VISTAS in SCIENCE

Edited by

DAVID L. ARM
DIRECTOR OF THE SEMINAR

The Thirteenth AFOSR Science Seminar

sponsored by

THE AIR FORCE OFFICE OF SCIENTIFIC RESEARCH

in cooperation with

THE UNIVERSITY OF NEW MEXICO
THE AIR FORCE SPECIAL WEAPONS CENTER

*The Air Force Office of Scientific Research
Is One Of The Major Components Of
The Office Of Aerospace Research
United States Air Force*

Library of Congress Catalog Card Number 68-59282

Preface

THIS VOLUME is a collection of articles based upon lectures presented at the Thirteenth Science Seminar of the Air Force Office of Scientific Research, held at Albuquerque, New Mexico, in June 1968. The seminar was held in cooperation with the University of New Mexico and the Air Force Special Weapons Center.

These seminars have been planned to assist in breaking down barriers to the flow of ideas between different specialized areas of scientific knowledge. Interdisciplinary in character, their programs have consisted of reports on, and discussions of basic research across the spectrum of Air Force interests. They have dealt with fundamental ideas in science—not in hardware or gadgets or instrumentation or weapons systems—important though all these may be. The lecturers have been internationally known in their fields and the research done by most of them has been accomplished with AFOSR support.

This book is not a verbatim transcript of the lectures which were presented. Instead, its chapters, written after the conclusion of the seminar by the people who appeared on the program, are, in the main, digests of what was discussed in the lectures and in the discussion periods. Collectively, they record a substantial measure of scientific achievement. Such a record is important, since world progress over the past several centuries has been greatly affected by advancements in pure science.

I am greatly indebted to my wife, Rena, who assisted in preparing the manuscripts for publication and to Mrs. Ann Masi and Miss Shirley M. Farmer for their assistance in reading proof.

D. L. A.

Arlington, Virginia
November 1968

Contents

I. Inquiries Into the Foundations of Science

WESLEY C. SALMON

IN 1950, L. RON HUBBARD published his book *Dianetics*,[1] which purported to provide a comprehensive explanation of human behavior, and which recommended a therapy for the treatment of all psychological ills. According to Hubbard's theory, psychological difficulties stem from "engrams," or brain traces, that are the results of experiences the individual has undergone while unconscious due to sleep, anesthesia, a blow to the head, or any other cause. Of particular importance are those that occur before birth. Hubbard gives strikingly vivid accounts of life in the womb, and it is far from idyllic. There is jostling, sloshing, noise, and a variety of rude shocks. Any unpleasant behavior of the father can have serious lasting effects upon the child. On a Saturday night, for example, the father comes home drunk and in an ugly mood; he beats the mother and with each blow he shouts, "Take that, take that!" The child grows up and becomes a kleptomaniac.

It is perhaps worth remarking that the author of this work had no training whatsoever in psychology or psychiatry. The basic ideas were first published in an article in *Astounding Science Fiction*. In spite of its origins, this book was widely read, the theory was taken seriously by many people, and the therapy it recommended was practiced extensively. A psychologist friend of mine remarked at the time, "I

WESLEY C. SALMON is the Norwood Russell Hanson Professor of Philosophy of Science at Indiana University. His chief area of research has been inductive logic and probability theory. He is presently working on major articles on the nature of statistical explanation and on the logical concept of probability. Another longstanding interest is in the philosophical problems of space and time. Dr. Salmon is currently Vice President of the Philosophy of Science Association. In addition to Indiana, he has served on the faculties of UCLA, Washington State, Northwestern and Brown. During the school year 1968-1969, Dr. Salmon is Visiting Professor of Philosophy at the University of Pittsburgh.

can't condemn this theory before it is carefully tested, but afterwards I will."

In the same year—it seems to have been a vintage year for things of this sort—Immanuel Velikovski published *Worlds in Collision*,[2] a book that attempted to account for a number of the miracles alleged in the *Old Testament,* such as the flood and the sun's standing still. This latter miracle, it was explained, resulted from a sudden stop in the earth's rotation about its axis which was brought about, along with the various other cataclysms, by the very close approach to the earth of a giant comet which later became the planet Venus. One of the chief difficulties encountered by Velikovski's explanation is that, on currently accepted scientific theory, the rotation of the earth simply would not stop as a result of the postulated close approach of another large body. In order to make good his explanation, Velikovski must introduce a whole body of physical theory which is quite incompatible with that which is generally accepted today, and for which he can summon no independent evidence. The probability that Velikovski's explanation is correct is, therefore, no greater than the probability that virtually every currently accepted physical theory is false.

Before the publication of the book, parts of Velikovski's theory were published serially in *Harper's Magazine.* When the astounding new theory did not elicit serious consideration from the scientific community, the editors of *Harper's* expressed outrage at the lack of scientific objectivity exhibited by the scientists.[3] They complained, in effect, of a scientific establishment with its scientific orthodoxy, which manifests such overwhelming prejudice against heterodox opinions that anyone like Velikovski, with radically new scientific ideas, cannot even get a serious hearing. They were not complaining that the scientific community rejected Velikovski's views, but rather that they dismissed them without any serious attempt at testing.

The foregoing are but two examples of scientific prejudgment of a theory; many other fascinating cases can be found in Martin Gardner's *Fads and Fallacies in the Name of Science.*[4] Yet, there is a disquieting aspect of this situation. We have been told on countless occasions that the methods of science depend upon the objective observational and experimental testing of hypotheses; science does not, to be sure, prove or disprove its results absolutely conclusively, but it does demand objective evidence to confirm or disconfirm them. This is the scientific ideal. Yet scientists in practice do certainly make judgments of plausibility or implausibility about newly suggested theories, and in cases like those of Hubbard and Velikovski, they judge the new hypotheses too implausible to deserve further serious consideration. Can it be that the editors of *Harper's* had a point, and that there is a large discrepancy between the ideal of scientific objectivity and the actual practice of prejudgment on the basis of plausibility considerations alone? One could maintain, of course, that this is merely an example of the necessary compromise we make between the abstract ideal and the practical exigencies. Given unlimited time, talent, money, and material, perhaps we should test every hypothesis that comes along; in fact, we have none of these commodities in unlimited supply, so we have to make practical decisions concerning the use of our scientific resources. We have to decide which hypotheses are promising, and which are not. We have to decide which experiments to run, and what equipment to buy. These are all practical decisions that have to be made, and in making them, the scientist (or administrator) is deciding which hypotheses will be subjected to serious testing and which will be ignored. If *every* hypothesis that comes along had to be tested, I shudder to think how Air Force scientists would be occupied with anti-gravity devices and refutations of Einstein.

Granted that we do, and perhaps must, make use of these plausibility considerations, the natural question concerns their status. Three general sorts of answers suggest themselves at the outset. In the first place, they might be no more than expressions of the attitudes and prejudices of individual scientists or groups of scientists. The editors of *Harper's* might be right in claiming that they are mere expressions of prejudice against ideas that are too novel—the tool used by the scientific establishment to enforce its own orthodoxy. If that suggestion is too conspiratorial in tone, perhaps they arise simply from the personal attitudes of individual scientists. In the second place, they might be thought to have a purely practical function. Perhaps they constitute a necessary but undesirable compromise with the ideal of scientific objectivity for the sake of getting on with the practical work of science. Or maybe these plausibility considerations have a heuristic value in helping scientists discover new and promising lines of research, but their function is solely in relation to the discovery of hypotheses, not to their justification. In the third place, it might be held that somehow plausibility arguments constitute a proper and indispensable part of the very logic of the justification of scientific hypotheses. This is the view I shall attempt to elaborate and defend. I shall argue that plausibility arguments are objective in character, and that they must be taken into account in the evaluation of scientific hypotheses on the basis of evidence.[5]

The issue being raised is a logical one. We are asking what ingredients enter into the evaluation of scientific hypotheses in the light of evidence. In order to answer such questions, it is necessary to look at the logical schema that represents the logical relation between evidence and hypotheses in scientific inference. Many scientific textbooks, especially the introductory ones, attempt to give a brief characterization of the process of confirming and disconfirming hypotheses. The usual account is what is generally known as the *hypothetico-deductive method*. As it is frequently described, the method consists in deducing consequences from the hypothesis in question, and checking by observation to determine whether these consequences actually occur. If they do, that counts as confirming evidence for the hypothesis; if they do not, the hypothesis is disconfirmed.

One immediate difficulty with the foregoing characterization of the hypothetico-deductive method is that from a general hypothesis it is impossible to deduce any observational consequences. Consider, for example, Kepler's first two laws of planetary motion: the first states that the orbits of the planets are elliptical, and the second describes the way the speed of the planet varies as it moves through the ellipse. With this general knowledge of the motion of Mars, for instance, it is impossible to deduce its location at midnight, and so to check by observation to see whether it fulfills the prediction or not. But with the addition of some further observational knowledge, it is possible to make such deductions—for instance, if we know its position and velocity at midnight last night. This additional observational evidence is often referred to as the "initial conditions;" from the hypothesis together with statements about initial conditions it is possible to deduce a concrete prediction that can be checked by observation. With this addition, the hypothetico-deductive method can be represented by the following simple schema:

H-D schema: H (hypothesis)
$\phantom{\text{H-D schema:}}$ I (initial conditions)
$\phantom{\text{H-D schema:}}$ —————————————
$\phantom{\text{H-D schema:}}$ O (observational prediction)

Although it is always possible for errors of observation or measurement to occur, and consequently for us to be mistaken about the initial conditions, I shall assume for purposes of the present discussion that we have correctly ascertained the initial conditions, so that the hypothesis is the only premise whose truth is in question. This is one useful simplifying assumption.

Another very important simplifying assumption is being made. In many cases the observational prediction does not follow from the hypothesis and initial conditions alone, but so-called "auxiliary hypotheses" are also required. For instance, if an astronomical observation is involved, optical theories concerning the behavior of telescopes may be implicitly invoked. In principle, a false prediction can be the occasion to call these auxiliary hypotheses into question, so that the most that can be concluded is that *either* an auxiliary hypothesis *or* the hypothesis up for testing is false, but we cannot say which. For purposes of this discussion, however, I shall assume that the truth of the auxiliary hypotheses is not in question, so that the hypothesis we are trying to test is still the only premise of the argument whose truth is open to question. Such simplifying assumptions are admittedly unrealistic, but things are difficult enough with them, and relinquishing them does not help with the problems we are discussing.

Under the foregoing simplifying assumptions a false prediction provides a decisive result: if the prediction is false the hypothesis is falsified, for a valid deduction with a false conclusion *must* have at least one false premise, and the hypothesis being tested is the only premise about which we are admitting any question. However, if the prediction turns out to be true, we certainly cannot conclude that the hypothesis is true, for to infer the truth of the premises from the truth of the conclusion is an elementary logical fallacy. And this fallacy is not mitigated in the least by rejecting the simplifying assumptions and admitting that other premises might be false. The fallacy, called *affirming the consequent,* is illustrated by the following example: If the patient has chickenpox, he will run a fever; the patient is running a fever; therefore, he has chickenpox. The difficulty is very fundamental and very general. Even though a hypothesis gives rise to a true prediction, there are always other different hypotheses that would provide the same prediction. This is the *problem of the alter-*

native hypotheses. It is especially apparent in any case in which one wishes to explain data that can be represented by points on a graph in terms of a mathematical function that can be represented by a curve. There are always many different curves that fit the data equally well; in fact, for any finite number of data, there are infinitely many such curves. Additional observations will serve to disqualify some of these (in fact, infinitely many), but infinitely many alternatives will still remain.

Since we obviously cannot claim that the observation of a true consequence establishes the truth of our hypothesis, the usual claim is that such observations tend to support or confirm the hypothesis, or to lend it probability. Thus, it is often said, the inference from the hypothesis and initial conditions to the prediction is deductive, but the inference in the opposite direction, from the truth of the prediction to the hypothesis is inductive. Inductive inferences do not pretend to establish their results with certainty; instead, they confirm them or make them probable. The whole trouble with looking at the matter this way is that it appears to constitute an automatic transformation of deductive fallacies into correct inductive arguments. When we discover, to our dismay, that our favorite deductive argument is invalid, we simply rescue it by saying that we never intended it to be deductive in the first place, but that it is a valid induction. With reference to this situation, the famous American logician Morris R. Cohen is said to have quipped, "A logic book is divided into two parts; in the first (on deduction) the fallacies are explained, and in the second (on induction) they are committed." Surely inductive logic, if it plays a central role in scientific method, must have better credentials than this.

When questions about deductive validity arise, they can usually be resolved in a formal manner by reference to an appropriate logical system. It has not always been so. Modern mathematical logic dates from the early nineteenth century, and it has undergone extraordinary development, largely in response to problems that arose in the foundations of mathematics. One such problem concerned the foundations of geometry, and it assumed critical importance with the discovery of non-Euclidean geometries. Another problem concerned the status of the infinitesimal in the calculus, a concept that was the center of utter confusion for two centuries after the discovery of the "infinitesimal" calculus. Thanks to extensive and fruitful investigations of the foundations of mathematics, we now have far clearer and more profound understanding of many fundamental mathematical concepts, as well as an extremely well-developed and intrinsically interesting discipline of formal deductive logic. The early investigators in this field could never have conceived in their wildest imaginings the kinds of results that have emerged.[6]

It is an unfortunate fact that far less attention has been paid to the foundational questions that arise in connection with the empirical sciences and their logic. When questions of inductive validity arise, there is no well-established formal discipline to which they can be referred for definitive solution. A number of systems of inductive logic have been proposed, some in greater and some in lesser detail, but none is more than rudimentary, and none is widely accepted as basically correct. Questions of inductive correctness are more often referred to scientific or philosophical intuitions, and these are notoriously unreliable guides.

We do have one resource which, although not overlooked entirely, is not exploited as fully as it could be. I refer to the mathematical calculus of probability. The probability calculus will not, by itself, solve all of our foundational problems concerning scientific inference, but it will provide us with a logical schema for scientific inference which is far more adequate than the H-D schema. And insofar as the probability calculus fails to provide the answers to foundational questions, it will at least help us to pose those problems in intelligible and, hopefully, more manageable form.

In order to show how the probability calculus can illuminate the kinds of questions I have been raising, I should like to introduce a very simple illustrative game. This game is played with two decks of cards composed as follows: deck 1 contains eight red cards and four black cards; deck 2 contains four red cards and eight black cards. A player begins by tossing a standard die; if the side one appears he draws a card from the first deck, and if any other side comes up he draws a card from the second deck. The draw of a red card constitutes a win. There is a simple formula for calculating the probability of a win resulting on a play of this game. Letting "$P(A,B)$" stand for the probability *from* A *to* B (i.e., the probability of B, given A), and letting "A" stand for tosses of the die, "B" for draws from deck 1 (which occur when and only when an ace is tossed on the die), and "C" for draws of red cards, the following formula, which is a special case of the "theorem on total probability" yields the desired computation:

$$P(A,C) = P(A,B)\,P(A\,\&\,B,C) + P(A,\overline{B})\,P(A\,\&\,\overline{B},C) \qquad (1)$$

The ampersand means "and" and the bar above a symbol negates it. Accordingly, the probabilities appearing in the formula are:

$P(A,C)$—probability of drawing a red card on a play of the game.

$P(A,B)$—probability of drawing from deck 1 on a play of the game $(= \frac{1}{6})$.

$P(A,\overline{B})$—probability of drawing from deck 2 on a play of the game $(= \frac{5}{6})$.

$P(A\,\&\,B,C)$—probability of drawing a red card if you play and draw from deck 1 $(= \frac{2}{3})$.

$P(A\,\&\,\overline{B},C)$—probability of drawing a red card if you play and draw from deck 2 $(= \frac{1}{3})$.

The theorem on total probability yields the result

$$P(A,C) = \frac{1}{6} \times \frac{2}{3} + \frac{5}{6} \times \frac{1}{3} = 7/18$$

Suppose, now, that this game is being played, and you enter the room just in time to see that the player has drawn a red card, but you did not see from which deck it was drawn. Perhaps someone even offers you a wager on whether it came from deck 1 or deck 2. Again, the probability calculus provides a simple formula to compute the desired probability. This time it is a special form of "Bayes' theorem" and it can be written in either of two ways:

$$P(A\,\&\,C,B) = \frac{P(A,B)\,P(A\,\&\,B,C)}{P(A,C)} \qquad (2)$$

$$= \frac{P(A,B)\,P(A\,\&\,B,C)}{P(A,B)\,P(A\,\&\,B,C) + P(A,\overline{B})\,P(A\,\&\,\overline{B},C)} \qquad (3)$$

The theorem on total probability (1) assures us that the denominators of the two fractions are equal; we must, of course, impose the restriction that $P(A,C) \neq 0$ in order to avoid an indeterminate fraction. The expression on the left evidently represents the probability that a draw which produced a red card was made from deck 1. Substituting known values in equation (2) yields

$$P(A \& C, B) = [\tfrac{1}{6} \times \tfrac{2}{3}] / [7/18] = 2/7$$

There is nothing controversial about either of the foregoing theorems or their applications to simple games of chance of the type just described.

In order to get at our logical questions about the nature of scientific inference, let me redescribe the game and what we learned about it, and in so doing I shall admittedly be stretching some meanings. It is nevertheless illuminating. We can think of the drawing of a red card as an effect that can be produced in either of two ways, by tossing an ace and drawing from the first deck or by tossing a number other than one and drawing from the second deck. When we asked for the probability that a red card had been drawn from deck 1, we were asking for the probability that the first of the two possible causes rather than the second was operative in bringing about this effect. In fact, there are two causal hypotheses, and we were calculating the probability that was to be assigned to one of them, namely, the hypothesis that the draw came from the first deck. Notice that the probability that the draw came from the first deck is considerably less than one-half, making it much more likely that the draw came from the second deck, even though the probability that you will get a red card if you draw from the first deck is much greater than the probability that you will get a red card if you draw from the second deck. The reason, obviously, is that many more draws are made from the second deck, so even though many more black than red cards are drawn from the second deck, still the preponderance of red cards also comes from the second deck. This point has fundamental philosophical importance.

Continuing with the bizarre use of terms, let us look at the probabilities used to carry out the computation via Bayes' theorem. $P(A,B)$ and $P(A,\overline{B})$ are known as *prior probabilities;* they are the probabilities, respectively, that the particular cause is operative or not, regardless of the result of the draw. These probabilities are obviously linked in a simple manner,

$$P(A,\overline{B}) = 1 - P(A,B),$$

so that knowledge of one of them suffices. P(A & B,C) and P(A & $\overline{B}$,C) are usually known as *likelihoods*. P(A & B,C) is the likelihood of the causal hypothesis that the draw came from deck 1 given that the draw was red, while P(A & $\overline{B}$,C) is the likelihood that that hypothesis is false (i.e., the likelihood of an alternative) given the same result. Note, however, that *the likelihood of a hypothesis is not a probability of that hypothesis;* it is, instead, the probability of a result given that the hypothesis holds. Note, also, that the two likelihoods need not add up to one; they are logically independent of one another and both need to be known—knowledge of one only does not suffice. These are the probabilities that appear on the right hand side of the second form of Bayes' theorem (3). In the first form of Bayes' theorem (2) we do not need the second likelihood, P(A & $\overline{B}$,C), but we require P(A,C) instead. This probability has no common name, but it is the probability that the effect in question occurs regardless of which cause is operative. But whichever form of the theorem is used, we need three logically distinct probabilities in order to carry out the calculation. P(A & C,B), the probability we endeavor to establish, is known as the *posterior probability* of the hypothesis. When we entertain the two causal hypotheses about the draw of the card, we may take the fact that the draw produced a red card as observational evidence relevant to the causal hypotheses. (A rapid calculation will show that the probability that the draw came from deck 1 if it was a black card $= 1/11$.) Thus, we may think of our posterior probability, P(A & C,B), as the probability of a hypothesis in the light of observational evidence. This is precisely the kind of question which arose in connection with the hypothetico-deductive method, and in connection with our attempt to understand how evidence confirms or disconfirms scientific hypotheses. Bayes' theorem therefore constitutes a logical schema, found in the mathematical calculus of probability, that shows some promise of incorporating the main logical features of the kind of inference the hypothetico-deductive schema is intended to describe.

The striking difference between Bayes' theorem and the H-D schema is the relative complexity of the former compared with the latter. In fact, in some special cases the H-D schema provides just one of the probabilities required in Bayes' theorem, but never does it yield either of the other two required. Thus, the H-D schema is inadequate as an account of scientific inference because it is a gross oversimplification which omits reference to essential logical features of the inference. Bayes' theorem fills these gaps. The H-D schema describes a situation in which an observable result is deducible from a hypothesis (in conjunction with initial conditions, and possibly auxiliary hypotheses, all of which we are assuming to be true); thus, if the hypothesis is correct, the result *must* occur and cannot fail to occur. In this special case, $P(A \,\&\, B,C) = 1$, but without two other probabilities, say $P(A,B)$ and $P(A \,\&\, \overline{B},C)$, no conclusion at all can be drawn regarding the posterior probability. Inspection of Bayes' theorem makes it evident that $P(A \,\&\, B,C) = 1$ is completely compatible with $P(A \,\&\, C,B) = 0$. At best, the H-D schema yields the likelihood of the hypothesis for that given evidence, but we need a prior probability and the likelihood of an alternative hypothesis on the same evidence.

That these other probabilities are indispensible, and the manner in which they function in scientific reasoning, can be indicated by examples. Consider *Dianetics* once more. As remarked above, this book contained not only a theory to explain behavior, but also it contained recommendations for a therapy to be practiced for the treatment of psychological disturbances. The therapeutic procedure bears strong resemblances to psychoanalysis; it consists of the elimination of those "engrams" that are causing trouble by bringing to consciousness, through a process of free association, the unconscious experiences that produced the engrams in the first place. The theory, presumably, enables us to deduce that practice of the recommended therapy will produce cures of psychological illness. At the time the theory was in vogue, this therapy was practiced extensively, and there is every reason to believe that "cures" did occur. There were unquestionably cases in which people with various neurotic symptoms were treated, and they experienced a remission of their symptoms. Such instances would seem to count, according to the hypothetico-deductive method, as confirming instances. That they cannot actually be so regarded is due to the fact that there is a far better explanation of these "cures." We know that there is a phenomenon of "faith-healing" that consists in the efficacy of any treatment the patient sincerely believes to be effective. Many neurotic symptoms are emenable to such treatment, so anyone with such symptoms who believed in the soundness of the dianetic approach could be "cured" regardless of the truth or falsity of the theory upon which it is based. The reason, in terms of Bayes' theorem, is that the second likelihood—the probability $P(A \,\&\, \overline{B},C)$ that the same phenomenon would occur even if the hypothesis were false—is very high.

Since this term occurs in the denominator, the value of the whole fraction tends to be small when the term is large.

A somewhat similar problem arises in connection with psychotherapy based upon more serious theoretical foundations. The effectiveness of any therapeutic procedure has to be compared with the so-called "spontaneous remission rate." Any therapy will produce a certain number of cases in which there is a remission of symptoms, but in a group of people with similar problems, but who undergo no therapy of any kind, there will also be a certain percentage who experience remission of symptoms. For a therapy to be judged effective, it has to improve upon the spontaneous remission rate; it is not sufficient that there be some remissions among those who undergo the treatment. In terms of Bayes' theorem, this means that we must look at both likelihoods, $P(A \& B,C)$ and $P(A \& \overline{B},C)$, not just the one we have been given in the standard H-D schema. This is just what experimental controls are all about. For instance, vitamin C has been highly touted as a cold remedy, and many cases have been cited of people recovering quickly from colds after taking massive doses. But in a *controlled* experiment in which two groups of people of comparable age, sex, state of general health, and severity of colds are compared, where one group is given vitamin C and the other is not, no difference in duration or severity of colds is detected.[7] This gives us a way of comparing the two likelihoods.

Let me mention, finally, an example of a strikingly successful confirmation, showing how the comparative likelihoods effect this sort of situation. At the beginning of the nineteenth century, two different theories of light were vying for supremacy: the wave theory and the corpuscular theory. Each had its strong advocates, and the evidence up to that point was not decisive. One of the supporters of the corpuscular theory was the mathematician Poisson, who deduced from the mathematical formulation of the wave theory that, if that theory were true, there should be a bright spot in the center of the shadow of a disk. Poisson declared that this absurd result showed that the wave theory is untenable, but when the experiment was actually performed the bright spot was there. Such a result was unthinkable on the corpuscular theory, so this turned into a triumph for the wave theory, because the probability on any other theory then available was negligible.[8] It was not until about a century later that the need for a combined wave-particle theory was realized. Arithmetically, the force of this dramatic confirmation is easily seen by noting that if $P(A \& \overline{B},C) = 0$ in (3), the posterior probability $P(A \& C,B)$ automatically becomes 1.

In addition to the two likelihoods, Bayes' theorem requires us to have a prior probability $P(A,B)$ or $P(A,\overline{B})$ in order to ascertain the posterior probability. These prior probabilities are probabilities of hypotheses without regard to the observational evidence provided by the particular test we are considering. In the card-drawing game described above, the prior probability was the probability of a draw from one particular deck regardless of whether the draw produced a red or black card. In the more serious cases of the attempt to evaluate scientific hypotheses, the probability of a hypothesis without regard to the test is precisely the sort of plausibility considered that was discussed at the outset. How plausible is a given hypothesis; what is its chance of being a successful one? This is the type of consideration that is demanded by Bayes' theorem in the form of a prior probability. The traditional stumbling-block to the use of Bayes' theorem as an account of the logic of scientific inference is the great difficulty of giving a description of what sort of things these prior probabilities could be.

It seems possible, nevertheless, to give many examples of plausibility arguments, and even to classify them into very general types. Such arguments may then be regarded as criteria which are used to evaluate prior probabilities—criteria that indicate whether a hypothesis is plausible or implausible, whether its prior probability is to be rated high or low. I shall mention three general types of criteria, and give some instances of each.

1. Let us call criteria of the first general type *formal criteria,* for they involve formal logical relations between the hypothesis under consideration and other accepted parts of science. This kind of consideration was illustrated at the outset by Velikovski's theory, which contradicts virtually all of modern physics. Because of this formal relationship we can say that Velikovski's theory must have a very low prior probability, since it is incompatible with so much we accept as correct. Another example of the same type can be found in those versions of the theory of telepathy that postulate the *instantaneous* transference of thought from one person to another, regardless of the distance that separates them. For, the special theory of relativity stipu-

lates that information cannot be transmitted at a speed greater than the speed of light, and so it would preclude instantaneous thought transmission. It would be even worse for precognition, the alleged process of direct perception of future occurrences, for this would involve messages being transmitted backward in time! Such parapsychological hypotheses must be given extremely low prior probabilities because of their logical incompatibility with well-established portions of physical science. A hypothesis could, of course, achieve a high prior probability on formal grounds by being the logical consequence of a well-established theory. Kepler's laws, for example, are extremely probable (as approximations) because of their relation to Newtonian gravitational theory.

2. I shall call criteria of the second type *pragmatic criteria*. Such criteria have to do with the evaluation of hypotheses in terms of the circumstances of their origin—for example, the qualifications of the author. This sort of consideration has already been amply illustrated by the example of *Dianetics*. Whenever a hypothesis is dismissed as being a "crank" hypothesis, pragmatic criteria are being brought to bear. In his fascinating *Fads and Fallacies in the Name of Science,* Martin Gardner offers some general characteristics by which cranks can be identified.[9]

One might be tempted to object to the use of pragmatic criteria on the ground, as we have all been taught, that it is a serious fallacy to confuse the *origin* of a theory with its *justification.* Having been told the old story about how Newton was led to think of universal gravitation by seeing an apple fall, we are reminded that that incident has nothing to do with the truth or justification of Newton's gravitational theory. That issue must be decided on the evidence.[10] Quite so. But there are factors in the origin of a hypothesis, such as the qualifications of the author, which have an *objective* probability relationship to the hypothesis and its truth. Crank hypotheses seldom, if ever, turn out to be sound; they are based upon various misunderstandings, prejudices, or sheer ignorance. It is *not* fallacious to conclude that they have low prior probabilities.

3. Criteria of the third type are by far the most interesting and important; let us call them *material criteria.* They make reference, in one way or another, to what the hypothesis actually says, rather than to its formal relation to other theories, or to the circumstances sur-

rounding its origins. These criteria do, however, depend upon comparisons of various theories or hypotheses; they make reference to analogies or similarities among different ones. Again, a few examples may be helpful.

Perhaps the most frequently cited criterion by which to judge the plausibility of hypotheses is the property of simplicity. Curve drawing illustrates this point very aptly. Given data which can be represented graphically, we generally take the smoothest curve—the one with the simplest mathematical expression—which comes sufficiently near the data points as representing the best explanatory hypothesis for those data. This factor was uppermost with Kepler, who kept searching for the simplest orbits to account for planetary motion, and finally settled upon the ellipse as filling the bill. Yet, we do not *always* insist upon the simplest explanation. We do not take seriously the "hypothesis" that television is solely responsible for the breakdown of contemporary morals, assuming that there is such a breakdown, for it is an obvious oversimplification. It may be that simplicity is more to be prized in the physical than in the social sciences, or in the advanced than in the younger sciences. But it does seem that we need to exercise reasonable judgment as to just what degree of simplicity is called for in any given situation.

Another consideration that may be used in plausibility arguments concerns causal mechanisms. There was a time when all scientific explanation was teleological in character; even the motion of inanimate objects was explained in terms of the endeavor to achieve their natural places. After the physics of Galileo and Newton had removed all reference to purpose from these realms, the remnants of teleological language remained: "Nature abhors a vacuum" and "Water seeks its own level." But though there have been a few attempts to read purpose into such laws as least action ("The Absolute is lazy"), it is for the most part fully conceded that physical explanation is nonpurposive.

The great success of Newtonian physics provided a strong plausibility argument for Darwin's account of the development of the biological species. The major difference between Darwin's evolutionary theory and its alternative contenders is the thoroughgoing rejection of teleological explanation by Darwin. Although teleological sounding language may sometimes creep in when we talk about natural selection, the concept is entirely nonpurposive. We ask, "Why is the polar bear white?" We answer, "Because that color provides a natural camouflage." It sometimes sounds a bit as if we are saying that the bear thinks the situation over and decides before he is born that white would be the best color, and so he chooses that color. But, of course, we mean no such thing. We are aware that, literally, no choice or planning is involved. There are chance mutations, some favorable to escaping from enemies and finding food. Those animals that have the favorable characteristics tend to survive and reproduce their kind, while those with unfavorable characteristics tend to die out without reproducing. The cause and effect relations in the evolutionary account are just as mechanical and without purpose as are those in Newtonian physics. This non-teleological theory is in sharp contrast to the theory of special creation according to which God created the various species because it somehow fit his plan.

The non-teleological character of Newton's theory surely must lend plausibility to a non-teleological biological theory such as Darwin's. If physics, which was far better developed and more advanced than any other science, got that way by abandoning teleological explanations for efficient causation, then it seems plausible for those sciences that are far less developed to try the same approach. When this approach paid off handsomely in the success of evolutionary theory, how much more plausible it becomes for other branches of science to follow the same line. Thus, for theories in psychology and sociology, for example, higher plausibility and higher prior probability would now attach to those hypotheses that are free from teleological components than to those that retain teleological explanation. When a biological hypothesis comes along that regresses to the pre-Darwinian teleology, such as Lecomte du Noüy's *Human Destiny,* it must be assigned a low prior probability.[11]

Let me give one final example of material criteria. Our investigations of the nature of physical space, extending over many centuries, have led to some rather sophisticated conceptions. To early thinkers, nothing could have been more implausible than to suppose that space is homogeneous and isotropic. Everyday experience seems clearly to demonstrate that there is a preferred direction—down. This view was expressed poetically by Lucretius in *The Nature of the Universe,* in which he describes the primordial state of affairs in which all the atoms are falling downward in space at a uniform speed.[12] On this view, not only was the downward direction preferred, but also, it was possible to distinguish absolute motion from absolute rest. By Newton's time it seemed clear that space had no preferred direction; rather, it was isotropic—possessed of the same structure in every direction. This consideration lent considerable plausibility to Newton's inverse square law, for if space is Euclidean and it has no preferred directions, then we should expect any force, such as gravitation, to spread out uniformly in all directions. In Euclidean geometry, the surface of a sphere varies with the square of the radius, so if the gravitational force spreads out uniformly in the surrounding space, it should diminish with the square of the distance.

Newton's theory, though it regards space as isotropic, still makes provision for absolute motion and rest. Einstein, reflecting on the homogeneity of space, enunciated a principle of relativity which precludes distinguishing physically between rest and uniform motion. In the beginning, if we believe Einstein's own autobiographical account, this principle recommended itself entirely on the grounds of its very great plausibility.[13] The matter does not rest there, of course, for it had to be incorporated into a physical theory that could be subjected to experimental test. His special theory of relativity has been tested and confirmed in a wide variety of ways, and it is now a well-established part of physics, but prior to the tests and its success in meeting them, it could be certified as highly plausible on the basis of very general characteristics of space.

Up to this point I have been attempting to establish two facts about prior probabilities: (1) Bayes' theorem shows that they are needed, and (2) scientific practice shows that they are used. But their status has been left very vague indeed. There is a fundamental reason. In spite of the fact that the probability calculus was established early in the seventeenth century, hardly any serious attention was given to the analysis of the meaning of the concept of probability until the latter part of the nineteenth century. There is nothing especially unusual about this situation. Questions about the meanings of fundamental concepts are foundational questions, and foundational investigations usually follow far behind the development of a discipline. Even today there is no real consensus on this question; there are, instead, three distinct interpretations of the probability concept, each with its strong adherents. A fortiori, there is no widely accepted answer to the question of the nature of the prior probabilities, for they seem to be especially problematic in character. Among the three leading probability theories, the *logical theory* regards probability as an *a priori measure* that can be assigned to propositions or states of affairs, the *personalistic theory* regards probability as a *subjective measure* of degrees of belief, and the *frequency theory* regards probability as a *physical characteristic* of types of events.

The logical theory is the direct descendent of the famous classical theory of Laplace. According to the classical theory, probability is the ratio of favorable to equally possible cases. The equi-possibility of cases, which is nothing other than the equal probability of these cases, is determined a priori on the basis of a *principle of indifference,* namely, two cases are equally likely if there is no reason to prefer one to the other. This principle gets into deep logical difficulty. Consider, for example, a car that makes a trip around a one mile track in a time somewhere between one and two minutes, but we know no more about it. It seems reasonable to say that the time could have been in the interval from one to one-and-one-half minutes, or it could have been in the interval of one-and-one-half to two minutes; we don't know which. Since these intervals are equal, we have no reason to prefer one to the other, and we assign a probability of one-half to each of them. Our information about this car can be put in other terms. We know that the car made its trip at an *average* speed somewhere in the range of 60 to 30 miles per hour. Again, it seems reasonable to say that the speed could have been in the range 60-45 miles per hour, or it could have been in the range 45-30 miles per hour; we don't know which. Since the two intervals are equal, we have no reason to prefer one to the other, and we assign a probability of one-half to each. But we have just contradicted our former result, for a time of one-and-one-half minutes corresponds with an average speed of forty, not forty-five, miles per hour.

This contradiction, known as the Bertrand paradox, brings out the fundamental difficulty with any method of assigning probabilities a priori. Such a priori decisions have an unavoidable arbitrary component to them, and in this case, the arbitrary component gives rise to two equally reasonable, but incompatible, ways of assigning the probabilities. Although the logical interpretation, in its current form, escapes this particular form of paradox, it is still subject to philosophical criticism because of the same general kind of aprioristic arbitrariness.

The personalistic interpretation is the twentieth century successor of an older and more naive subjective concept. According to the crude subjective view, a probability is no more nor less than a subjective degree of belief; it is a measure of our ignorance. If I assign the probability value one-half to an outcome of heads on a toss of the coin, this means that I expect heads just as often as I expect tails, and my uncertainty is equally divided between the two outcomes. If I expect twice as strongly as not that an American will be the first human to set foot on the moon, then that event has a probability of two-thirds.

The major difficulty with the old subjective interpretation arises because subjective states do not always come in sizes that will fit the mathematical calculus of probability. It is quite possible, for example, to find a person who believes to the degree one-sixth that a six will turn up on any toss of a given die, and who also believes that the tosses are independent of one another (the degree to which he believes in an outcome of six on a given toss is unaffected by the outcome of the previous toss). This same individual may also believe to the degree one-half, that he will get at least one six in three tosses of that die. There is, of course, something wrong here. If the probability of six on a given toss is one-sixth, and if the tosses are independent, this probability is considerably less than one-half (it is approximately 0.42). For four tosses, the probability of at least one six is well over one-half. This is a trivial kind of error that has been recognized as such for hundreds of years, but it is related to a significant error that led to the discovery of the mathematical calculus of probability. In the seventeenth century, the view was held that in 24 tosses of a pair of dice, there should be at least a fifty-fifty chance of tossing at least one double six. In fact, the probability is just under one-half in 24 tosses; in 25 it is just over one-half. The point of these examples is very simple. If probabilities are just subjective degrees of belief, the mathematical calculus of probability is mistaken, because it specifies certain relations among probabilities that do not obtain among degrees of belief.

Modern personalists do not interpret probabilities merely as subjective degrees of belief, but rather, as *coherent* degrees of belief. To say that degrees of belief are coherent means that they are related in such manner as to satisfy the conditions imposed by the mathematical calculus of probability. The personalists have seen that degrees of belief that violate the mathematical calculus involve some sort of error or blunder that is analogous to a logical inconsistency. Hence, when a combination of degrees of belief is incoherent, some adjustment or revision is called for in order to bring these degrees into conformity with the mathematical calculus. The chief objection to the personalist view is that it is not objective; we shall have to see whether and to what extent the lack of objectivity is actually noxious.

The frequency interpretation goes back to Aristotle who characterized the probable as that which happens often. More exactly, it regards a probability as a relative frequency of occurrence in a large sequence of events. For instance, a probability of one-half for heads on tosses of a coin would mean that in the long run the ratio of the number of heads to the number of tosses approaches and remains close to one-half. To say that the probability of getting a head on a particular toss is one-half means that this toss is a member of an appropriately selected large class of tosses within which the overall relative frequency of heads is one-half. It seems evident that there are many contexts in which we deal with large aggregates of phenomena, and in these contexts the frequency concept of probability seems well suited to the use of statistical techniques—e.g., in quantum mechanics, kinetic theory, sociology, and the games of chance, to mention just a few. But it is much more dubious that the frequency interpretation is at all applicable to such matters as the probability of a scientific hypothesis in the light of empirical evidence. In this case where are we to find the large classes and long sequences to which to refer our probabilities of hypotheses? This difficulty has seemed insuperable to most authors who have dealt with the problem. The general conclusion has been that the frequency interpretation is fine in certain contexts, but we need a radically different probability concept if we are to deal with the probability of hypotheses.

Returning to our main topic of concern, we easily see that each of the foregoing three probability theories provides an answer to the question of the nature of plausibility considerations and prior probabilities. According to the logical interpretation, hypotheses are plausible or not on the basis of certain a priori considerations; on this view, reason dictates which hypotheses are to be taken seriously and which not. According to the personalistic interpretation, prior probabilities represent the prior opinion or attitude of the investigator toward the hypothesis before he sets about testing it. Different investigators may, of course, have different views of the same hypothesis, so prior probabilities may vary from individual to individual. According to the frequency interpretation, prior probabilities arise from experience with scientific hypotheses, and they reflect this experience in an objective way. To say that a hypothesis is plausible, or has a high prior probability, means that it is of a type that has proved successful in the past. We have found by experience that hypotheses of this general type have often worked well in science.

From the outset, the personalistic interpretation enjoys a major advantage over the other two. It is very difficult to see how we are to find non-arbitrary a priori principles to use as a basis for establishing prior probabilities of the a priori type for the logical interpretation, and it is difficult to see how we are reasonably to define classes of hypotheses and count frequencies of success for the frequency interpretation. But personal probabilities are available quite unproblematically. Each individual has his degree of belief in the hypothesis, and that's all there is to it. Coherence demands that degrees of belief conform to the mathematical calculus, and Bayes' theorem is one of the important relations to be found in the calculus. Bayes' theorem tells us how, if we are to avoid incoherence, we must modify our degrees of belief in the light of new evidence. The personalists, who constitute an extremely influential school of contemporary statisticians, are indeed so closely wedded to Bayes' theorem that they have even taken its name and are generally known as "bayesians."

The chief objection to the personalist approach is that it injects a purely subjective element into the testing and evaluation of scientific hypotheses; we feel that science should have a more objective foundation. The bayesians have a very persuasive answer. Even though two people may begin with radically different attitudes toward a hypothesis, accumulating evidence will force a convergence of opinion. This is a basic mathematical fact about Bayes' theorem; it is easily seen by an example. Suppose a coin which we cannot examine is being flipped; but we are told the results of the tosses. We know that it is either a fair coin or a two-headed coin, we don't know which, and we have very different prior opinions on the matter. Suppose your prior probability for a two-headed coin is 1/100 while mine is one-half. Then as we learn that various numbers of heads have been tossed (without any tails, of course), our opinions come closer and closer together as follows:

Number of tosses resulting in head	Prior probability that coin has two heads	
	1/100	1/2
	Posterior probability on given evidence	
1	2/101	2/3
2	4/103	4/5
10	$1024/1123 \simeq .91$	$1024/1025 \simeq .99$

After only ten tosses, we both find it overwhelmingly probable that the coin that produced this sequence of results is a two-headed one. This phenomenon is sometimes called "swamping of the priors," for their influence on the posterior probabilities becomes smaller and smaller as evidence accumulates. The only qualification is that we must begin with somewhat open minds. If we begin with the certainty that the coin is two-headed or with the certainty that it is not, i.e., with prior probability of zero or one, evidence will not change that opinion. But if we begin with prior probabilities differing ever so little from those extremes convergence will sooner or later occur. As L. J. Savage remarked, it is not necessary to have an open mind, it is sufficient to have one that is slightly ajar.

The same consideration about the swamping of prior probabilities also enables the frequentist to overcome the chief objection to his approach. If it were necessary to have clearly defined classes of hypotheses, within which exact values of frequencies of success had to be ascertained, the situation would be pretty hopeless, but because of the swamping phenomenon, it is sufficient to have only the roughest approximation. All that is really needed is a reasonable guess as to whether the value is significantly different from zero. In the artificial coin tossing example, where there are only two hypotheses, it is possible to be perfectly open-minded and give each alternative a non-negligible prior probability, but in the serious cases of evaluation of scientific hypotheses, there are infinitely many alternative hypotheses, all in conflict with one another, and they cannot all have non-negligible prior probabilities. This is the problem of the alternative hypotheses again. For this reason, it is impossible to be completely open-minded, so we must find some basis for assigning negligible prior probabilities to some possible hypotheses. This is tantamount to judging some hypotheses to be too implausible to deserve further testing and consideration. It is my conviction that this is done on the basis of experience; it is not done by means of purely a priori considerations, nor is it a purely subjective affair. As I tried to suggest by means of the examples of plausibility arguments, scientific experience with the testing, acceptance, and rejection of hypotheses provides an objective basis for deciding which hypotheses deserve serious testing and which do not. I am not suggesting that we proceed on the basis of plausibility considerations to summary dismissal of almost every hypothesis that comes along; on the contrary, the recommendation would be for a high degree of open-mindedness. However, we need not and cannot be completely open-minded with regard to any and every hypothesis of whatever description that happens to be proposed by anyone. This approach shows how we can be reasonably openminded in science without being stupid about it. It provides an answer to the kind of charge made by the editors of *Harper's:* Science *is* objective, but its objectivity embraces two aspects, objective testing and objective evaluation of prior probabilities. Plausibility arguments are used in science, and their use is justified by Bayes' theorem. In fact, Bayes' theorem shows that they are indispensible. The frequency interpretation of probability enables us to view them as empirical and objective.

It would be an unfair distortion of the situation for me to conclude without remarking that the view I have been advocating is very definitely a minority view among inductive logicians and probability theorists. There is no well agreed upon majority view. One of the most challenging aspects of this sort of investigation lies in the large number of open questions, and the amount that remains to be done. Whether my view is correct is not the main issue. Of far greater importance is the fact that there are many fundamental problems that deserve extensive consideration, and we cannot help but learn a great deal about the foundations of science by pursuing them.

REFERENCES

[1] L. Ron Hubbard, *Dianetics: The Modern Science of Mental Healing* (Hermitage House, 1950).

[2] Immanuel Velikovski, *Worlds in Collision* (Doubleday and Co., 1950).

[3] *Harper's Magazine,* **202** (June, 1951), 9-11.

⁴ Martin Gardner, *Fads and Fallacies in the Name of Science* (Dover Publications, Inc., 1957). Gardner's excellent discussions of Hubbard and Velikovski provide many additional details.

⁵ In my book, *The Foundations of Scientific Inference* (University of Pittsburgh Press, 1967), I have discussed these issues in greater detail and have argued this case at greater length.

⁶ For a very readable account of recent developments, and a comparison with the earlier situation in the foundations of geometry see Paul J. Cohen and Reuben Hersh, "Non-Cantorian Set Theory," *Scientific American*, December 1967, Vol. 217, no. 6.

⁷ The Editors of Consumer Reports, *The Medicine Show* (Simon and Schuster, 1961), chapter 2.

⁸ See Max Born and Emil Wolf, *Principles of Optics* (Pergamon Press, 1964), p. 375.

⁹ See p. 12-14, Reference 4.

¹⁰ An elementary account of the distinction between discovery and justification is given in my *Logic* (Prentice-Hall, Inc., 1963), § 3.

¹¹ Pierre Lecomte du Noüy, *Human Destiny* (Longmans, Green and Co., 1947).

¹² Lucretius, *The Nature of the Universe*, trans. Ronald Latham (Penguin Books, 1951). Originally titled *De Rerum Natura*, and usually translated *On the Nature of Things*. The Latham translation is modern, and is far more intelligible than the older ones.

¹³ Albert Einstein, "Autobiographical Notes" in *Albert Einstein: Philosopher-Scientist*, ed., Paul Arthur Schilpp (The Library of Living Philosophers, 1949).

II. The Researcher and His Working Environment: Research Findings and Their Application

Floyd C. Mann

THE RESEARCHER HIMSELF has become an object of study in the last decade. There is now a small body of knowledge about the factors which distinguish the more from the less effective scientists and scientific work units. This knowledge bank includes studies by Shepard (7), Orth (5), Pelz and Andrews (6), Vollmer (8, 9, 10) Marquis, and others at MIT (2, 3, 4), and our small group (Neff, Erfurt, and Mann) studying the effectiveness of scientific work groups. This is not a large fund of knowledge, but it does contain some insights and suggestions for improving research operations. It is significant that already there is developing a gap between what is known and what is being used in the everyday management of our research and development laboratories.

It is the objective here to present one researcher's view of the present state of the art regarding the study of the organizational behavior of scientists and the utilization of this knowledge for organizational development. The means by which this will be done is to describe in some detail the life history of one sequence of studies on research management. This case study approach will provide an overview of the approach, models, and conceptualizations being used in this field,

FLOYD C. MANN is an organizational psychologist, Director of the Center for Research on the Utilization of Scientific Knowledge and Professor of Psychology at the University of Michigan. His research has focused on the social psychological factors that distinguish the more effective from the less effective units in business and industry, hospitals, government agencies, and research laboratories. He is now concentrating on the problems of knowledge utilization.

a look into the methodologies of measurement and change being employed, and some appreciation of the difficulties encountered in doing research that contributes to knowledge and, in addition, is helpful to the laboratory manager and his associates.

A STUDY OF WORKING ENVIRONMENTS OF PROFESSIONALS

Five or six years ago, an assistant secretary of a major department in the federal government, responsible for that unit's "R and D agencies," asked us to undertake a study that would introduce the managers of five bureaus and agencies to what behavioral scientists have been learning about the most effective ways of organizing and managing complex social systems. The charge was just that general and it was given in just that amount of time, as he left for a meeting with Congress and I was ushered into another room to talk with the personnel directors of these agencies. A long session then occurred in which I described the way in which our group of social scientists like to work, and they described the wide range of activities performed in their organizations and the problems they were facing. Our method of operation involves a good deal of collaboration and participation of the key members within the organization studied, the formation of study teams composed of members from inside the unit and members of our research group, and the joint development of study objectives, research designs, interviews and questionnaire forms.

As our study got underway, we learned that the work of the five units was indeed as varied as the personnel directors had indicated at that first meeting. Some of the units were concerned with global measurements and with the development and standardization of new measurements, others with the documentation and protection of new discoveries and the diffusion of new knowledge. Personnel in the agencies ranged in job grade from the lowest civil service ratings to the highest professional and managerial grades. Many of the professionals were trained in several disciplines. For some, their work took them all over the globe.

After familiarizing ourselves with the objectives of these agencies, their tasks, their personnel, and their principal problems through exploratory interviews, we proposed that we study the populations of professionals that existed within each agency. The most general statement of our objective was to investigate what social and psychological factors distinguish the more from the less effective working environments of such highly trained professionals. This was discussed first with the personnel directors, then with the agency heads, and finally with the assistant secretary.

More specifically, we proposed to study the way in which organizational factors, like leadership and supervision, coordination, and distribution of influence, affected member attitudes, perceptions, and motivation, and how these in turn were related to organizational unit effectiveness, such as productivity, efficiency, and adaptability, and to individual member feelings of self actualization, work and life satisfactions, sense of well-being and health. Our study design had two parts: random sample attitude and perception surveys of individual professionals at three levels—non-supervisory, supervisory, and management, and a more intensive study of high and low effectiveness units. Our approach was (1) to collect information through questionnaires, analyze the data to determine how members at various levels saw their working environments, and study in depth what factors were associated with high and low effectiveness units, (2) to report the simple descriptive findings and the results of the more complex analyses back into the organization for management review and use in better problem assessment, decision making, and action. The cycle we hoped would be followed was measurement, feedback, action, and remeasurement after a period of time to see if the action had been appropriate to meet the problem. Data from the remeasurement would serve as the basis for new goal setting and actions. In this manner, we expected to link research and action in a way that would be useful and meaningful both to supervisors needing information for formulating practical solutions to problems and to us as behavioral scientists concerned with adding new information about the factors affecting the effectiveness of professionals, and with learning more about how to increase the effective use of such information.

With the study design established and the approach agreed upon, data were then collected by paper and pencil questionnaires from about 1500 professionals. As simple, straight run findings became available, showing how the professionals at different levels within the same agency saw things, these were made available to key administrative personnel through the members of our joint research teams. The following are examples of some of these findings.

CHART #1   Job Needs and Opportunities Reported by Management in Agency A

Percent saying "Great" or "Utmost"

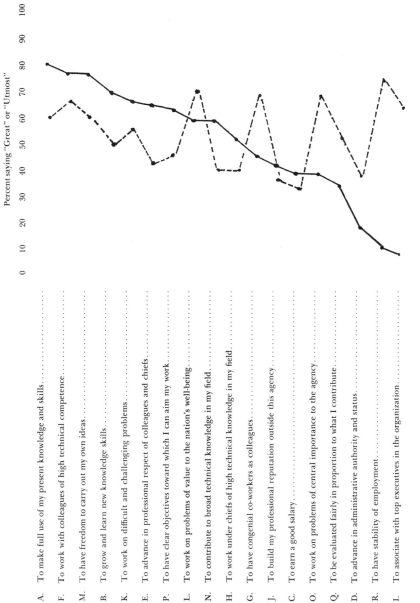

A.   To make full use of my present knowledge and skills . . . .
F.   To work with colleagues of high technical competence . . . .
M. To have freedom to carry out my own ideas . . . .
B.   To grow and learn new knowledge skills . . . .
K.   To work on difficult and challenging problems . . . .
E.   To advance in professional respect of colleagues and chiefs . . . . .
P.   To have clear objectives toward which I can aim my work . . . . . .
L.   To work on problems of value to the nation's well-being . . . .
N.   To contribute to broad technical knowledge in my field . . . .
H.   To work under chiefs of high technical knowledge in my field . . . . .
G.   To have congenial co-workers as colleagues . . . .
J.   To build my professional reputation outside this agency . . . .
C.   To earn a good salary . . . .
O.   To work on problems of central importance to the agency . . . .
Q.   To be evaluated fairly in proportion to what I contribute . . . .
D.   To advance in administrative authority and status . . . .
R.   To have stability of employment . . . .
I.   To associate with top executives in the organization . . . .

———— Importance attached to job factor ("job need")
- - - - - - Provision afforded in present job to meet this need ("job opportunity")

Two of the more extensive questions concerned the importance professionals attached to different aspects of a job, and the extent to which their present job actually provided an opportunity to meet these needs. The solid line on Chart 1 shows percent of top management personnel in Agency A who said that each job factor was of great or utmost importance to them. The dotted line indicates what percent of this same group felt their present job actually provided opportunity to meet these job needs.

Four out of five (80 percent) of the 30 top management personnel in Agency A indicated that it was of great or utmost importance to them to have a job in which they could make full use of their present knowledge and skills. Three out of five (60 percent) said that the provision in their present job was great or more to make full use of their present knowledge and skills. The chart indicates that this group had less of the job factors they prized most highly, and more of the factors they valued least. Thus, this chart shows "the fit" of expressed job needs and job provisions for the professionals in key administrative positions. Let us now look at a similar chart for the professionals who had no supervisory responsibility.

Chart 2 shows that the kinds of opportunities that non-supervisory professionals in Agency A want are similar but not identical in order to those reported as of great or utmost importance to top management. To grow and learn new knowledge and skills, to make full use of their present knowledge and skills, to have freedom to carry out their own ideas, to work on difficult and challenging problems are highly important to both groups of professionals. To associate with top executives in the organization, to advance in administrative authority and status, to work on problems of central importance to the agency were not of great or utmost importance to either population of professionals.

Perhaps more interesting from a motivational standpoint is the much larger gap between what the non-supervisory professional wants from his job and what he feels he is getting. A comparison of Charts 1 and 2 suggests that the managerial professionals in this agency are coming closer to obtaining the kinds of things they value the most than are the non-supervisory professionals. The gap between need and provision is a good deal larger for the non-supervisory professionals.

This gap between expressed job need and provision was even larger

CHART #2   Job Needs and Opportunities Reported by Non-Supervisory Professionals in Agency A

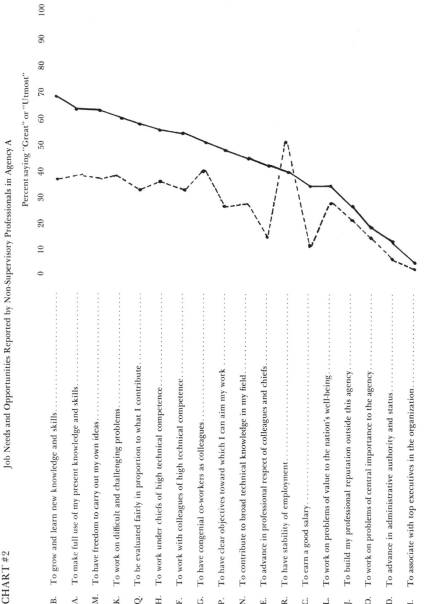

Percent saying "Great" or "Utmost"

B. To grow and learn new knowledge and skills. . . . .

A. To make full use of my present knowledge and skills. . . . .

M. To have freedom to carry out my own ideas. . . . .

K. To work on difficult and challenging problems. . . . .

Q. To be evaluated fairly in proportion to what I contribute. . . . .

H. To work under chiefs of high technical competence. . . . .

F. To work with colleagues of high technical competence. . . . .

G. To have congenial co-workers as colleagues. . . . .

P. To have clear objectives toward which I can aim my work . . . .

N. To contribute to broad technical knowledge in my field . . . .

E. To advance in professional respect of colleagues and chiefs. . . . .

R. To have stability of employment. . . . .

C. To earn a good salary. . . . .

L. To work on problems of value to the nation's well-being. . . . .

J. To build my professional reputation outside this agency. . . . .

O. To work on problems of central importance to the agency. . . . .

D. To advance in administrative authority and status. . . . .

I. To associate with top executives in the organization . . . .

———— Importance attached to job factor ("job need")

- - - - - Provision afforded in present job to meet this need ("job opportunity") for the non-supervisory professionals in two other agencies. Charts 3 and 4 show how dramatic these differences can be. In general, our straight run findings regarding these two sets of questions indicated that top managerial and intermediate level supervisors were meeting more of their job needs than professionals without administrative responsibility. The working environment that the top managers were creating for the non-supervisory professionals was a good deal less need-satisfying than the working environment in which they found themselves or which they could create for themselves.

Support for this interpretation of straight run findings was given in the responses of three different levels of professionals to a question about their involvement in their work.

"Some individuals are completely involved in their work—absorbed by it night and day. For others, their work is simply one of several interests. How involved do you feel in your work?

Level of Professional and Agency	Percent Saying Greatly or Completely Involved
Management	
Agency A	77%
Agency B	78
Agency C	88
Supervisory	
Agency A	58%
Agency B	41
Agency C	22
Non-Supervisory	
Agency A	30%
Agency B	29
Agency C	11

Top management personnel reported themselves as being more highly involved in their work than supervisors; supervisors were more highly involved than non-supervisory professionals.

Straight run findings generally showed a marked and significant gap between how top management and non-supervisory professionals saw such things as

(1) The effort made to place people,

(2) the opportunity given to people to react to proposed changes, and

CHART #3   Job Needs and Opportunities Reported by Non-Supervisory Professionals in Agency B

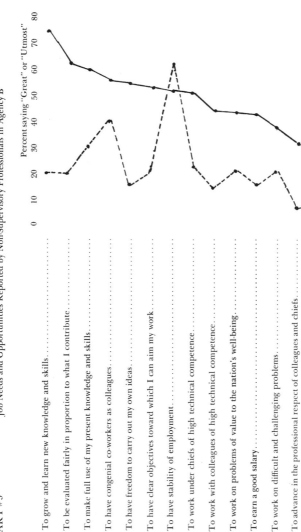

B.   To grow and learn new knowledge and skills. . . . .

Q.   To be evaluated fairly in proportion to what I contribute. . . . .

A.   To make full use of my present knowledge and skills. . . . .

G.   To have congenial co-workers as colleagues. . . . .

M.   To have freedom to carry out my own ideas. . . . .

P.   To have clear objectives toward which I can aim my work. . . . .

R.   To have stability of employment. . . . .

H.   To work under chiefs of high technical competence. . . . .

F.   To work with colleagues of high technical competence. . . . .

L.   To work on problems of value to the nation's well-being. . . . .

C.   To earn a good salary. . . . .

K.   To work on difficult and challenging problems. . . . .

E.   To advance in the professional respect of colleagues and chiefs. . . . . .

N.   To contribute to broad technical knowledge in my field. . . . .

O.   To work on problems of central importance to the agency. . . . .

D.   To advance in administrative authority and status. . . . .

J.   To build my professional reputation outside this agency. . . . .

I.   To associate with top executives in the organization. . . . .

————— Importance attached to job factor ("job need")

- - - - - Provision afforded in present job to meet this need ("job opportunity")

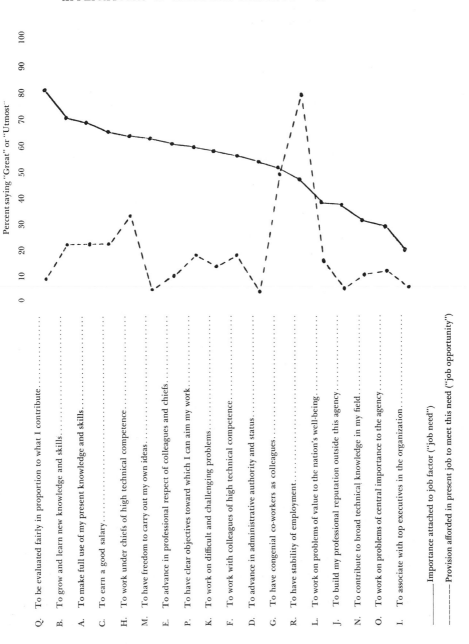

CHART #4 Job Needs and Opportunities Reported by Non-Supervisory Professionals in Agency C

Percent saying "Great" or "Utmost"

Q. To be evaluated fairly in proportion to what I contribute............
B. To grow and learn new knowledge and skills...........
A. To make full use of my present knowledge and skills...........
C. To earn a good salary...........
H. To work under chiefs of high technical competence...........
M. To have freedom to carry out my own ideas............
E. To advance in professional respect of colleagues and chiefs............
P. To have clear objectives toward which I can aim my work...........
K. To work on difficult and challenging problems............
F. To work with colleagues of high technical competence............
D. To advance in administrative authority and status............
G. To have congenial co-workers as colleagues............
R. To have stability of employment............
L. To work on problems of value to the nation's well-being...........
J. To build my professional reputation outside this agency............
N. To contribute to broad technical knowledge in my field............
O. To work on problems of central importance to the agency............
I. To associate with top executives in the organization...........

——— Importance attached to job factor ("job need")

------ Provision afforded in present job to meet this need ("job opportunity")

(3) the extent to which the immediate supervisor generally tries to get subordinates' ideas and opinions in solving job problems.

These are but a few of the mass of findings that emerged from this first step in our study of professionals. Sizeable sets of tables were prepared for each agency. Data from 165 numbered questions were presented by organizational levels and location—if the latter was relevant. Discussions of these straight run findings with a few key managers and members of the study teams in each agency produced relatively few positive steps toward action. There was little willingness to draw on the findings from other studies about the relationship of member attitudes and organizational unit effectiveness. A persistent question was "How do we know these attitudes would relate to effectiveness in scientific laboratories or units like ours?" The volume of findings seemed to be too large to handle with ease. Few of our research collaborators were familiar enough with the recent literature regarding organizational behavior to read such tables and to grasp the meaning of the finding for their agency. Even fewer were willing to try and think through the implications of the findings for change. Simple answers to complex questions were requested often. Old axes were brought out for regrinding—if the data seemed consistent with the position the men had taken some time before. Relatively little effort was committed to working through the meaning of the findings for immediate action.

A STUDY OF THE DIFFERENTIAL EFFECTIVENESS OF WORK SECTIONS

To sharpen the meaning of the findings, an intensive analysis was undertaken of the organizational and individual factors contributing to the effectiveness of work sections in one of the agencies. Before the data had been collected in this agency, we had selected at random two sections from each of fifteen divisions. We then asked the five key management men who were primarily responsible for the administration and direction of this agency to rank order these sections according to five dimensions of effectiveness: productivity, efficiency, adaptability, cooperativeness, and staff recruitment and development. The data generated by this process indicated that a single measure of overall unit effectiveness could be used as one criterion of unit effectiveness.

Measures from the questionnaires that had been given to supervisory and to non-supervisory personnel that were similar to the five dimensions on which key managers had ranked the sections were then combined into a single overall measure of effectiveness and compared with the key management's evaluation of the units. This analysis established that there was a good deal of similarity in the evaluation of three levels of professionals about the work of each unit. The unit supervisor's evaluation of his unit's effectiveness was highly correlated with that of the non-supervisors in the unit; the evaluators of both were significantly related to the five key managers' evaluations of each unit's effectiveness. Having established a rough but useable criterion of effectiveness, an extensive investigation was undertaken to see which of all the measures we had been studying were related significantly to the key manager's overall measure of unit effectiveness.

This analysis also revealed a large body of findings. More supervisors in high effectiveness sections (as opposed to those in the less effective sections);

—were younger
—had more education
—had higher civil service job grades
—were similar in age and educational achievement with the scientists in their sections
—considered their occupation more important in their lives than their family
—were more likely to prefer work situations which afford greater chances to exercise authority and achieve success at the risk of security than their counterparts
—viewed periods of major change as more exciting than annoying, and providing an opportunity to use their abilities
—perceived their own careers in terms of professions or specialties rather than the public service
—identified their professional colleagues in their part of the agency as their most important reference group
—tended to attach high importance to those work goals that are characteristic of the scientific professional

—saw research and development efforts as being crucial to their agency's basic mission, and indicated that the proportion of the agency's total resources devoted to research was either adequate or that a greater proportion should be devoted to research

—reported high levels of opportunity on their jobs to attain (1) their scientific goals, (2) their socio-emotional goals of having congenial co-workers, of being evaluated fairly, and of having stability of employment, and (3) their public service goals

—reported high overall job satisfaction

—were satisfied with their opportunities for technical and administrative training

—said their occupation was the most important sector of their lives, and were satisfied with their performance in this sector

—said they worry more often about money problems, about how good a job they were doing, and about feeling "in a rut"

—reported fewer mental health complaints and say they never worry about their own health

—rated their immediate superiors very high or high on (1) using supportive behaviors such as getting their ideas and suggestions, giving them help when they really need it, being available for discussion of job problems, being open to influence to a considerable extent, using general rather than close supervision, and being good at human relations, (2) on coordinating and integrating activities: being up-to-date on new policies and procedures, planning work so that time is not lost, assigning work so that there is no duplication of work assignments, doing administrative activities well, and giving little attention to enforcing rules and regulations

—reported reciprocal high understanding between themselves and their subordinates in the unit.

This was a partial list of the findings regarding the differences between supervisors in high effectiveness sections and those in the low effectiveness sections. Many, but not all, of these findings appeared to hold for the non-supervisory professionals in these same sections.

With the completion of these analyses and the identification of the factors associated with unit effectiveness, it was then possible to combine the findings from the random sample and these analyses to determine where action might be taken. It was found, for example, that supervisors of more effective sections rated their division heads higher than supervisors of less effective sections on the dimensions of supportive behavior. With this as a fact on which to build, it was then possible to discover by studying the random sample findings that while 90 per cent of the supervisors reported they felt completely or rather free to discuss job problems with their division head, only 48 per cent felt their division heads always or almost always try to get the supervisor's ideas and opinions in solving job problems. This combination of findings suggests that any investment of time and effort in trying to change the behavior of division heads might pay greater dividends by having division heads ask subordinate professionals for their ideas and opinions rather than simply continuing to be available to subordinates who wish to discuss job problems with them.

This full set of findings was then presented in the form of charts to the top management of the agency. In many respects, this was an evening of frustration again for both the managers and the researchers. There seemed to be too many findings and the implications for action were either not seen or not accepted. The researchers were, however, asked to summarize the findings in a few pages and present them to the division and section heads of the agency in a series of meetings.

A further summary was then prepared and a series of two to three hour meetings were initiated with fifteen different groups. Different groups of scientists and professionals responded in different ways, but all were generally dubious about the value of the findings and very hesitant to consider taking any action on the basis of the data— even the data that had been collected from their own agency. An example again may be helpful. The chemists meeting with us to review the data on the first day indicated that they found the charts and our summary of findings very complicated and difficult to understand. The physicists and the statisticians in the afternoon of the same day indicated they felt our charts and summaries were too simple and did not present enough detail about our measurements, the indices we had constructed, and our methodology. Careful questioning about our research design, our awareness of the limitations of the nature of the scales used in our questionnaires, and the statistics used, led them to grant that the study appeared to have been carefully done. They quickly added, however, that there was little or nothing that was new in the findings. As supervisors they generally mutually reassured each other that they not only knew these facts but used them in the day-to-day management of their units. Since neither top management nor the supervisors felt it was necessary, the findings of the study were not reported to the non-supervisory professionals. After fifteen sessions, both the key agency personnel and the members of our research team felt that not much more could be accomplished and no further efforts were made toward the utilization of these findings with the members of this agency.

A STUDY OF MANAGEMENT KNOWLEDGE UTILIZATION IN RESEARCH AND DEVELOPMENT LABORATORIES

The indifference, the misgivings, and the sharply expressed doubts about the usefulness of our findings for the everyday management of laboratories forced us to explore in greater depth the problems of communicating research results. To gain as much information as possible from a single study, a new group of researchers* developed a program of effort around an extended seminar which incorporated the following features:

1) A variety of inputs: e.g., research-based theory of management and human relations, research findings regarding scientists and engineers in general, findings about scientific work group effectiveness, and survey data about each laboratory director's own organization.
2) A variety of formats: e.g., extended readings, abstracts, lectures, role-playing and group discussion.
3) A variety of laboratory directors whose organizations represented a range of management problems from the most applied and operational to the most basic research.

---

* This study was directed by Mann and Havelock. A full account will be published under the title of *Learning About Research Management: A Study in Knowledge Diffusion and Utilization* (tentative title) by Ronald Havelock, Floyd Mann, William Morris, Marshall Sashkin, with the assistance of John Erfurt. Part of this description draws on a Final Report on Contract AF 49 (638) 1732 titled *Research and Development Laboratory Management Knowledge Utilization Study,* by Ronald Havelock and Floyd Mann.

4) A sequence of planned activities over a six month period to:
    Step (a)—develop an understanding of the social science research findings
    Step (b)—derive practical implications of findings for change in own management practices
    Step (c)—experiment and try out practices
    Step (d)—measure attitude in own laboratory
    Step (e)—allow for the involvement of the director's staff in the organizational diagnosis and change process

5) Continuous monitoring of the dissemination-utilization process by the project staff using tape recording and analysis of all input sessions, questionnaires after each session asking for evaluations of different types of inputs and different patterns of working together, and extended interviews with each participant before and after the series.

Participants for this seminar were selected from the available population of southeastern Michigan laboratories which were reported to have staffs of 30 or more professionals. Three steps were employed in this process: (1) a letter and brochure inviting them to consider investing four to five hours every two weeks for six months in a science management seminar, (2) a brief telephone interview regarding their interest, and (3) a visit to their laboratory for an extensive discussion and interview regarding the seminar. Eleven directors attended the first meeting; ten continued after the initial meeting; eight participated throughout the project—two succumbing to cancer and coronary attacks during the six month period. The laboratories of these eight had a wide variety of missions; their work ranged from basic through applied research to systems engineering and operational trouble-shooting. The staffs of these laboratories were generally small, all under 100 except for one with 270 professionals.

The seminar staff did not begin with any fixed ideas about what knowledge from the growing body of facts relevant to laboratory management ought to be used, or how this information might best be introduced and presented. It saw its role as that of introducing the managers to these ideas, to help them probe the implications of these findings, and to assist them in thinking through the meaning of these for changes in their own behavior or the operations within their laboratories. In short, our staff saw its goal as being to optimize the conditions for learning and changing, and to study the process of learning and changing as it occurred.

The seminar was conducted in twelve sessions, biweekly from January through June in 1967. Meetings were from 5 to 9 PM each Monday at the Fairlane Conference Center of the University of Michigan. Dinners were served at the Center, and were an integral part of the work sessions.

Four distinct types of knowledge were introduced as inputs: (1) empirical social research findings on the administration of scientific and engineering organizations, (2) knowledge of human relations skills having immediate practical application, (3) problem solutions and management practices from own experience of the participating directors, and (4) survey research data for each director especially collected for this project from members of his own laboratory. To elaborate on these a little further, the basic text for the seminar was *Scientists in Organizations,* by Donald Pelz and Frank Andrews. This was supplemented by the findings of the studies reported earlier in this paper, and a compendium of detailed abstracts of social science research on scientists. The practical human relations skills inputs included analyzing and critiquing the manner in which a group is functioning through the use of process evaluation techniques, learning to listen actively and understand fully the ideas and feelings of the other person, and behavioral skill practice and testing through role playing. Discussions of problems in the participants' own laboratories and their own experience in meeting these gave all members a more active contributing role in the seminar. The possibility of a survey at some time was touched on in the brochure and initial interviews, but this was not pressed. By the ninth meeting all participants were very eager to obtain and share this type of additional information about their laboratories.

The seminar sessions did not follow a fixed format. Indeed, an effort was made to change each meeting to accommodate the desires of the participants and incorporate the learnings of the staff. The design did call for some emphasis in each meeting on research findings, on human relations skills concepts and training, on colleague sharing, and most importantly on the practical implications of various inputs, including actual reports by participants on their back-home efforts to apply some idea derived from the seminar.

Typically a meeting would begin at about 5:15 PM with a brief report and analysis of the written reactions to the previous session. This was done to re-establish the sense of continuity through linking one session with another. Usually this review would be followed by the presentation of a problem by one of the participants or perhaps a human relations skill training exercise developed by the staff or the participants and a staff member. Dinner would follow at about 6:30 and would be given over to reports by various members on back-home efforts to try out seminar learnings. After dinner the staff might make a presentation of new findings or work with the participants to summarize and critique the readings. At some point a staff member would make an effort to turn this discussion toward implications for the laboratory. Finally at a little before nine, the staff member concerned with the process of the meeting would lead off the discussion of the evening's various parts. Each member would be encouraged to give his reactions to the meeting as a whole and to mention specific incidents in it that may have been bothersome. The airing of these "hang-ups" was consistently seen as a positive aspect of the meeting. At the end of each meeting a post meeting reaction questionnaire was filled out by all participants and staff.

The seminar began slowly, the early meetings being dominated by one or two individuals who argued strongly against the validity of the Pelz-Andrews research findings. Also noteworthy in these early sessions were unsatisfactory efforts to build group problem-solving discussions around real problems brought to the group by each director. In retrospect, these early meetings were very much like the fifteen three-hour meetings held to present the findings from the survey of data regarding professionals in the government agency. To a certain extent, the introduction of the human relations skill ideas helped the group through both of these difficulties.

A critical turning point in the movement toward acceptance of the research findings came about in the fifth session when the methodology and the findings from the study of professionals in government laboratories were presented. After this discussion, there were very few further questions about the validity and meaningfulness of the measures. The group was able to move on to a serious look at the implications of the findings for change.

In the following meeting, the sixth of the series, Donald Pelz joined the group and presented the synthesis of his work with Andrews. Par-

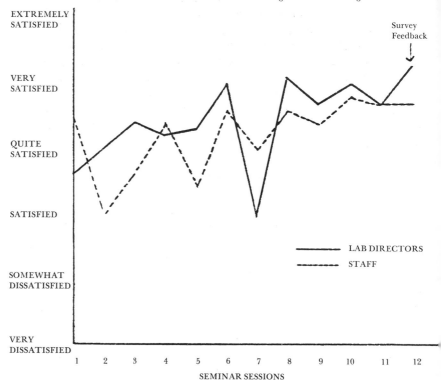

CHART #5:   Satisfaction Ratings After Each Meeting

In general, how satisfied were you with this meeting?

ticipants were very impressed with Pelz and were especially apprecia-
tive of the openness and scientific scepticism with which he approached his own data. This meeting with Pelz was the high point in
the first half of the seminar as indicated by the total satisfaction
ratings in Chart 5.

The seventh meeting was rated low, largely because of a very unsuccessful effort by two directors to role play an interview on a real
problem presented by one of them. They had met between sessions to
prepare and had effectively worked through any differences that they
had. In spite of this low rating, this meeting marked the initiation of
two new activities which would establish the pattern of the remainder
of the seminar. These were: first, a list of management practices implied as "good" from the findings, and second, a detailed discussion of

the possible uses of a survey on one's own laboratory. In each subsequent session some time was devoted to these elements.

The above mentioned list of possible applications is reproduced in Table I.

TABLE I
IMPLICATION FINDINGS DERIVED FROM
"CREATIVE TENSIONS IN THE RESEARCH
AND DEVELOPMENT CLIMATE,"

By Donald C. Pelz in *Science,* July 14, 1967

The management actions listed below are suggested as those which might bring about a greater sense of *security* on the one hand and *challenge* on the other to create a production climate in the R & D laboratory.

1. Insure that once or twice a year each man produces a product which bears his own name—even if a joint document must be broken into parts.
2. A single chief should not assign tasks, judge results, evaluate performance, and recommend pay increases or promotions by himself.
3. In review sessions with executives or clients, include the engineer who is doing the work, and let him do some of the talking, not just his chief.
4. Develop a flat organizational structure with fewer levels.
5. Individual and his supervisor should *jointly* determine assignments.
6. Give the younger man a year or two to dig into his main project.
7. In forming teams, managers can put together individuals who have *similar sources* of motivation—who are interested in the same kinds of problems.
8. The supervisor can encourage cohesion by giving credit to the group rather than to himself.
9. The supervisor can build mutual respect by publicizing the contribution of each member.
10. The supervisor can strengthen teamwork through competition with other groups in the solution of technical problems.
11. The R & D manager can often steer the scientist to others who can give or use help.
12. He can invite the individual to talk to a seminar.
13. Set up study teams and evaluation groups.
14. Pose problems which require consultation for their solution.
15. Invite members of an older group to shoot holes in each other's presentation.
16. When forming a new project committee, he can include individuals who like each other but who use different strategies.
17. Periodic regrouping of teams—always with the consent of persons involved.
18. Give a younger scientist each year a second shorter assignment which demands that he learn a new skill.
19. In an older man, interest in pioneering can be kept strong by tempting him with problems outside his area of expertise.
20. Set up refresher courses.
21. Arrange sabbatical exchanges with a university.

In subsequent sessions this list was subjected to intensive study and discussion and appeared to be a springboard to actual utilization efforts in each of the participating laboratories. It also became a key feature of our efforts to evaluate progress toward utilization. On the whole, the directors found little trouble in accepting items which would have created a greater sense of *security* (autonomy, self-reliance, specialized competence and self-confidence), but appeared to be more wary of actions which might bring about a greater degree of *challenge* (vigorous interaction, intellectual competition).

The twelfth and final session was an all day meeting held on a Saturday at the Institute for Social Research in Ann Arbor. It was given over almost entirely to a feedback of the survey findings in six of the eight laboratories. In spite of the great volume and complexity of the feedback data, all the directors were deeply involved throughout this day, focusing their attention on information in their own organization with the data from the five others listed side-by-side for comparison. As has been observed in the past in other studies, the impact of such self-relevant data was very powerful. It is noteworthy that all those who had data on their own laboratories rated themselves "extremely satisfied" with this last session.

A major effort was made to collect as much information as possible about the impact of this seminar. Meetings were taped and analyzed; questionnaires were administered after each session in which ratings for the meeting as a whole and each different segment were obtained, along with reports of efforts at utilization between sessions. In-depth, focused interviews were held with each participant after the seminar to learn what he had learned and what he was trying to apply. While the survey of laboratory staff was taken primarily to provide additional learning material for the directors, it also contributed to our understanding of the extent to which personnel within laboratories saw changes reported by the directors themselves. Actual on-site observations in the laboratories over a period of time and records of achievement and productivity could not be attempted because of budget and time limitations.

Analyses of the data collected during the life of this seminar and through interviews a year later indicate that:

(1) the directors generally reported increasing satisfaction throughout the seminar.

(2) behavioral science data discussions and intellectual inputs regarding research findings were well received, especially after early questions about validity were resolved.

(3) the practical human relations skills inputs were highly appreciated, particularly the procedures for ensuring man-to-man communication and for critiquing the process of a meeting.

(4) sharing with colleagues and problem-solving sessions around real problems brought to the group by participants were generally disappointing with one or two exceptions.

(5) all the laboratory directors were able to describe changes in attitude and practice which the staff rated as constituting genuine utilization of seminar learning. These ranged in number from three for one laboratory director to eighteen for another.

(6) there was a steady trend in all participants through a utilization scale from meeting to meeting, with cognitive awareness and understanding occurring first, with acceptance, internalization, and planning for use developing next, and with commitment to try, actual use, evaluation, and adoption for continued use coming much later—according to our tape analyses of the seminar sessions.

SUMMARY

What are some of the principal implications of these first years of research on the working environments and the study of the processes required to ensure utilization of such research findings in the management of laboratories?

1. Social scientists are able to identify individual and organizational factors which distinguish productive climates and working environments for scientists and engineers.

2. Most of these findings are consistent with what laboratory directors report they would expect—and few feel there is much they have to learn intellectually.

3. A major problem is the difference between what is known intellectually and what is known behaviorally and is regularly used in the management of their laboratories.

4. Exposure to empirical, quantitative findings from carefully designed surveys does not lead to quick acceptance of these facts. Challenge and resistance is a common response at first and

perhaps a necessary step toward real awareness and understanding, then acceptance, and perhaps the eventual adoption and use of such findings.

5. Effective seminars utilizing a variety of intellectual and behavioral inputs, building on own experiences and research findings from other laboratories can lead to the use of these findings.

It is evident from this account that careful research is just beginning in this complex field of research management. The energy and support required to develop this new area of investigation will not be small, but the value of such research in a society increasingly dependent on new discoveries and innovation is obvious.

ACKNOWLEDGEMENT

The major portion of the research reported on in this chapter was supported by the Division of Behavioral Sciences, Directorate of Life Sciences of the Air Force Office of Scientific Research.

REFERENCES

[1] Mann, Floyd C. "Work Unit Effectiveness in a Scientific Organization." in *The Fundamental Research Activity in a Technology-Dependent Organization.* Washington, D.C. Air Force Office of Scientific Research. USAF. 1965.

[2] Marquis, Donald G. "Organization and Management of Research and Development." Presented at 17th Annual Conference on Administration of Research, Estes Park, Colorado, 1963. University of Denver. Published Proceedings of Denver Research Institute. April, 1964.

[3] Marquis, Donald G. "Scientists in a Technology-Oriented Organization—Their Expectations, Incentives, and Career Patterns." in *The Fundamental Research Activity in a Technology-Dependent Organization.* Washington, D.C. Air Force Office of Scientific Research. USAF. 1965.

Marquis, Donald G. and Straight, David M. Jr. "Organizational Factors in Project Performance." Presented at Second Conference on Research Program Effectiveness. Washington, D.C. Office of Naval Research.

[5] Orth, Charles D. III. "The Optimum Climate for Industrial Research." *Harvard Business Review.* March/April, 1959. pp. 55-64.

[6] Pelz, Donald C. and Andrews, Frank M. *Scientists in Organizations: Productive Climates for Research and Development.* New York. Wiley and Sons. 1966.

[7] Shepard, Herbert A. "Nine Dilemmas in Industrial Research." *Administrative Science Quarterly.* December, 1956. pp. 295-309.

[8] Vollmer, H. M., LaPorte, T. R., Pedersen, W. C., and Langton, P. A. *Adapta-*

tions of Scientists in Five Organizations: A Comparative Analysis. Menlo Park, California. Stanford Research Institute. 1964.

[9] Vollmer, Howard M. *Work Activities and Attitudes of Scientists and Research Managers: Data from a National Survey.* Menlo Park, California. Stanford Research Institute. 1965.

[10] Vollmer, Howard M. *Applications of the Behavioral Sciences to Research Management: An Initial Study in the Office of Aerospace Research.* Menlo Park, California. Stanford Research Institute. 1964.

III. Communication—*Sine Qua Non* of the Behavioral Sciences

LEE THAYER

IT IS EXTREMELY DIFFICULT to talk sense about communication. There
are a number of reasons why this is so, and some awareness of the
reasons for that difficulty is an important preliminary for anyone who
is seriously interested in the subject. So that is where this paper must
begin.

SOME FUNDAMENTAL DIFFICULTIES

It would be impossible to indicate an order of importance of the
several difficulties to be faced in trying to talk sense about communication. What for one reader may stand as a serious obstacle may be
of little consequence for another. Hence I make no claim that the
sequence in which these difficulties are presented in any way represents the order of their importance. Since it is *conceptual* difficulties
we are faced with, the pertinence of any one of them for each reader
can be determined only by the individual reader.

FAMILIARITY, POPULARITY

One difficulty of major import is the fact that the phenomenon of
communication is a familiar one to most of us. And the term is a very
popular one these days. From an individual point of view, the more

*LEE THAYER is Professor of Administration and Director of the Center
for the Advanced Study of Communication in the University of Missouri
at Kansas City. He has been a consultant on communication and organization to a number of industrial organizations and governmental agencies.
His current research has been on the ways in which communication systems and processes affect human and organizational performance. He is
President of the National Society for the Study of Communication. In
September 1968, he joined the faculty of the University of Iowa as Gallup
Professor of Communication Research.*

familiar a phenomenon, the more difficult it is to develop a sound, empirical understanding of it. From an aggregate point of view, the more talked about a phenomenon is, the more difficult it becomes to develop scientifically-sound conceptualizations of it. It is furthermore quite difficult to come to grips with a phenomenon so vital to our behavior.[1]

LACK OF A DISCIPLINE

A second difficulty is the fact that there exists no single scientific discipline having an exclusive interest in communication or a systematic body of knowledge. There are loose "professional" associations of persons having some part interest in communication, of course, as well as academic programs built upon some special orientation; and there is undoubtedly an "invisible college" of scholars whose scientific interests and pursuits with respect to communication do overlap to some degree.[2] But there is nothing like the disciplinary foundations one sees in physics, for example.

Closely related is the fact that the phenomena of communication are so basic to the life and behavioral sciences that they transcend most of the arbitrary disciplinary boundaries which do exist. Each discipline thus appropriates some part-aspect of the total process of communication as a matter of proprietary concern, the consequence being a discontinuous and fractionated hodgepodge of terms and approaches which doesn't add up to much more than any of the pieces. Not only is there no single core of knowledge to draw upon, but there is often no way to relate the part-aspects to one another. Each discipline is destined to study its own myopias. Because the phenomena of communication are so basic as to have some relevance for all scientific disciplines, and because each of the often diverse points of view brought to bear is self-legitimizing, no comprehending body of knowledge is likely to emerge in the near future. It is like a piece of farmland which belongs to everyone for his own whimsical uses; it stands never to be properly cultivated or systematically productive.

APPROACHABLE BOTH OPERATIONALLY AND SCIENTIFICALLY

A third difficulty is the fact that communication, unlike most of the other subjects treated in this volume, can be approached either (or both) as an operational or as a scientific phenomenon. That is, communication is not only something that can be studied, it is something most of us *do*. While it would seem odd to try to talk about someone "physic-ing" or "psychology-ing," it is easy to talk about "communicating."

This is an especially potent difficulty, for there is no necessary relationship between our scientific knowledges and the uses to which those knowledges are put. What the physicist learns from his inquiries into the nature of things is not likely to alter significantly his own social behavior. So it is with the traditional psychologist. The difficulty arises from the pervasive ambiguity that surrounds most of the writing and the talk that goes on about communication; is it in the spirit of scientific inquiry or operational usefulness? Is the purpose to develop a reliable theory of the phenomenon, or to figure out how to "communicate" better in some way?

The fundamental issue, as Donald MacKay has often urged,[3] is whether or not there is a need for a theory of communication as distinct from a body of practical knowhow. It would require too much space to address that issue here. An awareness and an appreciation of this basic difficulty seems to me to be indispensable to an adequate posture for coming to conceptual grips with the phenomena of communication.

Scientism and the Mystique of Technology

A fourth difficulty lies in the incompatibility of our seemingly inexhaustible faith in scientism on the one hand,[4] and on the other the nature of the phenomenon itself. The power of the scientific approach is hardly to be doubted. But the cult of *scientism* is remarkably barren. The increasing efforts being made to "scientize" communication will likely reveal little more about the phenomenon than the limits of its scientizability.

Closely related is the fact that we suffer a deeply embedded cultural belief in technology as the answer to our problems. The illusion is that, no matter what the nature of our problems, we have only to await or urge on the development of some new technology and those problems will be solved. Yet the human and "organizational" communication problems we have today are not basically different from those Confucius pondered more than twenty centuries ago. A fantastic array of technology has evolved; but tacitly assuming these technologies to be an adequate substitute for a sound and comprehensive understanding of the phenomenon has led, not to the solution of our so-called "communication problems," but to an intensification of them.

In short, the inclination to assume that communication *is* whatever is easily and handily scientizable about it, and the inclination to assume that technological progress is equivalent to understanding, are basic difficulties standing in the way of talking sense about communication.

BASIC RECONCEPTUALIZATION

Finally, it is exceedingly more difficult to reconceptualize something as basic and as ubiquitous as communication, and to come to terms with the implications of that basic reconceptualization, than it is to accumulate new knowledges. The ways in which we traditionally and conventionally conceive of communication—those being inadequate and untenable—stand as obstacles to more adequate and more potent ways of conceiving of communication.[5] But the lifeblood of science has always been infused by its basic reconceptualizations, not its "research." What is needed now to provide this sort of impetus for conceptual progress in the study of communication is a basic reconceptualization of the underlying phenomena.

That is what I would like to try to do in this paper: suggest some ways of reconceptualizing the phenomena of communication which offer a means of organizing a wide range of facts and ideas from a wide range of disciplines of the life and behavioral sciences having some part interest in communication—cybernetics, information theory, psychology, systems theory, sociology and anthropology, cognitive studies, and so on.

The reason for this long digression is that this is a task to be faced only when the kinds of difficulties described above are in full and meaningful view.

OBJECTIVES

For these same reasons, it would not be especially profitable to survey here the "state-of-the-art" of human communication theory—

or research. The conceptual/theoretical foundations are neither sound enough, nor broadly enough based. Most of the "research" that has been produced to date is therefore of questionable value. Thus, my objectives here are directed not to the scientific *accomplishments* of this patchwork "field," but to the pressing scientific *need, viz.,*

1. To stimulate some thought about why, and in what ways, communication and its related phenomena are the *sine qua non* of the behavioral sciences;

2. To present a basic conceptual framework for approaching those phenomena empirically and systematically; and

3. To provide a way of generating some of the far-ranging implications of this conceptual foundation.

SOME BASIC CONCEPTS

At the outset, some basic propositions and distinctions need to be introduced.

COMMUNICATION

First, it will be useful, if not necessary, to conceive of communication as one of the two basic life processes—one, of course, being the ingestion and processing of energy, the other being the acquisition and processing of information, or communication. Just as the crucial component of physical metabolism is the conversion of raw environmental processes into energy forms consumable or processable by a particular living system, the crucial component of the communication process is the conversion of raw event-*data* into forms of *information* consumable or processable by that living system.

Communication is not, therefore, a uniquely human phenomenon. We have been greatly disadvantaged by the assumption that communication is something peculiarly human, when in fact the process is as basic and indispensable to living systems as is their physical metabolism.

COMMUNICATION AND INTERCOMMUNICATION

One immediate advantage is that a distinction must be made between communication and intercommunication.[6] The distinction can most clearly be made in terms of the separate functions each subserves.

The primitive functions of communication for all complex living systems are those of

a) "mapping" into itself relationships between itself and some temporary or recurrent aspect(s) of its environment (adaptation),[7] or

b) confirming those relationships or the resulting orientations, to the ends of the stability or the direction of growth or movement of that living system.

The primitive functions of intercommunication—the intentional and mutual production and consumption of event-data—are therefore those of

a) mutual adaptation and/or manipulation (or control), which in turn results in

b) the building and/or confirming of aggregate structures such as family units, communities, societies, etc., and, at the human level, of institutions, cultures, ideologies, etc.

Although an understanding of communication at the human level is hardly possible without a conception of intercommunication, it is necessary to keep in mind that communication and intercommunication are different processes subserving different (though often related) ends. The technologies employed in specifically *human* communication and intercommunication may differ, but the primitive functions subserved are similar throughout the phylogenetic scale.

The Communicational Environment

What *is* uniquely characteristic of human communication and intercommunication is the fact that the technological sophistication of human intercommunication has made possible the emergence and evolution of a purely communicational environment or reality—i.e., an environment or reality comprised of anything that can be and is talked about. Whatever can be and is talked about comprises a reality in the sense that it must be adapted to and dealt with in much the same way as that reality which is subject only to sensory validation.

In other words, man's position on the phylogenetic scale has made possible the emergence and evolution of a communicational environment which has as much or more significance for man than does the physical environment for the "lower" animals. All of those conditions which function as determinants of man's thought and hence his behavior, but which are not directly verifiable by his own sensorium, are aspects of his communicational environment. Thus most of what we term man's values, beliefs, ideologies, aesthetic standards, etc., are ultimately products of human intercommunication. Taken together, anything and everything which man can and does talk about comprises his communicational environment or communicational reality. Whatever one or more men can and do talk about, but which is not amenable to direct sensory contact by them, has no reality beyond what can be and is said about it. The significance of his communicational environment to modern man makes it the major aspect of his total ecology.[8]

TELEOLOGICAL VS. TELESITIC BEHAVIOR

At the level of man, it is necessary to make a distinction between what might be termed his "teleological" contrasted with his "telesitic" behavior. We can do so easily by taking a brief look backward along the phylogenetic scale.

At some vague point along that scale, self-reflexivity emerges as a biological possibility. What this emergent characteristic enables man to do is conceive of himself in relation to those aspects of his environments which he must or would encounter behaviorally.

All living systems, from the simplest to the most complex, exhibit what has been viewed as "purposive" behavior in the teleological sense;[9] that is, given that every healthy living system is continuously and unavoidably in the process of becoming what it is, the behavior it manifests can be viewed as having purposiveness about it.*

Man's complex biological architecture and sophisticated intercommunication technologies make possible an exceptional degree of

---

*Implying different degrees of "intelligence," of course. An interesting example cited by E. Laszlo (in a recent issue of *Main Currents*) is that of the cat and the amoeba. The amoeba evidences no anticipation (or "intelligence") in following a target such as a puddle of water with the appropriate salinity. It exhibits no ability to extrapolate the track of the source. But a cat will run to where he anticipates the mouse will be rather than where it is.

self-reflexivity; he is capable of behaving other than teleologically. Because he can conceive of very intricate and future-projected relationships between himself (as he conceives of himself) and his environments (including other people and his expectations of *their* conceptions of those relationships), man also exhibits *telesitic* behavior—that is, covert or overt behavior undertaken as rational or "intelligent" means to self-determined ends. Living systems and organized aggregates of living systems (such as human organizations) are through the behavior of their members both self-organizing and evolutionary. But overlaying the teleological behavior which occurs in the service of those ends, both man, and, to a greatly limited degree some of his demesticated animals and the "infrahuman" primates, evidence "entrepreneurial" behavior consistent with self-images or self-contrived ends or states. This capacity carries with it the possibility of failure to bring about intended states-of-affairs—a possibility having considerable import for the condition of man and for the evolution of his particular institutions and ideologies.[10]

Teleological behavior is that which a complex living system *can* or *must* engage in to its own end; telesitic behavior is that which man (e.g.) *would* engage in to some further end.

Of relevance here too is the fact that all emergent capacities, such as man's capacity for self-reflexivity and for the invention of communication and intercomunication technologies, are incipient incapacities. Because man's intercommunication abilities can be deployed "consciously," that is, consistent with his own self-images and intended states, they may disadvantage as well as advantage him. In and of themselves, man's capacities for communication and intercommunication are amoral. There is no more absolute good or right implicit in man's sophisticated intercommunication-abilities than in the apparent muteness of butterflies. The sole criterion lies in the consequences of the ways in which those capacities are deployed.

Hence the crucial importance, in the study of *human* communication and intercommunication, of distinguishing between teleological and telesitic behavior.

LEVELS OF ANALYSIS

As one of the two basic life processes, the phenomenon of communication and its concomitants have pervasive implications for all of man's behavior. Whatever it is a man does, qua man, can be carried out only in and through communication and intercommunication. It is for this reason inconceivable that man and his behavior and his artifacts and his institutions can ever be adequately and accurately described apart from a full description of the underlying processes of communication and intercommunication, the *sine qua non* of the behavioral sciences.

Yet the very pervasiveness and ubiquitousness of those processes and their concomitants make it necessary to approach them from the point of view of one or more "levels" of analysis.

The decisions one makes about which levels of analysis to use to guide his inquiries are at once both arbitrary and critical.[11] I have found it most useful, however, to approach communication and intercommunication phenomena from the standpoint of these broad levels of analysis:

a) the intrapersonal (the point of focus being one individual, and the dynamics of communication as such);

b) the interpersonal (the point of focus being a two or more person interactive system and its properties—the process of intercommunication and its concomitants);

c) the multi-person human enterprise level (the point of focus being the internal structure and functioning of multi-person human enterprises);

d) the enterprise ⟷ environment level (the point of focus being upon the interface between human organizations and their environments); and

e) the technological level of analysis (the focus being upon the efficacy of those technologies—both hardware and software—which have evolved in the service of man's communication and intercommunication endeavors).

For purposes of conceptual and empirical inquiry, each successive level of analysis overlays and subsumes the preceding level. Any way of comprehending intercommunication, for example, must be consistent with the way in which communication is comprehended. And so on. A systematic conceptual framework requires this sort of interlevel articulation, a requirement often overlooked.

It can be seen in Fig. 1 that the technological level of analysis transcends and overlays each of the other levels, as well as having an area of inquiry or discourse of its own. What this crude schematic is in-

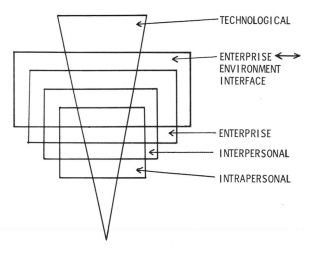

FIGURE 1. Levels of analysis.

tended to imply is that the phenomena of interest at each level of analysis *can* be studied either apart from the technologies that are employed, or in terms of those technologies; and that the technologies of communication and intercommunication *can* be studied apart from their uses at the various levels of analysis, or in terms of those levels or even outside of them. In short, this scheme is a matter of conceptual convenience, and has no necessary theoretical significance. Nor is it intended to be in any sense isomorphic.

It is further no more than a matter of expository convenience to organize the balance of this paper around those levels of analysis. However, the additional space given over to the discussion of the first two levels of analysis is intended to reflect their more fundamental significance.

THE INTRAPERSONAL LEVEL: COMMUNICATION

I have previously suggested that it is conceptually useful, if not necessary, to conceive of the communication process as being compounded of all of those subprocesses by which a living system acquires and converts ongoing event-*data* into *information,* for processing or "consumption" to some end. From that base, a comprehensive frame of reference for the study of human communication can be derived.

1. It is therefore consistent to define *communication* as all of those processes associated with the acquisition and conversion of raw event-data into consumable or processable information, culminating in an instance of taking-something-into-account. We can thus look to a given individual's take-into-account-abilities* and take-into-account-susceptibilities as the co-determining factor (along with the event-data) in the process of communication. Whatever other factors we may wish to include under the heading of "communication," the process does not occur in the absence of acquirable event-data which are at least potentially take-into-account-able by a given individual.

2. As indicated before, the ends or functions subserved by the process of communication are those of

a) enabling the individual to establish or maintain adaptive state-relationships with his two environments (the physical and the communicational) through the mapping-into himself concepts of himself vis-à-vis those aspects of his environments with which he must, or would have, transactions; and

b) enabling the individual to acquire and process or "consume" information, about himself and his environments, having relevance or utility for some present, past, or future behavior.

Although often indistinguishable empirically, conceptually distinguishing the two functions in this way has the advantage of emphasizing, in the first instance, the process of reality-attenuation or "invarianting" which all complex living systems engage in via the process of being-communicated-with by their environments (to the extent of their take-into-account-abilities). It permits us additionally to see, for example, the applicability of Ashby's "law of requisite variety," a very general translation for the present purpose being that an individual can reliably "invariant" his environments psychologically only as his own complexity approaches the complexity of those environments with which he transacts.[12]

In the case of the second of the two functions, it offers the advantage of emphasizing the strategic intelligence gathering and evaluation

---

*This term should be, I believe, attributed to Donald MacKay.

which culminates in some "intelligent" behavior. That is, it suggests the basic dynamic of human behavior as arising out of the continuous monitoring of apparent states-of-affairs relative to his intended states-of-affairs (teleological or telesitic) vis-à-vis those environments.

3. This reformulation also necessitates our making clear the distinction implied between event-data and information. All event-data potentially acquirable by an individual are neutral and "given," devoid in and of themselves of any significance or meaning. Event-data therefore *are;* information is always *information-about* something going on. Event-data and information are of different qualitative orders. The human sensorium is so evolved and structured as to be receptive to certain ranges of certain kinds of event-data. But the functional ingredient of human perception, thought, memory, etc., is *information-about.* Taking-something-into-account involves the acquisition of certain patterns or sequences of event-data, and the simultaneous conversion of that raw material into functionally processable and "consumable" information. In the same way that there is an important qualitative difference between the steer-on-the-hoof and the energy that is ultimately used by the human body subsequent to the ingestion and digestion of a steak, there is a critical qualitative difference between the event-data of one's environment (including verbal event-data) and the information-about it which he derives from it (*i.e.,* creates out of it).

Second, man and his environments are inextricably interdependent or co-determinate. This is inescapable by virtue of the fact that all of man's "intelligent" behavior with respect to himself vis-à-vis his environments is necessarily mediated by his conceptions of those environments, which in turn are his and his fellows' creations. Thus it is ultimately impossible to know whether those environments are orderly or chaotic.[13] So we have no way of knowing whether the process of converting raw event-data into processable *information-about* adds organization or reduces it; it would be impossible to say, for example, whether, in the process of being-communicated-with by his environments, an individual only imperfectly recreates what in its "natural" state is informationally perfect, or whether the individual's contribution to the process adds qualities of structure or organization and thus an order of "information" not intrinsic to the event-data.[14] What is observable and demonstrable is the development and exercise of *conventions* for acquiring and converting event-data. For purposes of communication, these may be personal and idiosyncratic, of course. It is only at the level of intercommunication that similar conventions of taking-into-account arise.

As "properly" socialized humans, we have similar take-into-account-abilities only to the extent that we are similarly skilled in the application of conventions for the acquisition and conversion of event-data. In the process of evolving workable models of what *is* in our environments, of what *matters,* and of *what to expect* as a consequence of the manner in which we relate aspects of our environments, an illusion of isomorphism is created. The validity of that illusion is not empirically testable. Given the dynamic complexity of the human environment, the number of ways of attenuating workable realities of it may be infinite. There is no way of determining the limits of the variety of conventions which would enable us to be communicated-with by our environments.

4. A fourth factor deserving of at least brief mention here is the fact that communication processes thus conceived may be either *morphostatic* or *morphogenetic* in character. That is, individuals (like other open systems) are in-formed* and altered by their environments to the extent that their communication experiences add to or alter their take-into-account-abilities, in which case the process is morphogenetic. Or, individuals in-form their environments to the extent that they impose upon them prior conceptions, for purposes of stability or confirmation—in which case the nature of the transaction is morphostatic. If morphostatic, attenuated states are reinforced or maintained. If morphogenetic, those attenuated states are altered or elaborated.

While one can exercise only those take-into-account-abilities he has in order to make sense of his environments, the possibilities for the elaboration or evolution of new take-into-account-abilities are initially omnipresent.

5. Those interactive systems comprised of an individual's "workable realities," those aspects of his environment with which he would interact, and his behavior in those environments—therefore vary from relatively closed to relatively open. A relatively closed communication system is one in which once-adequate comprehensions of some aspect of the environment are not altered (remain morphostatic) either (1) because no changes occur in the environment or in the individual

---
*A term for which I am indebted to Harley Shands.

which would impinge upon the adequacy of the particular take-into-account-abilities involved, or (2) because the anticipated instability of changing one's comprehensions of that environment exceed his tolerance limits, and he clings to now-inadequate conceptions in spite of their inadequacy.[15]

It should further be of keen interest to those concerned with human communication that it is only when an individual's self-defined ends are both completeable and fully determinate that his communication systems can be completely described; the extent to which they are not fully describable is the extent to which his communication systems are open.[16] The fact that people talk to themselves about their telesitic ends is in most cases sufficient to insure dimensions of indeterminate self-organization.

6. It is thus unavoidable that an individual's specifically human competence and efficacy depends ultimately upon the communication experiences he has had and is capable of having—and, as will be evident in the next section, upon his strategic intercommunication-abilities.

Some Implications

It is only in the implications of these basic concepts that their power and usefulness can be evaluated. The question must be: What are the implications of this way of conceiving of the process of communication for the way I look at X (any observable behavior, social phenomenon, etc.)?

It should be obvious that the great range of implications thus derivable defies any exhaustive listing—here or elsewhere. Yet it may be desirable to suggest one or two examples which might incite the thinking-through of a great many more implications of particular interest to the individual reader.

One of the most significant implications is that individuals behave, not on the basis of the ultimate realities of their environments, but on the basis only of the way they conceive of those realities. The determinants of behavior are not to be found in the event-data of the environments in which individuals exist, but in the interdependence of those environments with the ways they are taken into account—i.e., with the information about those environments (and the beliefs, ideas, etc. about them) which they have available to process. And any workable reality is useful for certain purposes (e.g., the earth is "flat" enough for purposes of walking upon it).

Individual orientations to one's environments are comprised of hypotheses with respect to what is likely to happen if. . . . The test is not whether those hypotheses are "true," but whether they are the most expeditious given the conditions, the objectives or mission, etc. The issue is not one of subjectivity vs. objectivity, as some have argued, but the fact that the ways in which we conceive of our worlds (and hence behave in them) often depend more upon our take-into-account-abilities — i.e., upon our communicate-abilities — than upon the "objective" realities of the environment (which are indeterminable of course).[17]

A second major complex of implications stems from the proposition that most individual behavior can be conceived of as the behaver's solution to a problem. But many commentators (and researchers) on human problem-solving and decision-making neglect the most critical aspects of the process—those of apprehending and identifying (naming) the problem which is to be dealt with.

There are two basic empirical errors made in conventional approaches to problem solving:

1. There is nothing "problematical" about event-data; event-data are meaningless in and of themselves. It is only in translation as information-about (human processing) that event-data (conditions, circumstances, etc.) are apprehended as problematical or not.

2. Second, the conditions identified as problematical are typically presumed to be eliminated by the proper (or adequate) solution. Yet it is empirically unavoidable that the solution to a problem (at least those which culminate in some action-in-the-environment) doesn't eliminate existing states-of-affairs, but consequents in the creation of new or altered states-of-affairs. Thus the criterion should not be sought in the excellence of the solution as such, but in the desirability of the altered state-of-affairs relative to the previous (before solution) state-of-affairs.

What is unavoidable, if we are to take what we know about communication seriously, is that

    a) Problems exist only in people;
    b) Problems exist only in the form they are conceived of;

c) The problem dealt with is the one named or identified (not the "objective" conditions of concern); and

d) Given that one can "get into contact" with his environment only via his own take-into-account-abilities, the solutions (or potential solutions) one has for problems generally determine the problems he "sees" or identifies.

It is in this way that the implications of these basic concepts can be drawn out.

Associated Technologies

The technologies that have evolved in the service of communication include all of those tools and techniques developed to enhance or facilitate the acquisition of event-data (e.g., the telescope, spectacles, ear horn) and its conversion and consumption (e.g., conceptual schemata, conventions of reality-attenuation, personal "maps" etc.).

Languages, as such, are not necessary to communication. They are, however, crucial to the development of complex social organizations via intercommunication—and hence are part of the technology of intercommunication.[18]

THE INTERPERSONAL LEVEL: INTERCOMMUNICATION

To avoid the mentalistic pitfalls of much of the literature on intercommunication, it is important to keep in mind these two basic points:

1. The way in which intercommunication is comprehended must be consistent with the basic phenomena of communication. The interpersonal level of analysis overlays and is in addition to, not in lieu of, the intrapersonal level of analysis.

2. There are but two ways of affecting and being affected by the environment—physically (coercively) and communicationally. Empirically, there are no alternatives. The vague mysticism that surrounds many popular conceptions of intercommunication—e.g., as the "transfer of meaning"—has greatly impeded progress toward a scientific understanding of the processes involved.

What I hope to provide here is a brief reformulation of the concept of intercommunication which is fully consistent with the empirical knowledge we do have of the underlying phenomena of communication.

3. What is characteristic of intercommunication (as contrasted with the individual process of communication) is the attempt by one or more individuals to influence, direct, control, or focus the communication experiences of one or more. One person presents himself as an aspect of another's environment and produces cultural artifacts in the conventional forms of messages, to be taken-into-account by that other in a way intended by (or acceptable to) the first.

4. The ends or functions subserved by intercommunication, then, are those of

a) Mutual adaptation, via the creation and perpetuation of shared communicational environments; and

b) Mutual control and manipulation, consequenting in the emergence and evolution of institutions, social organizations (of all types), cultures, ideologies, etc.

It is intercommunication which makes possible the emergence of higher-order systems, both social and communicational. Intercommunication is therefore both the means and the ends of creating, altering, maintaining, and exploiting the communicational environment, and of the social structures, ideologies, etc., embedded in it.

5. The process of communication is basic to all living systems. Required for successfully engaging in the sophisticated kinds of intercommunication we are all familiar with are

a) A language,

b) A minimal set of rules for the conduct of the participants of the encounter,

c) A relationship, mutually conceived of, and

d) A minimal degree of mutuality or complementarity with respect to intercommunicative intentions and their anticipated consequences.

To the extent that the process of intercommunication is "successful," we "map" each other into each other, and simultaneously "map" each other's adaptive mappings into each other. This produces an illusion of reality about those aspects of our environments which exist only in and through our intercommunication about them. But such similar or harmonious orientations, perceptions, beliefs, etc., are better conceived of as *intersubjectivities,* however, not as "reality" by tacit agreement. With respect to communicational realities, "right" and "wrong," "true" and "false," can have only normative relevance.

6. Two or more people in continuous or recurrent intercommunication comprise a second-order communication system. Such systems have properties of their own, which are not necessarily the properties of any of the individuals involved. These emergent properties function as system determinants. For example, the dynamic nature of a communicative relationship, once formed and always in evolution,* is a significant determinant of the behavior of the persons involved when they are in intercommunication.

All higher-order living systems may also be thought of as compound enterprises. Each individual involved is himself an enterprise to the extent he exercises his telesitic potentials, and the *raison d'etre* of any human organization identifies it as well as a collective enterprise. The conceptual difficulties this presents for comprehending higher-order systems from intercommunication up are perhaps obvious: not only are there individual communication systems subserving each individual, and interpersonal systems linking pairs intercommunicatively, and so on, but the collective enterprise achieves health and viability only to the extent that *its* communication system is efficacious.

7. Every intercommunicative relationship is an organization. Under scrutiny, it reveals the same conditions of "organization-ness" that any larger social structure does. So that concept should perhaps be introduced here.

Anything that is organized is organized only to the extent that its parts are subordinated to the whole. In effect, this means that at least task-relevant freedoms (variances) must be either abdicated by the components (à la humans) or designed out of them or denied them (à la complex biological organisms, machines, or humans to an extent via socialization and institutionalization). To be organized, the components must mutually control one another in some fashion—either by

---

*Relationships (i.e., intercommunication systems) are "purposive," too, in the teleological sense, even if not in the telesitic sense. To the extent the impetus of the evolutionary (teleological) thrust of such higher-order systems is not sourced in the one or the other person involved, or "managed" by them, it becomes a system determinant by default.

design (as in a digital computer) or by tacit accommodation (as in human social structures of all sorts) . Interpersonal relationships, however, as well as other organizational relationships, may be either *symbiotic* or *synergistic*.

Since intercommunication is the almost exclusive human means of mutual control and manipulation, it is through intercommunication that we "get organized"—whether that organization is parent-child, boss-subordinate, teacher-student, clerk-customer, husband-wife, friend-friend, or other relationship. Every continuing relationship (organization) requires the abdication or deprivation of certain degrees of freedom on the part of the members of that relationship. Intercommunicatively, it is the indeterminacy of the other's reaction which must be minimized. This is accomplished by mutually invarianting each other. Thus the ultimate trade-off in all intercommunication is between control and indeterminacy, an unavoidable trade-off of pervasive importance for all social (intercommunicative) behavior.

SOME IMPLICATIONS

Again, the implications of these reformulations go to the depth and breadth of man's social activities and endeavors, and hence defy even representative specification here. But two examples may be suggestive.

Intercommunication is the means via which communicational environments are created and maintained. All of our institutions, ideologies, beliefs, values, theories, etc., are created in and perpetuated through intercommunication. This communicational environment— these "realities"—are in effect the major portion of our human ecology. As such, they essentially determine the human condition: the kind of people we are going to have, our "human nature," human viability and efficacy, in short, the potentials and limits within which all other forces must operate.

Humans are in-formed within their communicational ecologies, and in turn perpetuate them. The widespread belief of not so many years ago that the best cure for many of man's ills was blood-letting is no more far-fetched than many beliefs held today—about human communication, for example! Because we intercommunicate and in-form or institutionalize one another, we are indeed carelessly fiddling with our own destinies as humans in the most vital ways. Urbanization and pollution do affect man's condition, but in pitifully minor ways by comparison to the potency of what we have done and continue to do to each other through the byproducts (cultures, beliefs, etc.) of our intercommunication.

We are the communication experiences we have had, and we can be what our communicational ecologies permit or force us to be. It is almost unbelievable that we continue to treat communication in a most superficial manner!

A second suggestive implication is revealed in the criterion we usually hold as the epitome of "good" communication: "effectiveness." An insidious and widespread assumption is the offhand belief that communication is in and of itself "good," and that if some of it is good, more of it would be better. Closely related is a similarly widespread assumption that the solution to most of the world's problems —from marital to international—is simply "better" communication.[19]

That assumption is extremely misguided and erroneous. There is nothing intrinsically good or bad about the process of communication —and particularly not about the practices of intercommunication. If a person satisfactorily achieves his communicative intentions vis-à-vis another person, we say he has "communicated" effectively. But this overlooks the compounding of enterprises when two or more people are involved. What is "effective" from one person's point of view may be detrimental to the other person(s) involved—as when schizophrenic mothers produce schizophrenic daughters via intercommunication, or when the commander's order, faithfully obeyed, leads to the death of all hands on board, or when the "I love you," "I love you too" exchange leads to hate or the degradation of one or both persons.

The much-hallowed notion of "effectiveness" is a completely inadequate one when a second or higher-order system is involved.[20] What is "effective" communication from one person's point of view in no way guarantees that the consequences will be efficacious for those higher-order systems of which that person is but one (of two or more) components.

Associated Technologies

In addition to those technologies pertinent to the intrapersonal level of analysis, the technologies involved at the interpersonal level

include all of those tools and techniques by which the cultural artifacts we call "messages" are produced and disseminated, stored and/
or retrieved, etc., whether individual or "mass."

Languages (or other such codes)[21] are thus a part of the technology
of intercommunication, as are the techniques of speech and writing
(and other aural or oral display). All of the media (hardware) via
which codified data are transported, etc., are pertinent to this level, as
are the forms and conventions by which those codified data are to be
interpreted and comprehended (software).

THE MULTI-PERSON HUMAN ENTERPRISE LEVEL

Human organizations exist in various forms—ranging from pro-
longed conversations to marriages to clans to communities to corpora-
tions to the "American society." What is organized about all of them
—i.e., their "organization-ness"—is very much the same in all instances.

The one distinction I want to emphasize, however, is between essentially *evolved* organizations like friendships or a society and essentially *contrived* organizations—like a corporation or a civic group. "Essentially," because neither type is purely evolved or purely contrived.
The difference is a matter of degree. A corporation is (at least at the
outset) more contrived than evolved, and the larger society (at least
as it matures) is more evolved than contrived.

The distinction is a useful one. The communication system(s) subserving an "evolved" human organization evolves with that organization; it is inductively formed (i.e., as needed and as a consequence of
the intercommunication that occurs). But the communication sys-
tem(s) of a contrived human organization is partially contrived along
with the goals and the structure of that enterprise; it is deductively
formed (i.e., rationally, to fit the ends, the structures, and the functions of the components of that enterprise, their task-relationships,
etc.). There are a great many implications of this distinction.

1. Multi-person human enterprises can be viewed as third-order
systems, compounded of individual enterprises, interpersonal enterprises of various complexities, and the rationalized ends and means of
the enterprise itself. Thus there are at least three orders of communication systems involved, and it is their integration or paralleling that
continues to challenge information system designers and managers
alike.

2. In addition to all of the factors of concern at the communication and intercommunication levels of analysis, what is appropriately of concern at this level of analysis is the design of enterprise communication systems for the purposes of generating, disseminating, storing, processing, displaying, and acquiring event-data pertinent to the performance of each subtask within the enterprise. The difficulty, of course, is that the enterprise must be "open" if it is to be adaptive and viable, yet it must be "closed" in order to be organized, predictable, and efficient.

Only tasks that are completeable and determinate have information requirements that can be defined (rationally specified in advance). To the extent tasks cannot or should not be closed in this sense, the information requirements for those tasks cannot be completely rationalized. Thus the design of enterprise communication systems must be both rationalized and "exigencized"—a condition that is logically unapproachable by the management and information "sciences." Stability and efficiency—which are quite approachable via cybernetics—are not the only criteria of enterprise viability, and in fact may be pathologic symptoms.

3. The efficacy of the design (or evolution) of an enterprise's communication systems is in part determined by the efficacy of the structure of the enterprise itself. Many so-called organizational "communication problems" are not at their source communication problems, but organization design problems.[22] Otherwise efficacious communication systems can compensate to a limited extent for poor enterprise design (or for human incompetencies in that enterprise), but that offsetting measure should be seen as compensation, not as elimination of the underlying fault.

4. If we think of the internal workings of an enterprise only in terms of its efficiency, control, or organization-ness, then what we would attempt ideally to do would be to design or constrain out of every member his cognizance of everything but what is necessary to the performance of his task. Then we would attempt to equip him with just those take-into-account-abilities which would enable him to apprehend and interpret problematicalness in precisely the desired way. Finally, we would organize his task-related intercommunication systems in such a way that his inputs and outputs were perfectly regulated and controlled. This is precisely what we do when we build an airplane or a computer. The difficulty is, however, that

while data transmission and acquisition may be highly rationalized, communication and intercommunication are not and largely can not be; people are relatively open systems, and to the extent they are open, their communication systems are open. It is human enterprising which energizes and organizes human enterprises, and which contributes whatever adaptive and telesitic viability they may have. Thus if enterprises are to evolve in an evolving environment consistent with their rationalized ends,[23] then their communication systems must be exigencized as well as rationalized.

IMPLICATIONS

If we recognize that it is the automatismic and nonconscious nature of an individual's behavior which makes possible higher degrees of competence or skill, what are the implications for the design and management of enterprises? The fact that the good pianist practices until he is not conscious of being communicated-with by the music on the page is the condition which increases his potential proficiency. If any of us had to make all of the actions necessary to driving a car consciously, we would have great difficulty.

What is the significance of this for the design of enterprise communication systems? It seems possible that attention has been concentrated upon communication issues and problems which are ultimately picayune, while ignoring other communication issues and design opportunities which might significantly alter the structure and the viability of human enterprises. I refer to the advantages of *non*communication or of *non*cognizance at successively higher levels in the enterprise. Similarly, the assumptions that information is the same thing as communication and that more information in decision-making is somehow better than less have led us down exceedingly unfruitful—and even disadvantageous—paths.

ASSOCIATED TECHNOLOGIES

Most of the technologies applied at the enterprise level of analysis are simply extensions of those available at the interpersonal level. However, a brief statement about the application of computers and "information systems" would be very much in order.

Confucius was concerned about much the same sorts of "organizational communication problems" that we read about today. Given that our current conceptions of the communication process are not much advanced over those held in Confucius' time (and in many respects less so), it is little wonder that the history of our concern with such matters is largely a history of our search for a technological panacea of one kind or another. The present-day faith in computerization and "information systems" as the solutions to our enterprise ills is a continuation of that historical search for panaceas.

An "information system" cannot compensate for the incompetencies of the members of an enterprise (particularly not its leaders), or for the inefficacy of the design of an enterprise. And in many cases, the applique-ing of computers and information systems onto ongoing enterprises has led to an intensification of underlying structural and human incompetencies. There is, of course, great potential in these technologies, both in their hardware and their software aspects. But this potential will never be realized apart from some fundamental progress in the comprehension of the phenomena of communication and intercommunication and their concomitants.

Related to the pitfalls of the technological mystique is the assumptive confusion between "information" and communication. What "information" systems and computers handle are data—not information. This is not "just" a semantic matter; the stuff the mind works with (i.e., that which is processable by humans) is not of the same order as the stuff which is carried along in coded form through wires and switches.

It should be emphasized again that only closed systems are completely describable. To the extent that one or more of the enterprises compounded in human organizations are telesitic, the communication systems subserving them will necessarily be open. Since only fully closed (or closeable) systems are rationalizable via deduced "information" systems, the applicability and usefulness of computers and their related data systems, as they exist today, are only partial. That is, they are fully applicable only to those tasks and enterprises which are determinate and completeable. Under any other conditions, their applicability is limited.

THE ENTERPRISE↔ENVIRONMENTAL LEVEL

Those who have contemplated the enterprise↔environment level of analysis over the years have frequently been tempted to analogize directly from the organism←→environment interface. But there are some differences.

1. As indicated before, it is useful to conceive of a human organization as a compound enterprise. The phenomena of communication and intercommunication are not basically different in this context; but they must be viewed as occurring within the context of a contrived social organization having rationalized task functions, data systems, decision prerogatives, etc. In addition, every complex enterprise has a life of its own; that is, as a result of the actions taken by its members on-behalf-of the enterprise, it is continuously in the process of evolving—irreversibly. A final overlay is that of the enterprise's telesitic existence. Its goals or ends (or its raison d'etre), and the means thereto are chosen by one or more members, or by all of the members tacitly (as a byproduct of their behaviors). This establishes the need for an additional communication system, one which links the enterprise with the relevant domains of its environment. What is observable at this level, then, is a complex hierarchy of communication systems which may or may not articulate one with another.

2. At this level of a fourth-order system, what must be organized are capacities for creating, maintaining, altering, or utilizing intercommunicative state-relationships between the enterprise and its relevant environmental domains. Because few "contrived" enterprises are developed and organized from the outside in, as "evolved" organizations are, they are in constant danger of "losing touch" with their environments, which are continuously changing as a result of the telesitic behaviors of other enterprises, of the evolving self-organization of those environments, and the like.

The internal operations of an enterprise can be controlled; relationships with its environments cannot be controlled, but must be strategically coped-with. This may be one reason why "management scientists" and "operations researchers" have so little of substance to say about this level of analysis.[24] Because telesitic behavior alters both the enterprise and its environment, is morphogenetic for both, and for the state-relationships that interlink them, and is neither completeable nor determinate, the consequences are hardly "scientizable," even probabilistically. But this does not mean the underlying processes are not understandable.

3. A further factor to be contended with is that the same ends can

be reached via different means and from different sets of circumstances where living systems are concerned *(equifinality),* and that similar sets of circumstances can consequent in different ends *(multifinality).* Such conditions place extreme limits upon the possibilities for arriving at "laws" of organizational behavior. But approaching such complex phenomena as communication concomitants and by-products may prove to be especially fruitful.

IMPLICATIONS

One implication is that, because the basic phenomena of communication are what they are, living (open) systems and their environments are interdependent. What this means, in turn, is that the success or failure of an enterprise is a function not of the enterprise alone (as is so often assumed), but of the nature of the state-relationships that obtain between the enterprise and the various relevant domains of its environments. Thus "profit" is not a measure of enterprise effectiveness, but of the efficacy of its state-relationships. No enterprise can be more efficacious than its subserving communication systems.

A second implication is the fact that our deeply-embedded scientistic orientations have led us to think in terms of "riskless" change. This is fallacious. The only out-of-risk living system is that one which is being perfectly controlled by its environment. Any exercise of telesitic capacities carries with it the risks of disequilibrium and even of failure. Telesitic choices are made on the basis of information-about, and hence carry with them all of the imperfections and potential risks of morphogenetic communication.

ASSOCIATED TECHNOLOGIES

There are very few technologies appearing at this level of analysis that have not been appropriated from the other levels. There is currently some interlocking of computers amongst buyers and sellers, government agencies, etc., for purposes of expediency. But these are capabilities which exist within enterprises.

In the years just ahead, however, new technologies will emerge to enhance and facilitate the communication systems of the enterprise *qua* enterprise. These will greatly modify the conceptions of enterprise design and functioning which we now hold. The impetus for these changes will come from our increasing cognizance and understanding of the basic nature of communication and communication systems for the functioning of all living systems.

THE TECHNOLOGICAL LEVEL

The technologies of communication and intercommunication can be and often are studied apart from the basic phenomena to which they are applied.

For example, descriptive linguistics focuses upon one particular technology of intercommunication—language forms and patterns. Similarly, the study of media characteristics and codes, deriving from the "communication" and information theory formulations of scholars such as Shannon and Weiner, is the study of but one aspect of the technology of human intercommunication.

These are perfectly valid and useful endeavors. However, the technological mystique so deeply imbedded in our culture, along with the remarkable faith we seem to put in scientism, have led some researchers and perhaps a great many laymen to assume that the "secrets" of human communication will ultimately be revealed through these studies of the technology. There is seductive appeal, but considerable danger, in attributing too much relevance (for human communication and inter-communication) to the mathematical models, the formulae, and the other trappings connected with purely technological studies. It may be useful to study and refine horse harness, but one would hardly expect to find therein the "secrets" of the horse's behavior (or the driver's, for that matter).[25]

Much more care needs to be taken to avoid the confusion that often exists between the phenomena of communication and the technologies employed.

What I have attempted here is to suggest an empirically-sound conceptual frame of reference for approaching and comprehending the fundamental nature of human communication and intercommunication. To the extent that these reformulations are acceptable and useful, the frame and substance of the behavioral sciences will be subject to radical changes, both in method and approach. It is likely that the failure to build those sciences on a firm understanding of this one of the two basic life processes has contributed to the fact that little real progress has been made.

To accommodate these basic reformulations in our thinking will require widespread and continuous searches for their implications for all of man's thinking and his behavior, which are both cause and effect of his communication and intercommunication, and of their social and institutional byproducts.

REFERENCES

[1] "Sciences most intimate to man and thus most frightening for power structures have come last. Astronomy developed before geography, physical science before biology, medicine before psychology—although in each case the availability of data was in the reverse order" (Joseph H. Monane, *A Sociology of Human Systems.* New York: Appleton-Century-Crofts, 1967, pp. 86-7). Cf. B. Berelson and G. A. Steiner, *Human Behavior: An Inventory of Scientific Findings.* New York: Harcourt, Brace & World, 1964, p. 11. But cf. R. R. Grinker, Sr. (ed.), *Toward a Unified Theory of Human Behavior.* 2nd ed. New York: Basic Books, 1967.

[2] The recent spate of "readers" in the field attests to this. The "Macy meetings" were an early attempt to pull these scholars together, as are the current symposia sponsored by the University of Missouri at Kansas City and its Center for the Advanced Study of Communication.

[3] E.g., in the discussion, pp. 164-65, in L. Thayer (ed.), *Communication: Theory and Research.* Springfield, Ill.: C. C. Thomas, 1967.

[4] Cf., for example, Susanne Langer, *Mind: An Essay on Human Feeling.* Vol. 1, Baltimore: The Johns Hopkins Press, 1967, Ch. 2; and M. Polanyi in "A Conversation with Michael Polanyi," *Psychology Today,* 1968, 1 (No. 12), p. 20.

[5] Those preconceptions, our traditional concepts of communication, are often insidious. "Communication is the 'transfer of meaning'" has an appealing ring to it. But none of our receptors is capable of receiving "meaning," the notion of "transfer" is a flagrantly untenable one. The typical formula, $A \rightarrow B = X$ (A "communicates" something to B with X result), is similarly misleading. What one person says to another is no more the product of the utterer than it is of the receiver; in fact, it is in practice difficult if not impossible to partial out their separate contributions to the overall consequence. It is quite observable that the process is neither linear nor algebraic. Why we continue to cling to those faulty orientations is perhaps partly explained by the difficulties outlined at the beginning of this paper.

[6] There is a mysterious but widely-held belief that when one talks about communication he ought to use totally familiar language. Yet conceptual progress in the study of communication has been greatly impeded by the lack of a special set of terms by which to do so. Perhaps more than any other field, the study of communication sorely needs inventive constructs and special-purpose terms, like *intercommunication.*

[7] There are many other terms for this process, which Bohm has referred to as "invarianting."

[8] See, e.g., the author's "Communication: Tool, Game, Ecology," in the publication of the Communication Colloquium, University of Wisconsin—Milwaukee, 1968. Cf. J. Ruesch and G. Bateson, *Communication: The Social Matrix of Psychiatry.* New York: Norton, 1951.

[9] Cf. the section on "Cybernetics and Purpose" in W. Buckley (ed.), *Modern Systems Research for the Behavioral Scientist.* Chicago: Aldine, 1968.

[10] As described, for example, in Helen Merrill Lynd, *Shame and The Search for Identity* (New York: Science Editions, Wiley, 1961), and Allen Wheelis, *The Illusionless Man* (New York: Norton, 1966), among hundreds of other books of recent years. I should also note the similarity between the distinction I am making here, and the distinction Kenneth Burke makes between "motion" and "action" (in, e.g., the discussion on pp. 358-59 of L. Thayer, *Communication: Concepts and Perspectives.* Washington, Spartan Books, 1967, and his earlier volumes and papers).

[11] The linguist or psycholinguist might employ the more familiar levels of the *syntactical,* the *semantic,* and the *pragmatic.* But few psycholinguists conceive of language as a technology of intercommunication. Thus these categories, being anchored in language, are limiting. The biologist would probably prefer the categories of *metabolic, epigenetic,* and *genetic.* But, again, these seem to me limiting for the purposes of a comprehensive approach to communication.

[12] W. Ross Ashby, *An Introduction to Cybernetics,* New York: Science Editions, Wiley, 1963.

[13] See Stafford Beer's "Below the Twilight Arch—A Mythology of Systems," in D. P. Eckman (ed.), *Systems: Research and Design.* New York: Wiley, 1961.

[14] It is not the "Information Theory" issue I would raise here (i.e., the matter of uncertainty reduction). It is the issue of whether, communicationally, man filters out uncertainty or *adds* whatever uncertainty there is.

[15] That those tolerance limits vary greatly from person to person, and typically shrink under certain conditions, is suggested in M. Rokeach, *The Open and Closed Mind.* New York: Basic Books, 1960. Cf. J. Ruesch, *Disturbed Communication.* New York: Norton, 1967.

[16] Cf. M. Toda and E. H. Shuford, Jr., "Logic of Systems." Tech. Doc. Rep. No. ESD-TDR-64-193. Bedford, Mass.: L. G. Hanscom Field, A. F. Systems Command, 1964; and P. M. Fitts, *Notes and Selected Readings on Human Engineering.* Ann Arbor: University of Michigan, College of Engineering, 1959.

[17] The notion of "objective reality" is a purely abstract construct, of course. However, the issue I want to raise is not the philosophic issue of how one's conceptions of the world compare with "objective reality," but simply that one bases his behavior not upon "objective reality" but upon his personal conceptions of "it."

[18] See, for example, the author's *Communication and Communication Systems.* Homewood, Ill.: Irwin, 1968, esp. Chap. 6, "People, Behavior, and Communication," and Chap. 17, "The Technology of Communication."

[19] " . . . an important cornerstone of American middlelore holds that communication can be counted on to spread emotional warmth, that any interpersonal or intergroup problem is really a lack-of-communication problem, that conflicts domestic and international will disappear when people get to know one

another and 'reason together' . . . The amount of communication among components, however, appears to have little impact in either setting or changing a system's emotional tone." J. H. Monane, *op. cit.*, p. 59. Cf. E. Goffman, *Encounters.* Indianapolis: Bobbs-Merrill, 1961.

[20] Cf. the author's "On Communication and Change: Some Provocations, in *Proceedings* of the 11th Annual Institute in Technical and Organizational Communication. Ft. Collins: Colorado State University, 1968.

[21] The distinction often made between signs and symbols may or may not be a useful one. The danger lies in the mentalistic connotations of symbols, when in fact one person's symbolic utterances in the presence of particular others may be both the necessary and sufficient conditions for the responses of those others (as in the *kumpan* theory of the ethologists—which does not need "symbols" as an explanator).

[22] This and other distinctions are further detailed in my "Communication Problems: Organizational 'Virus X' " in *Proceedings* of the 15th International Conference of the Society of Technical Writers and Publishers, in press.

[23] Some engineering-oriented writers refer to this condition as "ultrastability," but I believe that more than ultrastability is involved—that "more" being the people who energize enterprises.

[24] Those who approach such complex phenomena scientistically can bring to bear methods appropriate only to *closed* systems. So closed system methods are either applied to essentially open systems, or open system factors are simply assumed away as being irrelevant. The search for riskless choices and decisions exponentially increases employment in these technologically-based industries, however!

[25] That McLuhanism, "the medium is the message," is catchy, but even horses can discriminate drivers better than they can harness.

IV. The Microwave Sky

Ronald N. Bracewell

SOME EARLY HISTORY

EVERYONE IS FAMILIAR THESE DAYS with the reports of new discoveries in radio astronomy, such as the remarkable quasars, to quote one example that has been mentioned widely in the news; and so we tend to forget that a few years ago it was a very surprising idea that one could receive radio waves merely by pointing a directional antenna at the sky. However, it often leads to a better understanding to have a historical view of how things came about, and so let us go back to the closing years of the last century and, by reminding ourselves of the state of knowledge of physics that existed at that time, we shall see the steps by which our present picture of the radio sky unfolded.

At that time a period of experimental investigation of the laws governing the emission of light and heat from hot bodies was coming to a close. Essential features of the theory were still missing, but the experimental facts were reaching the degree of precision that would allow Planck's quantum theory to show itself clearly superior to the theories of radiation that preceded it. For example, it had been shown that a hot wire at a given temperature emits most strongly at a wavelength that is inversely proportional to the absolute temperature and that the power emitted per unit wavelength interval is inversely pro-

RONALD N. BRACEWELL is Professor of Electrical Engineering at Stanford University. His investigations are of solar disturbances and flares, radiations from the moon, planets, nebulae, star clusters and distant galaxies by the use of interferometers and also high resolution observations made on galactic and extragalatic radio sources. He has done ionospheric research at the Cavendish Laboratory, Cambridge University, and was concerned with very long wave propagation and radio astronomy at the Commonwealth Scientific and Industrial Research Organization, Sydney, Australia, where he was a Senior Research Officer in the Radiophysics Laboratory. He has served on advisory panels for the National Science Foundation, the Naval Research Laboratory, the Office of Naval Research, the National Academy of Sciences, the National Radio Astronomy Observatory and the Advanced Research Projects Agency.

portional to the square of the wavelength, if the wavelength is long.

At that time also, Hertz had just performed the experiments in generation and detection of radio waves which, for the first time, demonstrated the connection between light and electricity and magnetism that had been predicted by Maxwell on theoretical grounds. It was therefore quite clear that light, heat and radio waves were all electromagnetic phenomena of the same kind, differing mainly in wavelength.

Given this state of knowledge you will see that one could confidently deduce that radio waves would be found to be emitted by hot objects. When I say hot I mean merely some temperature that is above absolute zero, so that even the human body, which is generally thought of as only warm, comes within the category of hot objects, and would therefore also be expected to be a source of radio waves. This rather startling idea is an unfamiliar one but can be seen to be an absolutely necessary consequence of laws of physics that were well established over seventy years ago. Of course, we all know that the body emits electromagnetic waves in the infrared region and that this radiation can be felt by placing the palm of the hand close to the skin. To detect the radio waves, however, is a different matter, and if one wanted to demonstrate the emission of radio waves from a hot object, the wise thing to do would be to look around for the hottest object available. That object is the sun, and the basic idea of looking for the solar radio waves that ought to be there occurred to several nineteenth century scientists simultaneously.

Now a little quantitative consideration will indicate the magnitude of the experimental difficulty involved. Since the radiation intensity falls off inversely as the square of the wavelength, then when we bear in mind that radio waves are, very roughly, one million times longer than light waves, we see that the radio frequency radiation will be 10^{-12} times fainter than the light. Still, at 6000 degrees the sun is very bright and, who knows, there may be some surprises. Among those attempting the experiment was Nordmann, who ran an aerial 175 meters long out on snow-covered Mont Blanc. Why he went to this altitude I do not know. In any case this attempt and the others failed, but the very next time it was attempted, by Southworth, in 1942, the experiment succeeded.

Meanwhile, radio waves from the galaxy had been picked up by Jansky in the course of a survey to determine the general levels of radio interference. This is a matter of economic importance because the cost of the expensive part of a communications link, the transmitter, is set by the precise level of the very faint interference background against which the received signal is to be heard. To be brief, Jansky very cleverly identified an interference component of extraterrestrial origin and was able to prove beyond any doubt that it had its origin in the galaxy of which our sun is a part.

With the passage of years many more discoveries of radio signals from space were made. We may now jump forward in time and look at the picture as we know it today in a number of the modern fields of radio astronomy. To a large extent I will concentrate on the microwave end of the radio spectrum, which provides an ample number of examples for description.

GENERAL ASPECT OF THE SKY

One way of thinking about the radio sky is to suppose that the human race had evolved with radio antennas instead of eyes and then to describe what we would see as we peered about us. It is such a fascinating thought to the radio designer, however, that I cannot refrain at this point from talking about how one would go about designing people with antennas. The first design parameter to settle would be the wavelength of operation and, of course, this would make a profound difference to the general appearance. If we settled on the short microwaves, a tidy arrangement with waveguides and electromagnetic horns can be imagined; but if they had to operate in the meter wavelength region, some awkward problems with dipoles and TV-type antennas would have to be handled.

Of course, this discussion immediately makes us realize that there are real advantages and disadvantages associated with different wavelength regions and makes us wonder what the considerations were that led to the eye working in the visible range of the electromagnetic spectrum. It so happens that the spectrum of sunlight reaches its peak in the general neighborhood of the visible (the precise wavelength ranging from 4829 to 8497 angstroms, according to one's definition of peak) and so this might be the reason. On the other hand, the atmosphere in the present epoch happens to be opaque in the infrared and ultraviolet, and if we had infrared eyes, we would be living practically in darkness; so perhaps the physical properties of the atmosphere were the determining consideration.

However, the window in the atmosphere at visible wavelengths is not the only one; as we go farther through the infrared, the atmosphere opens up again at a radio wavelength of a few millimeters and remains open out to wavelengths of many meters before again becoming opaque. So, if we had radio eyes we would be able to view the universe and here are the principal features as they would appear to us.

First, we would notice a band running across the sky, and this band would occupy the same location in the sky as the Milky Way does. In addition, there would be many bright points sprinkled about at random. As far as this brief description goes, you would say the appearance is about the same as that of the night sky as we know it—a Milky Way plus many stars. Also, we have known since Galileo turned his homemade telescope on the sky, that the Milky Way itself is just stars and these stars are the same as the foreground stars, only more distant and more numerous. Their concentration into a band merely reveals that the stars extend to greater depths of space in the plane of the Galaxy than perpendicular to that plane. In view of the introductory discussion about the sun, which is a typical star, it would be reasonable to expect the radio sky to exhibit the features described. This interpretation is completely upset, however, by the observed fact that the radio point sources do not agree in position with the stars. In fact, with the exception of the sun, virtually no stars are found to be sources of detectable radio waves. In other words, the radio waves that we know they must emit are too faint to detect in comparison with the signals coming to us from the numerous "radio stars," which, evidently, are not stars. For this reason the term *radio star,* which was current for a time, has practically dropped out of use. To confirm this conclusion we have the further fact that the sun, as seen by radio, is a pale spectacle compared with the galaxy. As a matter of fact, the concept of night and day would have a completely different significance to a man with radio eyes because the rising and setting of the sun would make little difference to the general level of illumination. (Presumably, though, it would determine whether he felt warm or cold.)

Thus we see that the very first facts about the radio sky reveal a profound difference from the sky as we know it and they raise important questions about the nature of the world we live in. From radio information alone, our picture of the universe external to the earth would be quite different from that based on the information conveyed to us by visible light. It would be substantially a catalog of invisible things whereas, of necessity, our traditional astronomy has shown us the visible contents of space. At first, astronomers were bewildered by the failure of radio astronomy to tell them much, if anything, about the universe as they understood it from centuries of patiently accumulated observation. The new facts all seemed to be irrelevant. Now we see radio astronomy in the role of filling in enormous blanks in our knowledge of the environment around us, and as progress has been made in filling in these blanks, the radio and optical techniques in one field after another have become welded together to permit a more powerful combined attack on outstanding problems.

THE RADIO SUN

Let us look at the sun with our microwave eyes and then, having noted its appearance, tune to progressively longer wavelengths. At a wavelength of 10 centimeters the sun has a disc about 10 per cent bigger than the visible sun. It has spots, in about the same locations as visible sunspots, but instead of their being dark, they are bright. Another difference is that the sun's temperature is about 5 times greater than the 6000 degrees we remember. I do not believe anyone could have deduced from theory the three facts stated here in which the microwave sun differs from the visible sun. Indeed, on first encounter with these reported observations, one's tendency is to feel a conflict with theoretically based expectation, especially as regards the higher temperature. What we have to remember is that the microwave emission comes from outer layers of the sun which are invisible, being transparent to light, and that therefore our conception of the sun based on the facts revealed to us by visible light has little bearing on the state of its invisible envelope, which indeed does turn out to be hotter than the underlying visible surface. Even so, we depend a lot on very reliable principles such as the laws of thermodynamics, which we confidently extrapolate beyond the limits of actual experience. We are generally not disappointed, and yet here we seem to have a contradiction of the principle that heat always flows from the colder to the hotter. This principle is applied without scruple to the theory of the internal constitution of the sun and we say that, since everywhere within the sun, heat is on the average flowing radially outward, therefore the temperature must everywhere be decreasing outward. On this basis one deduces that the temperature at the center of the sun is 20,000,000 degrees, or some different value depending on precisely what chemical composition is adopted, and everyone seems to be generally happy with this kind of calculation in spite of the fact that radiation from the inside of the sun is absolutely unavailable for observation. I think there is food for thought in the fact that the temperature gradient runs the wrong way in the outer envelope of the sun; the clue to the difficulty lies in the fact that the envelope is mostly transparent in the spectral region where the vast flood of outward bound radiation is concentrated.

If we now take another look at the sun at a still longer wavelength, we find that the size has increased further, the shape has become noticeably elliptical with flattening at the poles, the temperature has gone up further, and that occasional fireworks are noticed. By the time we reach the longest wavelengths that can penetrate to ground level through the terrestrial ionosphere, the sun is five times bigger than the visible sun, approaching a million degrees in temperature, and in a disturbed state where great eruptions and flashes occur which may take the brightness up by further factors of millions.

IMPACT OF THE RADIO SUN ON PRACTICAL MATTERS

Because of the controlling influence of the sun on our environment, it is not hard to give examples of the practical utility of the new knowledge about the sun that has come from the pursuit of radio astronomy. For example, for astronauts there is concern about the damaging effect that could occur if large solar flares were to take place during a lengthy mission, such as a trip to the moon. Just as with expeditions to the Antarctic it is necessary to avoid the bad weather, so it will be in interplanetary space with expeditions to the moon. In this case it will be the solar weather that dominates, not the weather on earth. Solar flares emit ultraviolet light and high energy protons that could be lethal and so it becomes important to have a weather prediction service that can forecast the likelihood of the occurrence of flares. Unfortunately, not enough is yet known to do this with any great accuracy, (a situation that one can appreciate, knowing how difficult it is on earth to forecast the weather, in spite of much longer experience). However, there are some clues. For example, flares always occur in sunspot groups and, therefore, if there are no sunspots on the sun on a particular day, it is safe to predict that there will be no flares. But a lunar mission will take many days so if there were a large sunspot group due to appear on the east limb of the sun the day after launch, it would be a bad thing. How to see what is on the other side of the sun presents quite a problem, but with the aid of radio we can do this and so contribute just a little extra input to the total solar prediction effort. The way this happens is as follows. As mentioned earlier, the microwave sun exhibits bright spots approximately in the position where the dark sunspots are seen in visible light. Although the visible sunspot is a cool region, being only at a temperature of 5000 degrees, nevertheless it is overlain by a volume that is hotter and denser than its surroundings. It is from this volume that the extra microwave energy comes that we describe as a radio hot spot. When the sunspot is just behind the solar limb, and so invisible, there is a distinct possibility that the hot spot above it, because of its elevation, may still be perceptible from earth. This proves to be the case at wavelengths around 10 centimeters, where advance notice of three days has been shown to be possible on some quite modest hot spots that were approaching the sun's limb from the far side. With the strongly active regions that are feared in the space travel context this microwave contribution to advance warning will be welcome. The range of wavelengths in which this job can be done is rather narrow. At a wavelength of 1 centimeter the hot regions tend to become obscured by poor visibility and can only be detected when they are in the vicinity of the center of the sun's disc; so there is no possibility of prediction at all. At a wavelength of 1 meter, one is dealing with levels so far above the sun's surface that the connection with visible surface features can only be made with difficulty and it is not yet known whether it will be possible to associate the radio events with sunspot groups on the far side of the sun.

Another example of the impact of the radio sun on practical affairs may be taken from the field of navigation technology. It has been demonstrated that a microwave antenna can be caused, by means of a servomechanism, to point itself at the sun and to do this with full accuracy even when there is cloud and the sun cannot be seen. This instrument therefore takes the place of the sextant. Its use is suggested in situations where a ship might have to keep station with a high degree of accuracy in a cloudy ocean out of range of other navigational aids. A rescue operation for an astronaut in the south Indian Ocean in poor weather would pose such unusual navigational difficulties and there are military applications also.

Finally, I might mention an imaginary case to illustrate how new discoveries about our radio environment can have a bearing on a weapons system. When an atomic explosion occurs or a rocket is launched, the hot gas generated must give out a burst of radio waves, a phenomenon that might be made the basis of a satellite-borne surveillance system to monitor explosions or launchings. But the sun may emit similar bursts of radio waves. So, before such a system could be properly designed, taking the false alarm rate into account, it would be absolutely necessary for radio astronomical research to have stockpiled a sufficient backlog of information. A solar burst prediction service would seem desirable and, at the very least, simultaneous solar monitoring would seem to be required. Then, countermeasure tactics would have to be taken into account—perhaps the surveillance system would be confused if the events to be detected were deliberately synchronized with large solar events. This is a perfectly valid illustration of the way in which new research results in apparently far-out fields can have a direct bearing on some practical matter in another field of human interest entirely. It reminds one of that other connection between the sun and weapons that arose with magnetic mines, which could be so sensitively adjusted that the sun could, and did, set them off by virtue of the small changes in the earth's magnetic field that it produces during times of solar disturbance.

THE RADIO MOON

The moon is not as warm as the earth and therefore any thermal radiation that could be picked up from the moon on radio wavelengths would be less than could be picked up by pointing the same antenna at the ground. Anyone with experience with antennas knows that the ground is not a good source of radio emission although, of course, we recognize from the laws of thermal radiation from hot objects that it must give out something. We receive even less from the moon. Nevertheless, in the microwave range the moon can be readily studied because the sky background against which the moon is projected sends us even less radio emission than the moon. Therefore, if the antenna beam is kept fixed, and earth rotation carries the beam across the moon, an increase in received energy will be detectable. By this type of experiment the lunar radiation was first detected by Dicke and Beringer in 1946. As with almost every new detection of radio signals from the sky, prior expectation turned out to be insufficiently accurate to avert surprises. In the case of the moon the surprise was that full moon, as observed on a wavelength of 1.25 centimeters, comes three or four days later than full moon as we perceive it by eye.

An explanation for this phenomenon was immediately forthcoming and it evoked the existence of a surface layer having very low thermal conductivity. The material required had to have very much higher thermal insulation than any material occurring on earth, and the obvious way to get such properties is from a finely structured rock with a large percentage of voids. When placed in vacuo, such material cannot conduct heat across its pores by gaseous conduction but only around them, which forces the heat to flow in a tortuous path and to negotiate many highly resistive constrictions. Radiation transfer, which is the only other mode of heat transfer allowable, depends for its efficacy on the temperatures of opposite walls of a pore being sufficiently different, and if the pore structure is on a fine enough scale radiative transfer of heat becomes negligible. Laboratory experiments on powders in vacuo completely documented these ideas and for this and other reasons the insulating lunar surface was often described as dust. The thermal resistance required by observations could be expressed in terms of a layer thickness. A good deal of literature exists in which mathematical models are discussed which are equivalent to a moon covered with a layer of dust so many millimeters thick. Of course, the thermal resistance was a better expression of the radio observations, which did not bear at all on the state of comminution, or presence or absence of cohesiveness, of the particles of material. As it later developed from soft landings on the moon's surface, the material does not blow about loosely like dust, and fears that camera lenses and windows would be fogged by dust were not realized.

The effect of an insulating surface can be understood as follows. If you spread a large rug out on the ground, you find that after sunset the ground underneath the rug will still preserve some of the heat of the afternoon and will be warmer than areas where there is no rug. Likewise, when morning has come, the ground under the insulating rug will still have the pre-dawn coolness. In the same way, the temperature of the subsurface lunar material lags behind the surface temperature. The surface temperature is controlled by incident sunlight and rises and falls with a period of 29.53 days, which is one synodic month. Now the thermal microwave radiation does not come from the surface where visible moonlight (and lunar infrared radiation) originate, because the lunar material is a reasonably good dielectric that allows microwave radiation to pass through it, at least to some extent. Thus what we receive on earth is a combination of rays originating at all depths down to a meter or so, the radiation from the deeper layers showing the greater time lags, which is, of course, most weakened by attentuation on the way out. The net result is that maximum emission is not reached until three or four days after full moon.

The possibility of seeing below the surface is potentially important for subsurface mapping which may be especially necessary on the moon to penetrate the monotonous gray coating that it has developed through exposure to its harsh environment of bombardment by particles and radiation.

JUPITER

One of the unique compartments of radio astronomy is the story of unfolding discoveries about the radio emission from Jupiter. First accidentally detected as a strong source by Burke and Franklin in 1955, Jupiter has since remained a fascinating object as more and more new things have come out about it. It will be immediately appreciated that severe technical problems are involved in determining where on Jupiter radio signals originate since the angular diameter of the planet as seen from the earth is under one minute of arc. The techniques of fine angular discrimination developed well beyond the preexisting state of the antenna art by radio astronomers have been the key to the unraveling of some of the difficult observational items, and form an interesting topic in themselves. However, here it must suffice to state the facts baldly. To begin with, one might expect Jupiter to be at a temperature of about 140 degrees Kelvin, on the grounds that a sphere at that temperature would radiate thermal powers at a rate balancing the solar radiation intercepted by Jupiter. Of course, if Jupiter had its own internal source of heat, its surface could be hotter, but as a matter of fact, optical evidence as to the temperature of the visible cloud surface supports the figure of about 140 degrees. This is cold enough to mean that the clouds could be composed of solid particles of many gases other than H_2O, which is the only gaseous constituent of the earth's atmosphere that can freeze in the earth's atmosphere. But Jupiter's clouds can contain crystals of methane and ammonia. When the temperature was measured by Mayer, McCullough and Sloanaker, by radio methods at a wavelength of 3 centimeters, they obtained a value of 140 degrees. Now when the application of a new observational tool tells us approximately what was already expected, the scientists do not regard this as a very exciting development, but fortunately for their enjoyment, new measurements soon revealed a temperature of 2000 degrees at 21 centimeters and 5000 degrees at 31 centimeters. In reading these temperatures we have to bear in mind the explanation given above in connection with the sun as to how one and the same body can appear to have different temperatures when the wavelength is changed. The real fact is that as the wavelength is changed the source does not remain exactly the same because of the wavelength dependent opacity and emissivity of its various parts. Furthermore, in the case of Jupiter, the calculated temperatures include an allowance for the angular diameter of Jupiter which varies between about 14 and 21 seconds of arc depending on the date. But this is the optical diameter, and if the source of radio emission were to have a diameter that was different for different wavelengths, then again the apparent temperature could change with wavelength.

The interesting speculations raised by the radio observations that Jupiter was not behaving merely as a cold cloudy sphere as regards its emission of microwaves led quickly to a determination by Radhakrishnan and Roberts that the microwaves were coming, not from the visible surface, but from an invisible ellipsoid surrounding the planet and having three times its diameter, in the equatorial plane. In view of the small angular size of Jupiter, it will be appreciated that this was an impressive observational achievement.

It thus seemed that Jupiter must possess a radiation belt, similar to the earth's radiation belts, containing electrons at relativistic energies, this interpretation being confirmed by the high degree of linear polarization detected in the radiation, a feature that is not characteristic of thermally generated radiation.

Much more could be said about Jupiter, especially its sporadic emission in the vicinity of 25 MHz, the source of which is localized and rotates with the planet. Because of this fact, the rotation period can be measured, the radio value being 09^h 55^m 29^{s}37. The very high apparent precision of this value comes from the fact that a large number of rotations could be counted over the decade of observation on which the value rests. Rather interestingly, this period is in distinct disagreement with values obtained by watching the motion of features in the cloud surface with the telescope, a disagreement that can be explained by assuming that the upper surface of the clouds does not necessarily move in perfect synchronism with the solid surface below but is convected by global winds, just as on earth. The good stability of the radio value thus suggests the conclusion that we have here the true period of solid-body rotation of Jupiter. It might also lead one to infer that the source of this radiation is below the clouds, perhaps in some sporadically erupting volcano, whose eruptions have unprecedented ferocity by earthly standards, even causing lightning or other electrical phenomena on a scale sufficient to explain the level of interference received on earth. (Jovian lightning would have to be on a magnificent scale because the static it gives us dominates that produced by our tropical electrical storms despite the immensely greater distance of Jupiter. In fact, Jupiter noise is the strongest kind of non-manmade interference in the 20 MHz neighborhood.)

It is now clear, however, that this type of Jupiter emission is not a ground level phenomenon but originates some distance out in space from the planet. One indicator of this conclusion is the extraordinary discovery by Bigg that our reception of Jupiter noise is influenced by the satellite Io, which is the same size as our moon and moves in an orbit not much further from the surface of Jupiter than our moon does from the earth. When Io is in the right place in its orbit, it can practically turn off the signal that we receive and so it seems that the volume of space responsible for the emission is well out from Jupiter's surface.

THE COSMIC FIREBALL

When the universe originated 10^{10} years ago in the great expanding fireball whose still receding fragments are visible today as the remote galaxies (if indeed the universe did originate this way), the temperature, for a time, exceeded 10^7 degrees, which reduces matter to a state of ylem, to use Gamow's term for it. Gamow proposed that the atomic species formed as the expanding fireball cooled and also said that the radiation existing at the time when the density fell to the point of allowing the material to become transparent, would still be with us today. Because of the expansion that has taken place since, however, this radiation would now be weak. The recent fact is that weak microwave radiation corresponding to a temperature of 3 degrees above absolute zero has indeed been found by Penzias and Wilson and by Dicke's colleagues at Princeton and it possesses the attribute of arriving uniformly from all directions, which is just what the fireball radiation would be expected to do. So it may be that we are seeing the origin of the universe when we look at this radiation. We do not know yet whether this interesting discovery is the beginning of a new branch of radio astronomy, but if it is to be, then there will have to be structure discernable in different directions, for there is nothing that can be said about a strictly isotropic radiation field once its intensity has been established. Conklin has been looking for such structure and as of now has failed to find any but can say that departures from the nominal temperature value of 3 degrees cannot exceed 2 millidegrees. For the time being this result is less exciting than would have been a discovery of a pattern showing how the fireball originally broke up, but it does enable us to contemplate a different line of development.

Everyone remembers the famous Michelson-Morley experiment which aimed to detect the absolute velocity of the earth through the ether, and how the null result became a cornerstone of relativity theory. Today we always proceed on the assumption that there is no favored frame of reference, and this thought, embodied in the theory of special relativity, has proved a reliable daily basis for the design of all manner of instruments, devices and machines involving high speed particle streams. Still, if you think globally about the universe it is a hard thought to accept that there is no favored frame. A very interesting new observational possibility is now opening up.

Suppose that there are two observers at the same place and that one of them observes himself to be surrounded by an isotropic radiation field, let us say using an antenna connected to a 3-centimeter receiver. The other observer has identical equipment and is in motion with a speed v relative to the first, in a certain direction that I can call the forward direction. Now it can be shown from classical considerations, not involving relativity, that the second observer will not observe an isotropic field but in the forward direction will see a temperature that is higher by a factor $1 + v/c$, where c is the speed of light, and in the backward direction the temperature will be lower. Thus, if an isotropic radiation field exists, an observer embedded in it can tell in what direction he is moving and with what speed, relative to the radiation field, simply by surveying the temperature distribution over the sky. The considerations involved in demonstrating the effect include (a) astronomical aberration, which changes the apparent direction of arrival of light from a star and consequently crowds the forward hemisphere into less than a hemisphere, and (b) the increase of electric and magnetic field strengths when a measuring instrument is in motion with respect to the source of the fields.

In the case of the earth, the highest systematic velocity component of which we know is the motion around the center of the galaxy at 250 kilometers per second, which is about one thousandth of the speed of light. Therefore, we expect the sky to appear 3 millidegrees hotter in the direction in the sky where we know the galactic rotation is carrying us. There are some corrections to be made for the peculiar motion of the sun and for the earth's motion about the sun, but they are rather small. The prerequisite for the absolute velocity experiment is that there be an isotropic field to begin with and it appears now from Conklin's measurements that the degree of isotropy is really adequate. The only difficulty remaining, therefore, is the experimental one of reliably determining temperature differences of a few millidegrees between different directions. I am quite sure these difficulties can be overcome but not yet sure how long it will take to make progress in this unfamiliar type of measurement.

PULSARS

In a most exciting development, radio astronomers in Cambridge, England, discovered four radio sources that are ticking. Yes, they are giving out brief radio pulses about once a second, and the stability of the pulse interval is extremely high as clocks go. For the moment, our knowledge of the stability is subject to observational limitations on our part. The stability could prove to be better than we can generate under the best conditions in our laboratories, in which case the definition of the second could be uprated, as has already happened once recently. However, there are reasons to think that the present standard of time will be hard to supplant. Nevertheless, the pulsars are unique as astronomical objects go, and they have raised much agitated discussion as to their nature.

One class of suggestions invokes neutron stars or white dwarfs, with sizes comparable to that of the earth and masses like that of the sun, and these extraordinarily dense objects are supposed to be undergoing mechanical vibrations. Other suggestions invoke rotation of such an object on its axis or of two objects about each other. These suggestions are prompted by the need to propose mechanical systems that can vibrate at the very short period required, have good frequency stability, and at the same time be substantial enough to furnish the energy needed to account for the observed strength of the pulses when they reach earth. Of course, to work back from the received energy to the energy developed at the source, one needs to determine how far away the pulsar is. In radio astronomy, distance measurement has always been a vexing problem. But in the case of the pulsars a bonus in the form of dispersion in time of arrival on different frequencies permits a reasonable order of magnitude estimate of the distance that would have to be traversed by the radiation in order that the interstellar electrons might introduce the observed dispersion. This measurement, which is not available on a source that is not pulsed, has yielded distances of the order of 60 parsecs (comparable with the thickness of the galaxy, but less than one per cent of its radius). The energy at the source then proves to be large and requires something massive to be able to afford it. However, the mechanical models proposed must be able to generate radio pulses and it may be some time before the explanation is forthcoming, but during this time much interesting reading is likely to be generated.

Here I would like to digress on a potential application to general relativity, which is an important part of physics and still in need of good experimental support. According to the theory, a photon falling into a gravitational field gains energy and accordingly appears at a higher frequency. Therefore, if a remote source of sinusoidal oscillations was received when the earth is closest to the sun (perihelion), the frequency would appear higher than when received six months later at aphelion. From the difference in gravitational potential between the two places, the change in frequency can be calculated to be one part in 2×10^9. Clearly, to do this experiment, all that is needed is a stable remote source, because laboratory clocks have ample capacity to detect the small frequency change expected. Now, it is suggested by Hoffman, the pulsars may fill the bill. You may object that the pulsars are not sources of a single pure oscillation but give out pulses, and you may not feel that radio pulses falling into a gravitational field can speed up so as to be observed in greater numbers per unit time. However, it appears that, if the constituent photons of a pulse are raised in frequency, then the interval between successive pulses will shrink as a consequence, and to encourage you to continue thinking about radio astronomy I shall close leaving this interesting item for you to think about.

ACKNOWLEDGMENT

This research has been supported in part by the General Physics Division, Directorate of Physical Sciences of the Air Force Office of Scientific Research.

V. Recent Advances In Glass Science and Technology

J. D. MACKENZIE

INTRODUCTION

GLASS IS ONE OF THE MOST important and oldest materials of engineering. The value of the current annual production of glass in the United States is approximately $3 billion. By far the most common of all glasses are those based on sand (SiO_2), soda (Na_2CO_3) and lime (CaO). Such silicate glasses are also the cheapest because of the raw materials involved. For more than 10,000 years the chemical compositions of these soda-lime glasses have not been changed significantly. Despite the long history of the technology and the relative constancy of the chemical compositions, however, glass science is actually a fairly recent development. In Table 1, it is seen that although mass-

TABLE 1
SOME MILESTONES IN THE HISTORY OF GLASS
SCIENCE AND TECHNOLOGY

First man-made glass	10,000 B.C.
First glass with date	2,100 B.C.
First glass light bulb	1879
Pyrex glass	1904
Fiber glass	1931
First theory on structure	1932
First theory on glass formation	1933
Surge of scientific interest	1950's

JOHN D. MACKENZIE has been Professor of Materials Science at Rensselaer Polytechnic Institute since 1963. Dr. Mackenzie has been studying the relationship between physical properties and structure of glasses. In 1964, he was presented with the S. B. Meyer Award of the American Ceramic Society for the most creditable papers published in glass science in 1963 and 1964. He is currently a member of the Executive Committee of the International Glass Commission and also Chairman of the Commission's Committee on Electrical Properties of Glass.

production of glass had taken place before 1900, it was not until the 1930's when the first theoretical attempts were made to gain an understanding of the structure and nature of common glasses. This belated fundamental study of glasses is partly due to the lack of economic competition from other engineering materials, since there are few cheaper raw materials than sand, soda and lime. What little progress was made in the 1930's was soon halted because of World War II. Since the 1950's, the need for newer and better glasses and competition from plastics have generated much more fundamental as well as applied research. In this paper, I will attempt to review some of the important advances which have resulted from such recent studies.

WHAT IS A GLASS?

Most crystalline solids will form a relatively fluid liquid on fusion. The viscosity of most liquids at or near the melting temperature is usually less than 1 poise[1]. The viscosity of water, for example, is less than 0.1 poise. Second, the viscosity of most liquids does not increase significantly on cooling. Although a liquid can often be supercooled some tens of degrees below its thermodynamic freezing temperature, its viscosity is still fairly low. Slight physical disturbances or the presence of impurities will lead to rapid crystallization. The transformation of a liquid to the corresponding crystalline solid involves migration of atoms, ions or molecules. Such motion is, of course, easier for a fluid melt. Thus for most liquids exposed to the atmosphere it is difficult to maintain the supercooled state indefinitely.

Some solids, however, do yield extremely viscous melts on fusion. The viscosity of molten silica (SiO_2), for instance, is about 10^7 poises at the melting temperature of 1710°C. Further, small decreases of temperature can lead to large increases of viscosity. Molecular motion is now difficult. Thus crystal nucleation, as well as growth, also becomes difficult. It is now relatively easy to undercool molten silica appreciably without crystallization. The viscosity increases rapidly on cooling and by about 1200°C, it reaches a value of 10^{14} poises. For most practical purposes the liquid has now become a rigid solid. At such a higher viscosity, this solidified liquid is termed a glass. The material is said to be in the vitreous state. Silica (or sand) is called a "glass-former". The highly viscous melt which forms on the fusion of crystalline silica is termed a "network liquid" on account of its polymeric structure. Other materials of this family are boric oxide, germanium dioxide and phosphorus pentoxide.

Because of its high viscosity and high fusion temperature, silica glass is difficult to form. Sodium oxide and calcium oxide are added to the fusion mixture to lower the liquidus temperature as well as the viscosity. The reaction which results can be conveniently represented by a bond rupture of the type: :

$$
-\overset{|}{\underset{|}{Si}} - O - \overset{|}{\underset{|}{Si}} - + M_2O \rightarrow -\overset{|}{\underset{|}{Si}} - O^- \quad \overset{M+}{\underset{M+}{}} \quad {}^-O - \overset{|}{\underset{|}{Si}} -
$$

Such fusion products which have solidified without crystallization are thus common glasses. Theoretically, any liquid which can be rendered highly viscous (viscosity greater than 10^{14} poises) without crystallization will give a glass. The condition of "highly viscous without crystallization" is, of course, a difficult experimental problem. Nevertheless, even liquid gold-silicon alloys and other "metallic" melts have been rapidly quenched to the glassy state[2]. The earlier concept that only "glass-formers" like SiO_2 can form glasses is now considered incorrect.

The most convenient figure which illustrates the differences between crystal, liquid, supercooled liquid and glass is probably the simple volume-temperature diagram shown in Figure 1. The specific volume of a glass and its so-called glass transition temperature, T_g, are dependent on cooling rates. The specific volume of a supercooled liquid does not vary with time, whereas that of a glass at high temperatures does change on holding. The difference between the slopes of the V-T plot for liquid and glass, that is, the occurrence of T_g, is the result of the extremely high viscosity of 10^{13} to 10^{14} poises at the temperature in question. At such high viscosity, the molecular relaxation times are now greater than the duration of the experiments. A lower value of T_g will be expected with slower cooling rates. There has been considerable theoretical work on the limiting value of T_g. It is now generally considered that such a limiting value does exist and that, depending on the material, it is some 10-100° below the average experimental T_g.

Because a glass is a "rigid liquid" and yet at low temperature it is physically a solid, a number of technological advantages are evident. First, one can regard a glass as a fluid solution at high temperatures.

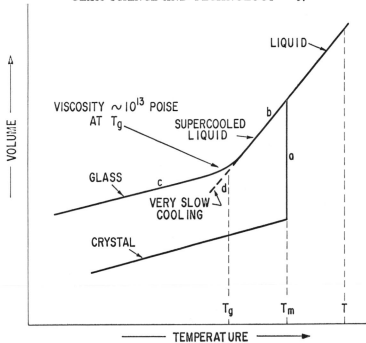

FIGURE 1. Volume-temperature relationship for an ideal glass-forming system.[1]

As long as immiscibility does not occur, "solutes" can be dissolved. On cooling, they may be precipitated out and are uniformly suspended in the solidified glass. The precipitate is normally crystalline and the sizes can now be controlled accurately through heat treatment of the glass. Second, as a liquid mixture, the constituents can be varied in any desired proportions. It is easy to imagine how optical, electrical and mechanical properties can be "tailored to measure" this way. Third, since a glass does not "melt" on heating, but only softens slowly, it lends itself to many advantageous forming techniques. Sheet glass, fiber glass, pressed wares, and blown wares are all examples of such advantageous forming methods which result from the uniqueness of the nature of glass.

STRUCTURE OF GLASSES

Techniques which have been successfully used to determine the structure of crystalline solids have proven to be disappointing when applied to glasses. A typical x-ray diffraction pattern of a glass and its "parent" crystal is exemplified by germanium dioxide (GeO_2) in Figure 2. Because of the diffuseness of the pattern, it is extremely difficult to perform detailed structural analysis. B. E. Warren and his associates have made significant contributions in this field[3]. However, the significant information which has been obtained is confined to "nearest neighbor" interactions. From x-ray analysis, for example, it has been found that *on the average,* the number of oxygen ions surrounding a silicon ion is four for silicate glasses; the building unit

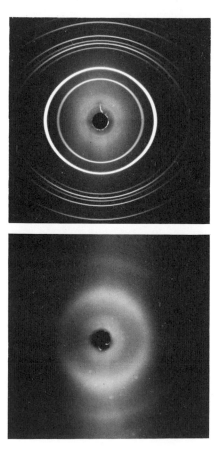

FIGURE 2. X-ray diffraction pattern of crystalline and glassy germanium dioxide.

is a SiO_4 tetrahedron; the oxygen-silicon separation is about 1.60A and the Si-O-Si angle is about 150°. This "short-range" structure of silicate glasses is thus essentially the same as that for crystalline silicates. X-ray diffraction, however, is unable to furnish "long-range" information. For instance, in crystalline silicates of the same SiO_2: Metal Oxides ratio, the long range structure may take different forms such as rings, chains, sheet or three-dimensional groups. It is not possible from diffraction experiments to say which of these structures are present in a glass. Relatively little additional information is obtained from other diffraction measurements such as electron diffraction or neutron diffraction.

Since the physical properties of glasses are similar to those of the corresponding crystalline solids, and since their short-range structures are also similar, it is not unreasonable to assume that their long-range structures are also not too different. The difference in the x-ray diffraction patterns is then explained by the lack of long-range *order* in glass. Such a hypothesis was first advanced by W. H. Zachariasin and formed the basis of the so-called "Random Network Theory" of glass structure. In the last twenty years many modifications of this theory have been made but experimental verification of the different models is still lacking. Often, indirect information, for example a particular physical property, is used to augment short-range structural results to indicate long-range structures.

Although the short-range nature of silicate glasses is relatively easy to obtain, this is not so for other glasses such as borates and germanates. In crystalline borates, it is known that the coordination number of boron can be three and/or four. That is, the boron ion can be surrounded by three or four oxygens. There were numerous controversies concerning borate glasses. This age-old problem was only solved recently through the use of nuclear magnetic resonance absorption techniques by Bray and co-workers.[5] The coordination number of germanium in crystalline germanates can be four or six. Here again there are controversies regarding the coordination number in germanate glasses and the problem remains unsolved at present.

Relative to silicate and borate glasses, much less structural information is available on other glasses, especially non-oxide glasses. In general it can be concluded that a combination of many different experimental tools, both direct and indirect, are necessary to obtain unambiguous structural information on glasses.

IONIC PROPERTIES

Most oxide glasses are good electrical insulators. The room temperature resistivity generally exceeds 10^{13} ohm-cm. At higher temperatures, however, the metal ions, especially alkali ions, become mobile and are the main cause for ionic conductivity[6]. For common glasses it has been proven that the transference number for alkali ions is unity. Since the random network theory suggests that oxide glasses have open three-dimensional disordered structures with the metal ions randomly distributed throughout the silicon-oxygen framework, it would seem logical to assume that ionic properties, especially conductivity, are directly dependent on the nature and concentration of the alkali ions present. However, this proves to be an erroneous assumption.

In Figure 3, a glass of the composition 18w/o Na_2O — 82w/o SiO_2

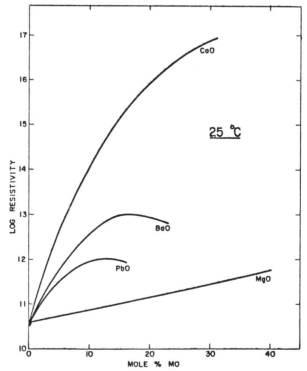

FIGURE 3. Effects of divalent ions on the electrical resistivity of a binary glass of the composition 18 w/o Na_2O-82 w/o_2.[7]

was modified by replacing the SiO_2 with a number of divalent oxides[7]. The concentration of NaO_2 was kept constant. Since the Na^+ ions are the current carriers, the resistivity is not expected to alter drastically. However, it is seen that only 10 w/o of CaO is sufficient to increase the resistivity by three orders of magnitude. It is now considered that the Ca^{++} ions are themselves immobile and that they tend to block the motion of the Na^+ ions. This, of course, indicates that the random network theory on structure is oversimplified. Perhaps "fine structures" or "preferred paths" exist in glass which govern the motion of ions. The verification of such models, however, must await further experimentation.

A detailed understanding of ionic transport is of obvious importance to the use of glasses as insulators as well as substrates in microelectronics. It is not generally appreciated that it is also intimately related to the strengthening of glasses.

STRENGTH AND STRENGTHENING[8]

The theoretical tensile strength of oxide glasses has been estimated to be E/5 to E/10 where E is Young's modulus. Since E is $1 - 2 \times 10^7$ psi, the theoretical strength must be at least one million psi. The reason is the presence of so-called Griffith flaws (surface defects). However, even "pristine", that is untouched, glasses do not approach theoretical strengths. Further, the strengths of different samples of the same pristine glass can vary significantly. It is clear then, besides the common Griffith flaws which are present and which are caused by mechanical handling, molecular defects of another type must also be present, and these also affect the strength of glass. The exact nature of such molecular defects is not known at present.

Since Griffith flaws are always generated in use, and since fracture of a glass invariably occurs through tension rather than compression, the only practical methods to increase glass strength must be the creation of a compressive "skin" on the surface. Thus, tensile forces must first overcome the surface compression before they are effective towards normal breakage.

The first successful attempts to strengthen glass this way were by "tempering". The glass object is first heated to near T_g and the surface is quenched by cold air. The surface layer is now relatively cold and rigid. When the whole object is cooled the interior contracts against a rigid skin. The skin is thus put into compression. Strengths in excess of 20,000 psi have been achieved by this method.

A second method to strengthen glass can be termed "ion stuffing". This is conveniently illustrated by Figure 4. The sample is immersed in a bath of fused salt at a temperature just below T_g. The glass is

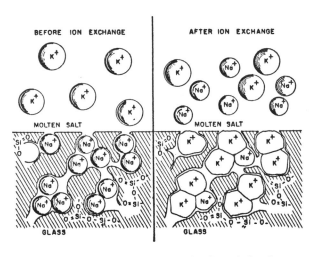

FIGURE 4. Ion stuffing strengthening of glass.[9]

still rigid but now the temperature is sufficiently high to enable alkali ions to undergo ion-exchange. In Figure 4, for instance, Na^+ ions in the glass are exchanging with K^+ ions of the fused salt. The larger K^+ ions migrated into the surface layers of the glass will exert a pressure on the rigid silicon-oxygen network resulting in surface compression. Strengths of abraded glass samples in excess of 40,000 psi have been obtained by this technique.

In yet another technique, surface compression is obtained via differential thermal expansion. A sodium alumino-silicate glass, for instance, is immersed in a molten salt containing Li^+ ions. Exchange between Na^+ in the glass and Li^+ in the salt occurs to give a surface composition enriched with lithium. The glass is now heat treated outside the bath. In the presence of suitable nucleating agents, beta-Eucryptite ($Li_2O \cdot Al_2O_3 \cdot 2SiO_2$) will be crystallized in the surface layers. The average thermal expansion coefficient of beta-Eucryptite crystals formed this way is negative. Thus on cooling to room temperature, a compressive skin will be formed on the glass. Tensile strengths in excess of 100,000 psi have been obtained with no decrease of transparency. It is obvious that such "chemical strengthening" methods will lead to a much wider usage of glass as a structural material.

EFFECTS OF HIGH PRESSURE AND HARDNESS OF GLASS

Glasses are generally considered as "perfectly" elastic solids. It is not widely known that under high pressure, particularly in the presence of shear forces, glasses can flow readily, even at very low temperatures. This type of flow is anomalous in that it is not plastic flow nor viscous flow. It has been separately observed in two areas of experimental studies of glass. In 1953, Bridgman and Simon[10] first reported that if silica glass is compressed at room temperature and at pressures in excess of 100 kilobars, its density will be "permanently" increased. Subsequent work showed that this increase of density is very sensitive to the degree of shear forces present.[11] Under shear conditions, densification will take place for silica glass at pressures of less than 30 kilobars. For glasses with lower T_g, pressures of less than 10 kilobars will cause densification at room temperature. Recent work also showed that the densification is not "permanent."[12] In Figure 5, it is illustrated that the density of a sample of densified silica glass need only be heated to 300°C to show a decrease of density. At room temperature, however, densified samples have shown no variation of density even after three years at ambient atmosphere. Since T_g for silica glass is about 1200°C, this volume flow to give a lower density at 300°C is anomalous. Glasses of lower T_g, for instance, boric oxide glass which has been densified, will exhibit such anomalous volume flow even at room temperature. It is likely that such anomalous densification and subsequent "cold" flow is the result of entanglement and disentanglement of the glassy network. The effect of shear on the entanglement leading to densification is illustrated by Figure 6. The behavior of glasses under pressure is thus very different from that exhibited by crystalline solids.

The hardness of a material is often measured by some form of load-induced indentation. The indentation is essentially the result of high local pressure under conditions of shear, because of the geometry of the indentox. Indentations made on silica glass, for ex-

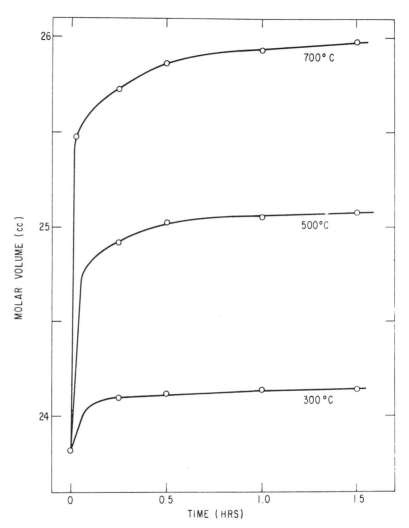

FIGURE 5. Decrease of density of compressed silica glass at low temperatures.[11]

ample, will show partial "healing" at temperatures as low as 300° C.[13] This is again anomalous volume flow probably similar to that described above for densified samples. The nature of atom transport giving the indentation is different between a glass and a crystal. Thus it is scientifically not meaningful to compare the hardnesses of crys-

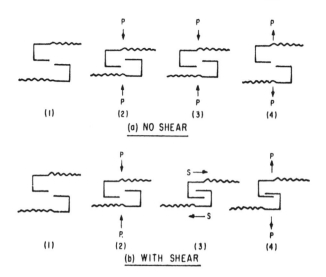

FIGURE 6. Idealized mechanism of shear-pressure induced densification of glass.[11]

talline and non-crystalline solids. Hardness of glass has frequently been correlated with strength. It is obvious that it is also related to "scratchability" and modulus. It is, therefore, an extremely important physical property, the further understanding of which is most necessary.

Another interesting effect of high pressure on glass is the exposure of molten glass to gases at elevated pressure. Many gases will undergo appreciable solution and can be trapped when the glass solidifies. As much as 5% solution is common. When hydrogen was dissolved in the glass (0.02 to 2%), it had a remarkable effect on radiation resistance towards x-rays, gamma-rays and neutrons.[14] Normally the glass would color on irradiation. The hydrogen-containing glasses, however, did not. This was attributed to the following reactions:

$$O\text{-}\overset{|}{\underset{|}{Si}}\text{-}O\text{-}\overset{|}{\underset{|}{Si}}\text{-}O \xrightarrow{\text{irradiation}} O\text{-}\overset{|}{\underset{|}{Si}} \oplus \ominus O\text{-}\overset{|}{\underset{|}{Si}}\text{-}O \xrightarrow[\text{of } H_2]{\text{diffusion}}$$

(color centers)

$$-\overset{|}{\underset{|}{Si}}\text{-}H + HO\text{-}\overset{|}{\underset{|}{Si}}-$$

(destruction of color centers)

The measurement of physical properties, for example viscosity, under pressure can give useful structural information. This has been recently carried out on borates and has provided interesting insights into the mechanism of flow as well as the polymeric nature of glass.[15]

OPTICAL PROPERTIES

Colored glasses have been in use for many centuries. Although empirical information exists which tells us what metal oxides will give what color to a glass under certain conditions, scientific understanding is still minimal. Perhaps the most significant and impressive experimental achievement is that glasses of extreme purity (less than 10 p.p.m. of coloring ions) can be made.[16] The empirical assignment of absorption bands in the visible region of the spectrum is no longer ambiguous. This, together with the application of crystal-field theory, will no doubt lead to rapid advances in fundamental studies of color in glass. It is perhaps worth remarking that, at present, there is still controversy concerning the exact nature of the brown color in common beer bottles.

If silver nitrate and sodium chloride are dissolved in a molten glass at high temperatures, controlled cooling can produce silver chloride crystals. Such crystals can be as small as 50A in diameter and are uniformly distributed in the glass. The resulting material is still transparent but is now *photochromic,* that is, it can be colored on exposure to light of one wavelength and then bleached by another light source.[17] Glass made this way differs from photographic films in that the latter are not reversible. Corning Glass Works claimed that their photochromic glasses are stable after more than 300,000 cycles of coloring in the ultraviolet and bleaching. Photochromic, or phototropic, glasses hold promise in ophthalmic, automotive, architectural, optical display, data processing and data storage applications.

Ordinary oxide glasses will not transmit further than 4 or 5 microns in the infrared. Preliminary attempts to produce infrared transmitting glasses were oriented toward the replacement of small ions in the glass with larger and heavier ions.[18] Thus germanate glasses were considered to replace silicate glasses. Since the oxygen ions were not replaced, the improvements gained were really insignificant. In the 1950's, it was recalled that oxides are not the only known glass-formers. Sulphides and selenides also form glasses readily. Arsenic trisulphide (As_2S_3) immediately proved to be a good infrared transmitting glass.[19] Its main disadvantage is the relatively low value of T_g. The search for higher softening non-oxide glasses has led to the discovery of many new glass-forming systems based on covalent-type elements such as Si, Ge, P, etc.[19] Glasses are now available which can transmit to beyond 15 microns and with T_g as high as 400° C. Some of these are shown in Table 2.

TABLE 2
PROPERTIES OF SOME INFRARED TRANSMITTING
GLASSES FROM TERNARY SYSTEMS

System	Max. Soft. Point °C	Refrac. Index	Absorption 8-14μ
Si-P-Te	180	3.4	Slight
Si-Sb-Se	270	3.3	Yes
Si-Sb-S	280	—	Yes
Ge-P-Se	420	2.4-2.6	Yes
Ge-P-S	520	2.0-2.3	Yes
Si-As-Te	475	2.9-3.1	Slight
Ge-As-Te	270	3.5	v. slight
Ge-P-Te	380	3.5	v. slight

ELECTRONIC PROPERTIES

The infrared transmitting glasses based on S, Se, etc. are generally known as chalcogenide glasses. They are also electronic conductors and form a new family of semiconductors of low conductivity.[20, 21] Unlike common semiconductors such as silicon and germanium, the conductivity of chalcogenide glasses range from 10^{-13} to only 10^{-3} at room temperature. Most of them are also photoconducting. The combination of relatively low electrical conductivity and photoconductivity leads to the very useful application of amorphous selenium in Xerography. The carrier mobility in these semiconducting glasses is extremely low and perhaps accounts for their high resistivity. Under a field gradient, however, they often undergo electronic switching. At some critical field, the insulator abruptly switches to a highly conductive material. This switching behavior is reversible and switching times are less than nanoseconds.[22] Considerable efforts are now directed towards the exploitation of this switching phenomenon in electronic devices.

Electronic conduction in glass is not confined to the chalcogenides.

In 1957, Baynton and co-workers first reported that phosphate glasses containing more than 10% vanadium oxide were semiconductors.[23] Since then many other semiconducting oxide glasses have been reported.[24] Electronic conduction is thought to occur by a charge-transfer type mechanism exemplified by:

$$V^{4+} - 0 - V^{5+} \quad \rightarrow V^{5+} - 0 - V^{4+}$$

The extra electron attached to the V^{4+} ion "hops" to an adjacent V^{5+} ion to constitute the current. The same principle is applicable to glasses containing Fe^{2+} and Fe^{3+} ions. These glasses, like the chalcogenides, also have relatively low conductivity 10^{-3} to 10^{-13} ohm^{-1} cm^{-1}. We again have a new class of "semi-insulators," which for many electrical applications are preferable to the ordinary "ionic-insulators," such as soda-lime glasses. Since conduction occurs through the

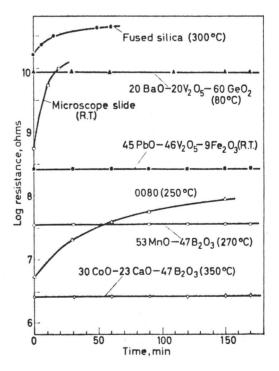

FIGURE 7. Effects of 200 volt DC on electrical resistance of glasses.[24]

motion of electrons rather than ions, electrolysis is absent and material deterioration will not occur under a DC field. This is illustrated in Figure 7 in which the deterioration of the ionically-conduction glasses is evident. Some important applications have already been found for these semiconducting oxide glasses.[25] As for the chalcogenide glasses, scientific understanding is far behind empirical knowledge and applications for these oxides.

GLASS CERAMICS[26]

A glass is essentially a metastable solid and under certain conditions will devitrify, that is transform to the appropriate crystalline phase. Normally, if the crystallization is not controlled, a mechanically weak material is formed. This is primarily because nucleation is relatively easy on the exposed glass surface after which crystals are formed. These crystals grow inward toward the interior of the sample and tend to be columnar in shape. A large-grained and anisotropic polycrystalline material results, which is generally undesirable for structural purposes.

S. D. Stookey of Corning Glass Works discovered that crystallization can be controlled by the addition of suitable nucleating agents to glass. The nucleating agents are added to the glass batch before melting and are therefore uniformly distributed through the body. Examples of nucleating agents are copper, gold, platinum, titanium dioxide, zirconium dioxide, phosphorus pentoxide and metal fluorides. Because of the uniformly distributed nucleating particles, crystallization now takes place simultaneously at all parts of a sample as soon as the appropriate temperature is reached. The large number of nucleating particles results in the formation of many small crystals. Dense and fine-grained bodies with crystal size of less than one micron can be formed. The glass-ceramic so formed can be more than 99% crystalline and yet can still be highly transparent in the visible region of the spectrum.

In the production of a piece of glass-ceramic, the appropriate oxides containing small amounts of the nucleating agents are first melted to form the glass. The glass is then rendered into the desired shape before a controlled heat-treatment schedule as depicted in Figure 8. The sample is usually nucleated at a lower temperature A, before it is taken to a higher temperature B, for maximum crystal growth rate.

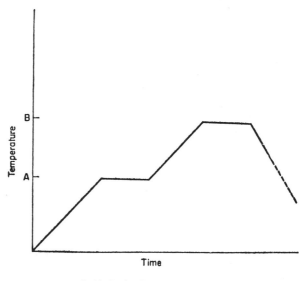

A. Nucleation temperature
B. Maximum crystallization temperature

FIGURE 8. Heat-treatment schedule for a glass-ceramic. *A* is the nucleation temperature and *B* is maximum crystallization temperature.[26]

Temperature A is sufficiently low so that, during the time necessary to complete the nucleation treatment, no deformation of the sample will occur. Further increase in temperature to B is accompanied by crystal growth and the sample is progressively stiffened because of the crystals now present in the glassy matrix. An almost entirely crystalline piece of ceramic is thus formed with no change in shape of the starting solid glass.

Glass-ceramics have many advantages over both the "parent" glass and conventional ceramics. Because they are essentially crystalline and the liquidus or melting temperatures of ceramic crystals are very high, glass-ceramics can be used at higher temperatures than the corresponding glass. Their obvious advantage over conventional ceramics is that of ease of fabrication. A common piece of ceramic is usually fabricated by sintering or hot pressing the powder or by slipcasting. Both methods are accompanied by large volume shrinkage and also necessitate higher temperatures than those required for glass-ceramics.

TABLE 3
DENSITIES OF GLASSES AND CORRESPONDING GLASS-CERAMICS[26]

Glass composition—weight per cent										Density of parent glass (g/cm³)	Density of glass-ceramic (g/cm³)
SiO_2	B_2O_3	Al_2O_3	ZnO	MgO	BaO	CdO	Li_2O	TiO_2	ZrO_2		
57.6	4.7	15.2	—	—	—	—	5.2	12.1	3.6	2.52	2.57
48.5	—	14.6	34.0	—	—	—	—	2.9	—	3.17	3.13
41.7	—	9.3	41.6	—	—	—	—	7.4	—	3.23	3.23
50.9	—	23.2	18.5	—	—	—	—	7.4	—	2.92	2.99
48.5	—	21.3	—	4.8	—	15.0	—	10.1	—	2.87	2.86
46.0	—	24.1	—	—	17.6	—	—	12.3	—	2.96	2.96

In Table 3, the density of glass-ceramics is compared with that of the "parent" glass. It is seen that the density differences are either negligibly small or are absent. This clearly illustrates the absence of shrinkage during processing. In Table 4, a comparison is made of the

TABLE 4

THERMAL EXPANSION COEFFICIENTS AND DILATOMETRIC
SOFTENING TEMPERATURES OF GLASSES AND CORRESPONDING
GLASS-CERAMICS[26]

Weight percentage composition					Thermal expansion coefficients x 10^7 (20-400 °C)	
SiO_2	Li_2O	MgO	Al_2O_3	K_2O	Glass	Glass-ceramic
81.0	12.5	—	4.0	2.5	84.3	113.0
77.5	12.5	—	10.0	—	78.0	50.0
62.1	1.9	17.6	18.4	—	42.0	50.3
66.4	10.0	3.0	20.6	—	63.4	0.7
60.2	8.5	2.8	28.5	—	60.5	−42.4
76.7	14.7	8.6	—	—	92.8	92.5
62.4	12.4	25.2	—	—	78.8	74.8

thermal expansion coefficients of some glass-ceramics and those of the glasses from which they are prepared. It is to be noted that glass-ceramics can have a very wide range of thermal expansion. Large sheets of glass ceramics which have a negligibly small expansion co-efficient and are as transparent as a piece of glass are now being made by some glass companies in this country.

Another versatility of glass-ceramics is their adaptability to chemical machining. When a glass containing small amounts of copper, silver or gold ions is irradiated with ultraviolet light through a mask, metal atoms are formed in the unmasked region via reactions of the kind:

$$Cu^+ + h\gamma \rightarrow Cu^{2+} + e \tag{1}$$

and
$$Cu^+ + e \rightarrow Cu \tag{2}$$

A sensitizing agent such as cerium oxide can be present to enable the following reactions to occur:

$$Ce^{3+} + h\gamma \rightarrow Ce^{4+} + e \tag{3}$$

and
$$Cu^+ + e \rightarrow Cu \tag{4}$$

The irradiated glass is then heated to cause the metal atoms to aggregate together to become a nucleation catalyst. A ceramic crystalline phase is thus formed in those unmasked regions which were exposed to the ultraviolet light. In some $Li_2O \cdot Al_2O_3 \cdot SiO_2$ type systems, the crystalline regions are many times more soluble in dilute hydrofluoric acid than the surrounding glass. These regions can therefore be etched away, leaving the clear glassy regions relatively untouched. Intricate patterns or holes can be produced on the glass. Now the entire sample is exposed to the ultraviolet, nucleated and subsequently totally crystallized to give the glass ceramic. Holes up to $1/4$ inch in diameter can be produced to within one thousandth of an inch tolerance and 360,000 fine holes have been chemically machined per square inch of glass-ceramics.

Because the structure of glass-ceramics is essentially made up of interlocking fine crystals of high melting oxide phases with negligble porosity between grains, good tensile strengths are expected. The strengths of glass-ceramics are comparable to those for high alumina ceramics.

Similar to the case described for glass, chemical strengthening can also be applied to glass ceramics through surface compression.[27] Nepheline ($Na_6K_2Al_8Si_8O_{32}$) glass-ceramics have been subjected to ion-exchange in molten KNO_3 or KCl or K_2SO_4. The Na^+ ions in the glass-ceramic are replaced by K^+ ions from the fused salt resulting in the formation of a compressed surface layer. The abraded modulus of rupture of the untreated sample is about 8,000 psi. After chemical strengthening, it has increased to 200,000 psi.

Because of their transparency, high strength, negligibly small thermal expansion, chemical inertness, relatively low density, and ease of fabrication and machining, glass-ceramics are rapidly becoming an important material of engineering. Although most glass-ceramics now made are insulators, it is obviously possible to apply the same principle to the preparation of electronic ceramics. For instance, ferrites and ferroelectrics have been made via the glass-ceramic technique.[25] Similar studies can be made on chalcogenide glasses and will, no doubt, generate a new area for scientific studies as well as technical exploitation in the near future.

Related to glass-ceramics is the study of phase-separation in glass. In addition to so-called classical nucleation which leads to formation and growth of spherical droplets, another mode of phase-separation termed "spinodal decomposition" is possible. This latter mechanism leads to the formation of continuous "channels" of a second phase. A well-known product which is made via this mechanism is Vycor glass which has a negligible thermal expansion coefficient.

SUMMARY AND CONCLUSION

In the last two decades, under pressure of competition from plastics and the demand for glasses with superior properties, a "renaissance" has taken place in the field of glass science and technology. This review is an attempt to present some of the important advances made. A valid conclusion is that the phrase "people in glass houses shouldn't throw stones" is certainly no longer valid.

ACKNOWLEDGMENT

I am extremely grateful to the Directorate of Chemical Sciences of the Air Force Office of Scientific Research for the support of our glass research program.

REFERENCES

[1] J. D. Mackenzie, *Modern Aspects of the Vitreous State*, Vol. 1, Butterworths, London (1960).

[2] J. D. Mackenzie, *Glass Industry*, **47**, 488 (1966).

[3] J. E. Stanworth, *Physical Properties of Glass*, Oxford University Press, Oxford (1950).

[4] W. H. Zachariasen, *J. Am. Chem. Soc.* **54**, 3841 (1932).

[5] P. J. Bray and A. H. Silver, *Modern Aspects of the Vitreous State*, Vol. 1, Butterworths, London (1960).

[6] J. M. Stevels, *Handbuch der Physik*, Vol. 20, Springer-Verlag (1957).

[7] M. Fulda, *Sprechsaal*, **60**, 769 (1927).

[8] F. M. Ernsberger, *Glass Industry*, **47**, 481 (1966).

[9] M. E. Nordbereg et al., *J. Am. Ceram. Soc.* **47**, 215 (1964).

[10] P. W. Bridgman and I. Simon, *J. Appl. Phys.* **24**, 205 (1953).

[11] J. D. Mackenzie, *J. Am. Ceram. Soc.* **46**, 461 (1963).

[12] J. D. Mackenzie, *J. Am. Ceram. Soc.* **47**, 76 (1964).

[13] W. B. Hillig, *Advances in Glass Technology*, Part 2, Plenum Press, N.Y. (1960).

[14] S. P. Faile and D. M. Roy, *Bull. Am. Ceram. Soc.* **47**, 401 (1968).

[15] L. L. Sperry and J. D. Mackenzie, *Phys. Chem. Glasses*, June (1968).

[16] H. Smith and A. J. Cohen, *Science*, **137**, 981 (1962).

[17] W. H. Armistead and S. D. Stookey, *Science*, **144**, 150 (1964).

[18] I. Simon, *Modern Aspects of the Vitreous State*, Vol. 1, Butterworths, London (1960).

[19] A. R. Hilton, *Glass Industry*, **48**, 550 (1967).

[20] A. D. Pearson, *Modern Aspects of the Vitreous State*, Vol. 3, Butterworths, London (1964).

[21] B. T. Kolomiets, *Phys, Stat. Solid*, **7**, 713 (1964).

[22] S. Ovshinsky, *Bull. Am. Ceram. Soc.* **47**, 383 (1968).

[23] P. L. Baynton, H. Rawson and J. E. Stanworth, *J. Electrochem. Soc.* **104**, 237 (1957).

[24] J. D. Mackenzie, *Modern Aspects of the Vitreous State*, Vol. 3, Butterworths, London (1964).

[25] J. D. Mackenzie, *Electronics*, **39**, 129 (1966).

[26] P. W. McMillan, *Glass Ceramics*, Academic Press, N.Y. (1964).

[27] D. A. Duke, J. F. MacDowell and B. R. Karstetter, *J. Am. Ceram. Soc.* **50**, 67 (1967).

VI. On The Theory of Optimum Aerodynamic Shapes

Angelo Miele

1. INTRODUCTION

The determination of optimum aerodynamic shapes has interested the scientific community for centuries. Historically speaking, the first problem of this kind was the study by Newton of the body of revolution having minimum drag for a given length ℓ and thickness t (Fig. 1). Not only did Newton employ analytical techniques analogous to the modern calculus of variations, but he also formulated pressure laws which are good approximations for certain physical flows. In studying the impact of a gas molecule with the body, Newton postulated two possible models: (a) the normal velocity component is reversed, while the tangential velocity component is conserved; and (b) the normal velocity component is annihilated, while the tangential velocity component is conserved. In modern aerospace terminology, we recognize that Model (a) is the specular-reflection model of free-molecular flow and Model (b) is an approximation to that of a hypersonic, inviscid flow.

In the early part of this century, the use of advanced mathematical techniques in the analysis of subsonic and supersonic flows stimulated a renewed interest in optimization problems. In particular, Munk

ANGELO MIELE is Professor of Astronautics and Director of the Aero-Astronautics Group in the Department of Mechanical and Aerospace Engineering and Materials Science, Rice University, Houston, Texas. Presently, he is Associate Editor of the Journal of the Astronautical Sciences and Editor-in-Chief of the Journal of Optimization Theory and Applications. His current research interests include optimization theory, optimum aerodynamic shapes, and optimum flight paths. Prior to Rice University, he served on the faculties of the Polytechnic Institute of Brooklyn and Purdue University and on the staff of the Boeing Scientific Research Laboratories.

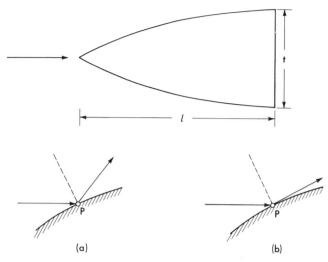

FIGURE 1. Newton's problem.

determined the lift distribution which minimizes the induced drag of a subsonic wing having given span and lift; furthermore, Von Kármán determined the shape of the slender forebody of revolution of given length and thickness which minimizes the pressure drag in linearized supersonic flow. In more recent times, the advent of jet and rocket engines as aircraft propulsion systems and the parallel increase in flight velocities and altitudes have made it necessary to extend the optimization of aerodynamic shapes to a wider range of Mach and Reynolds numbers, thereby including the hypersonic and free-molecular flow regimes.

Since the distributions of pressure coefficients and friction coefficients depend on the flow regime, it is clear that a single optimum body does not exist; rather a succession of optimum configurations exist, that is, one for each flow regime and set of free-stream conditions (Ref. 1). In addition, the optimum geometry'depends on the quantity being extremized as well as the constraints employed in the optimization process, whether aerodynamic constraints or geometric constraints. A summary of the variety of problems which may be encountered in the study of optimum aerodynamic shapes is shown in Table 1.

TABLE 1
STUDY OF OPTIMUM AERODYNAMIC SHAPES

Flow regimes	Subsonic, transonic, supersonic, hypersonic, free-molecular
Criteria of optimization	Pressure drag, total drag, lift, lift-to-drag ratio, heat-transfer rate, sonic boom, thrust
Aerodynamic constraints	Lift, pitching moment, center of pressure
Geometric constraints	Length, thickness, wetted area, planform area, frontal area, volume

Ideally, one would like to optimize an aircraft or a missile as a whole. Since this approach is extremely difficult, optimization studies have been concerned only with the main components of a configuration. In this connection, the categories of shapes most frequently investigated are shown in Table 2.

TABLE 2
CATEGORIES OF SHAPES

Wings	Two-dimensional, three-dimensional
Bodies	Axisymmetric, three-dimensional
Nozzles, diffusers	Axisymmetric, two-dimensional, three-dimensional

In this paper, the physical models of interest in the theory of optimum aerodynamic shapes are reviewed in Section 2. Then, the corresponding mathematical models are illustrated in Section 3. Concerning variational problems, those involving one independent variable are reviewed in Section 4 and those involving two independent variables are reviewed in Section 5. The solution process is considered in Section 6. Finally, new trends in the theory and certain physical problems of interest in the immediate future are outlined in Section 7. Here, only considerations of a general nature are presented; for detailed results, the reader should consult the specialized literature on the subject (see, for example, Refs. 1 and 2).

2.   PHYSICAL MODELS

In this section, some of the physical models of current interest in the theory of optimum aerodynamic shapes are reviewed.

2.1. <u>Linearized Supersonic Flow.</u> For relatively slender shapes in flight at Mach numbers not too close to unity and yet not too large with respect to unity, the small-perturbation theory can be employed when estimating the aerodynamic forces acting on a body. In other words, the set of nonlinear equations governing the motion can be replaced by one which is linear: this is equivalent to assuming that the Mach lines originating from the surface of the body are parallel (Fig. 2).

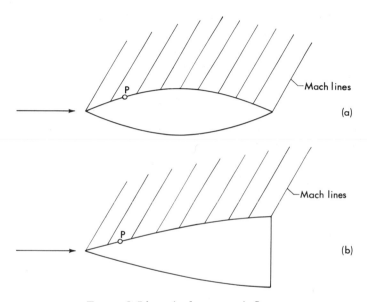

FIGURE 2. Linearized supersonic flow.

Because of the linearity, the method of superposition can be employed, and general analytical solutions can be derived for the aerodynamic forces acting on either a two-dimensional shape or an axisymmetric shape whose contour is arbitrarily prescribed. For a two-dimensional shape (Fig. 2-a), the pressure coefficient at a point P has the form

$$C_p = C_1 \dot{y} \tag{1}$$

where C_1 is a constant which depends on the free-stream Mach number and y is the inclination of the tangent to a surface element with respect to the free-stream direction*. On the other hand, for an axisymmetric shape (Fig. 2-b), the pressure coefficient no longer depends on the local slope of a surface element, but it is governed by the geometry of the entire body portion preceding that element. Symbolically, this can be written as

$$C_p = C_p \text{ (shape)} \tag{2}$$

2.2. <u>Nonlinearized Supersonic Flow.</u> Whenever the combination of thickness ratio and Mach number is such that the linearization process is not permissible, a more precise approach to the determination of the fluid properties is necessary. In this connection, one can employ a pressure coefficient derived from second or higher order approximations to the equations of motion or, where possible, one can use the complete set of equations.

Neglecting the interaction between the shock wave originating at the leading edge of the body I and the Mach lines originating at points downstream (Fig. 3), one can employ a pressure coefficient derived from a second-order approximation to the compression processes and expansion processes. Thus, for a two-dimensional shape, the pressure coefficient at a point P has the form

$$C_p = C_1\dot{y} + C_2\dot{y}^2 \tag{3}$$

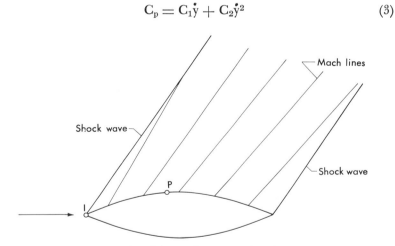

FIGURE 3. Higher order approximations.

* The symbol x denotes a coordinate in the undisturbed flow direction, y a coordinate perpendicular to x, and $\dot{y}$ the derivative dy/dx.

where C_1 and C_2 are constants which depend on the free-stream Mach number.

If more precision is desired, one can employ shock-expansion theory. That is, the compression through the shock wave originating at the leading edge I is calculated using the exact equations of a shock wave; the subsequent expansion from point I to point P is calculated using the equations of a Prandtl-Meyer expansion. For a two-dimensional shape, this leads to the following functional expression:

$$C_p = C_p(\overset{\bullet}{y},\overset{\bullet}{y}_i) \qquad (4)$$

If further precision is desired, the interaction between the shock-wave and the Mach lines must be accounted for (Fig. 4). That is, one

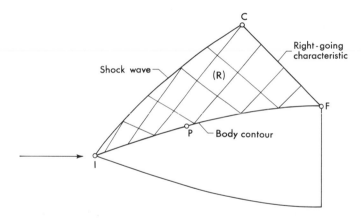

FIGURE 4. Nonlinearized supersonic flow.

must study the fluid region (R) limited by the body surface IF, the shock wave IC originating at the leading edge, and the right-going characteristic line CF passing through the final point. Along the line IF, the fluid velocity must be tangent to the body; along the line IC, the equations of a shock wave are valid; and, along the line CF, the direction and compatibility conditions hold. Finally, within the region (R), the partial differential equations governing the gas flow must be satisfied. This type of study is called *method of characteristics* and leads to a pressure law of the form

$$C_p = C_p \text{ (shape)} \qquad (5)$$

This means that the pressure coefficient at a point P depends on the geometry of the entire body portion preceding this point.

2.3. <u>Newtonian Hypersonic Flow.</u> Whenever the free-stream Mach number is sufficiently large with respect to unity, the shock wave generated at the leading edge of the body lies so close to the body that it can be regarded to be identical with it (Fig. 5). Consequently, the

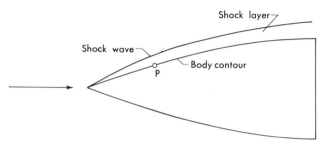

FIGURE 5. Newtonian hypersonic flow.

pressure distribution can be determined with the assumption that the tangential velocity component of the particles striking the body is conserved, while the normal velocity component is annihilated. This is precisely Model (b) of the introduction. For slender, two-dimensional shapes and axisymmetric shapes, the pressure coefficient at a point P is given by

$$C_p = 2\dot{\bar{y}}^2 \qquad (6)$$

2.4. <u>Newton-Busemann Hypersonic Flow.</u> A basic hypothesis of the Newtonian flow model is that the pressure at a point immediately behind the shock wave is identical with the pressure at the corresponding point of the body. Even if one admits that the layer of gas between the shock wave and the body is infinitely thin, the equality of the pressures is justified only if the gas particles, after crossing the shock wave, move along rectilinear paths; this is precisely the case for a wedge or a cone. On the other hand, if the body is either convex or concave, the gas particles in the thin layer between the shock wave and the body move along curvilinear paths, that is, they are subjected to centripetal accelerations. Therefore, the actual pressure on the body is lower than that predicted with the Newtonian theory for convex bodies but higher for concave bodies.

The resulting pressure correction was first calculated by Busemann; hence, this flow model is called the Newton-Busemann model and, while more complicated than the Newtonian model, it is still relatively simple for analytical purposes. The reason is that, if the slender body approximation is made, the pressure coefficient at a point P is given by

$$C_p = 2\dot{y}^2 + k y \ddot{y} \tag{7}$$

where $k = 2$ for two-dimensional flow and $k = 1$ for axisymmetric flow. Therefore, C_p depends only on the geometric properties of a surface element and is independent of the geometry of the body portion preceding that element.

2.5. Free-Molecular Flow. In the previous sections, it was tacitly assumed that the gas is a continuum, that is, the mean free path is small with respect to a characteristic dimension of the body. Whenever the mean free path is large with respect to a characteristic dimension of the body, the nature of the flow is free-molecular. The incident molecules are undisturbed by the presence of the vehicle, that is, the incoming and reflected flows are transparent to each other. For analytical purposes, two idealized models have been employed thus far and are now illustrated.

In the *specular reflection model* (Fig. 6-a), the molecules hitting the surface are reflected optically, which means that the tangential velocity component is unchanged while the normal velocity component is reversed. This is Model (a) of the introduction. Under convenient approximations, the pressure coefficient at a point P of a slender body is given by

$$C_p = 4\dot{y}^2 \tag{8}$$

that is, it is twice that of Newtonian hypersonic flow.

In the *diffuse reflection model* (Fig. 6-b), the molecules hitting the surface are first absorbed and then reemitted with a Maxwellian velocity distribution corresponding to an equilibrium temperature intermediate between that of the incoming flow and that of the solid surface. Under convenient approximations, the pressure coefficient at a point P of a slender body is give by

$$C_p = 2\dot{y}^2 + 2k\dot{y} \tag{9}$$

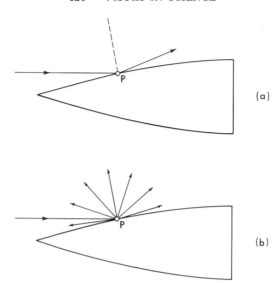

FIGURE 6. Free-molecular flow.

where the constant k depends on the surface temperature and the free-stream conditions. Clearly, C_p depends only on the orientation of a surface element with respect to the free-stream direction and is independent of the geometry of the body portion preceding that element.

3.   MATHEMATICAL MODELS

In the previous section, a discussion of the principal flow regimes was given. After the physical model has been established, and after the criterion of optimization, the aerodynamic constraints, and the geometric constraints have been decided upon, a well-defined optimization problem arises. In this connection, two mathematical models can be identified: (a) problems in which the optimum is sought with respect to a finite number of parameters and (b) problems in which the optimum is sought with respect to a finite number of functions. Problems of type (a) belong to the *theory of maxima and minima,* also called *mathematical programming;* problems of type (b) belong to the *calculus of variations,* also called *optimal control theory.* For the sake of brevity, only problems of type (b) are reviewed in the following sections. Specifically, the case of one independent variable is considered in Section 4 and the case of two independent variables is considered in Section 5.

4. VARIATIONAL PROBLEMS IN ONE INDEPENDENT VARIABLE

In the theory of optimum aerodynamic shapes, certain functional forms involving one independent variable and one or several dependent variables are of frequent interest.

4.1. <u>Simplest Problem.</u> The simplest problem of the calculus of variations consists of extremizing the line integral

$$J = \int_{x_i}^{x_f} f(x,y,\dot{y})dx \tag{10}$$

with respect to the class of continuous functions $y(x)$ which satisfy certain prescribed boundary conditions. In this relation, x denotes the independent variable, y the dependent variable and $\dot{y}$ the derivative dy/dx; the subscripts i, f stand for the initial and final points respectively.

Variational problems of this type arise whenever two requirements are met. First, the configuration must have special geometric properties so that the body is described by a single curve; this is precisely the case with a two-dimensional wing, a body of revolution, and a conical body. Next, the flow regime must be such that the pressure and friction coefficients are functions of, at most, the local coordinates and the slope of the contour; this situation occurs in linearized supersonic flow, Newtonian hypersonic flow, and free-molecular flow.

Examples of functionals of type (10) are the following:

$$D_p/2C_1q_\infty = \int_0^\ell \dot{y}^2 dx \tag{11}$$

and

$$D_p/4\pi q_\infty = \int_0^\ell y\dot{y}^3 dx \tag{12}$$

where D_p is the pressure drag, q_∞ the free-stream dynamic pressure, x a coordinate in the flow direction, and y a coordinate perpendicular to x. Equation (11) pertains to a two-dimensional wing, symmetric with respect to the chord, in linearized supersonic flow; Eq. (12) pertains to a body of revolution in Newtonian hypersonic flow.

4.2. Isoperimetric Problem. A modification of the previous problem arises whenever the following integrals are considered:

$$J = \int_{x_i}^{x_f} f(x,y,\dot{y})dx, \qquad K = \int_{x_i}^{x_f} \varphi(x,y,\dot{y})dx \qquad (13)$$

where K is a given constant. The extremization of (13-1) is sought with respect to the class of continuous functions y(x) which satisfy certain prescribed boundary conditions and the isoperimetric constraint (13-2).

The following are examples of this type:

$$D_p/2C_1q_\infty = \int_0^\ell \dot{y}^2 dx, \qquad A/2 = \int_0^\ell y dx \qquad (14)$$

and

$$D_p/4\pi q_\infty = \int_0^\ell y\dot{y}^3 dx, \qquad V/\pi = \int_0^\ell y^2 dx \qquad (15)$$

Problem (14) pertains to a two-dimensional wing, symmetric with respect to the chord, in linearized supersonic flow: the pressure drag D_p must be minimized for a given enclosed area A. Problem (15) pertains to a body of revolution in Newtonian hypersonic flow: the pressure drag D_p must be minimized for a given volume V.

4.3. Ratio of Integrals. A modification of the isoperimetric problem arises whenever the following integrals are considered:

$$J_1 = \int_{x_i}^{x_f} f_1(x,y,\dot{y})dx, \qquad J_2 = \int_{x_i}^{x_f} f_2(x,y,\dot{y})dx \qquad (16)$$

and the extremization of the ratio

$$J = J_1/J_2 \qquad (17)$$

is sought with respect to the class of continuous functions y(x) which satisfy certain prescribed boundary conditions.

The following example illustrates the above situation:

$$L/2q_\infty = \int_0^\ell \dot{y}^2 dx, \qquad D/2q_\infty = \int_0^\ell (\dot{y}^3 + C_f) dx \qquad (18)$$

$$E = L/D \qquad (19)$$

where L is the lift, D the total drag, E the lift-to-drag ratio, and C_f the surface-averaged friction coefficient. Problem (18)-(19) pertains to a two-dimensional, flat-top wing in Newtonian hypersonic flow: the lift-to-drag ratio E is to be maximized for given length ℓ and thickness t.

4.4. <u>Bolza Problem.</u> In the previous sections, several particular problems were considered. Here, we formulate a very general problem, which includes all of the previous problems as particular cases. We consider the set of derivated variables

$$y_k = y_k(x), \qquad k = 1,....,n \qquad (20)$$

and nonderivated variables

$$u_k = u_k(x), \qquad k = 1,....,m \qquad (21)$$

which satisfy the isoperimetric constraints

$$K_j = \int_{x_1}^{x_f} \varphi_j(x, y_k, \dot{y}_k, u_k) dx + [\gamma_j(x, y_k)]_i^f, \qquad j = 1,....,p \qquad (22)$$

the differential constraints

$$\psi_j(x, y_k, \dot{y}_k, u_k) = 0, \qquad j = 1,....,q \qquad (23)$$

and certain prescribed boundary conditions. It is required to find the combination (20)-(21) which extremizes the functional

$$J = \int_{x_1}^{x_f} f(x, y_k, \dot{y}_k, u_k) dx + [g(x, y_k)]_i^f \qquad (24)$$

This problem, called the Bolza problem, is the most general problem of the calculus of variations in one independent variable. It reduces to the *Lagrange problem* for

$$g = 0, \qquad \gamma_j = 0, \qquad j = 1,...,p \qquad (25)$$

and to the *Mayer problem* for

$$f = 0, \qquad \varphi_j = 0, \qquad j = 1,....,p \qquad (26)$$

In turn, the Mayer problem reduces to the *Pontryagin problem* when the differential constraints (23) have the form

$$\dot{y}_j - \omega_j(x,y_k,u_k) = 0, \qquad j = 1,...,q \qquad (27)$$

with

$$q = n \qquad (28)$$

Problems of the Bolza type arise in the study of two-dimensional or axisymmetric bodies in nonlinearized supersonic flow, providing the aerodynamic forces and the geometric constraints can be expressed as one-dimensional integrals to be evaluated along the same reference line (e.g., the contour of the body or a characteristic line of the flow field). As an example, consider the shock-free, supersonic expansion of a gas in a two-dimentional or axisymmetric nozzle of given length (Fig. 7). In this problem, the thrust, the mass flow, and the length can

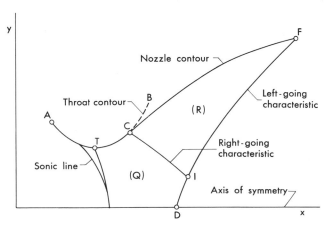

FIGURE 7. Rocket nozzle.

be expressed as integrals of quantities evaluated along the left-going characteristic line DIF joining the axis of symmetry with the final point. The minimal problem is a Bolza problem, with this understanding: the quantity J is the thrust; the constants K_j are the mass flow and the length; and the constraints $\psi_j = 0$ are the differential equations to be satisfied along a characteristic line, namely, the direction and compatibility conditions.

Problems of the Bolza type also arise in the study of two-dimensional or axisymmetric bodies in Newtonian hypersonic flow, Newton-Busemann hypersonic flow, and free-molecular flow whenever an inequality constraint is imposed on the configuration and/or derivatives of second and higher order are present. At first glance, these problems do not seem to be covered by the Bolza formulation: in Eqs. (22)-(24), inequality constraints are not mentioned and only first-order derivatives are present. However, by the judicious use of auxiliary variables, each problem can be converted into a Bolza problem. As an example, the slope of a configuration in Newtonian hypersonic flow may be required to be nonnegative everywhere, that is, the inequality constraint

$$\dot{y} \geq 0 \qquad (29)$$

is to be accounted for. This inequality constraint can be converted into a differential constraint if the auxiliary variable u defined by the relationship

$$\dot{y} - u^2 = 0 \qquad (30)$$

is introduced.

5. VARIATIONAL PROBLEMS IN TWO INDEPENDENT VARIABLES

In the theory of optimum aerodynamic shapes, certain functional forms involving two independent variables and one or several dependent variables are of frequent interest.

5.1. Simplest Problem. The simplest problem of the calculus of variations consists of extremizing the surface integral

$$J = \iint_S f(x,y,z,z_x,z_y)dxdy \qquad (31)$$

with respect to the class of continuous functions $z(x,y)$ which satisfy certain prescribed boundary conditions. In this relation, x and y denote the independent variables, z the dependent variable, z_x the derivative $\partial z/\partial x$, and z_y the derivative $\partial z/\partial y$; the symbol S denotes the domain of integration in the xy-plane.

Variational problems of this type arise whenever the flow regime is such that the pressure and friction coefficients are functions of, at most, the local coordinates and the slopes of the surface defining the body. This situation occurs in certain problems of linearized supersonic flow, Newtonian hypersonic flow, and free-molecular flow.

Examples of functions of type (31) are the following:

$$D_p/2q_\infty = \iint_S z_x^3 dxdy \tag{32}$$

and

$$D/2q_\infty = \iint_S (z_x^3 + C_f)dxdy \tag{33}$$

where x and y are planform coordinates and z is a coordinate perpendicular to the xy-plane. Equation (32) represents the pressure drag of a three-dimensional, flat-top wing in Newtonian hypersonic flow; Eq. (33) is the total drag of the same wing.

5.2. <u>Isoperimetric Problem.</u> A modification of the previous problem arises whenever the following integrals are considered:

$$J = \iint_S f(x,y,z,z_x,z_y)dxdy, \qquad K = \iint_S \varphi(x,y,z,z_x z_y)dxdy \tag{34}$$

where K is a given constant. The extremization of (34-1) is sought with respect to the class of continuous functions $z(x,y)$ which satisfy certain prescribed boundary conditions and the isoperimetric constraint (34-2).

The following is an example of a problem of this type:

$$D/2q_\infty = \iint_S (z_x^3 + C_f)dxdy, \qquad V = \iint_S zdxdy \tag{35}$$

Problem (35) pertains to a three-dimensional, flat-top wing in Newtonian hypersonic flow: the total drag D must be minimized for a given volume V.

5.3. <u>Ratio of Integrals.</u> A modification of the isoperimetric problem arises whenever the following integrals are considered:

$$J_1 = \iint_S f_1(x,y,z,z_x,z_y)dxdy, \qquad J_2 = \iint_S f_2(x,y,z,z_x z_y)dxdy \tag{36}$$

and the extremization of the ratio

$$J = J_1/J_2 \tag{37}$$

is sought with respect to the class of continuous functions $z(x,y)$ which satisfy certain prescribed boundary conditions.

The following example illustrates the above situation:

$$L/2q_\infty = \iint_S z_x^2 dx dy, \qquad D/2q_\infty = \iint_S (z_x^3 + C_f) dx dy \tag{38}$$

$$E = L/D \tag{39}$$

Problem (38)-(39) pertains to a three-dimensional, flat-top wing in Newtonian hypersonic flow: the lift-to-drag ratio E is to be maximized for a given planform.

5.4. Bolza Problem. In the previous sections, several particular problems were considered. Here, we formulate a very general problem, which includes all of the previous problems as particular cases. We consider the set of derived variables

$$z_k = z_k(x,y), \qquad k = 1,....,n \tag{40}$$

and nonderivated variables

$$u_k = u_k(x,y), \qquad k = 1,....,m \tag{41}$$

which satisfy the isoperimetric constraints

$$K_j = \iint_S \varphi_j(x,y,z_k,z_{kx},z_{ky},u_k) dx dy + \oint_B \gamma_j(x,\dot{x},y,\dot{y},z_k,\dot{z}_k) ds, \qquad j = 1,....,p \tag{42}$$

the differential constraints

$$\psi_j(x,y,z_k,z_{kx},z_{ky},u_k) = 0, \qquad j = 1,....,q \tag{43}$$

and certain prescribed boundary conditions. Here, S is the domain of integration, B the boundary of this domain, and s a curvilinear abscissa along B; the dot sign denotes total derivative with respect to s. It is required to find the combination (40)-(41) which extremizes the functional

$$J = \iint_S f(x,y,z_k,z_{kx},z_{ky},u_k) dx dy + \oint_B g(x,\dot{x},y,\dot{y},z_k,\dot{z}_k) ds \tag{44}$$

This problem, called the *Bolza problem,* is the most general problem of the calculus of variations in two independent variables. It reduces to the *Lagrange problem* for

$$g = 0, \qquad \gamma_j = 0, \qquad j = 1,....,p \qquad (45)$$

and to the *Mayer problem* for

$$f = 0, \qquad \varphi_j = 0, \qquad j = 1,....,p \qquad (46)$$

Problems of the Bolza type arise in the study of axisymmetric bodies in linearized or nonlinearized supersonic flow, whenever constraints are imposed, not only on the length and the diameter, but also on integrated quantities such as the wetted area or the volume. As an example, consider the problem of finding the axisymmetric closed body which minimizes the drag in linearized supersonic flow for given constraints imposed on the length and the volume (Fig. 8). One deals

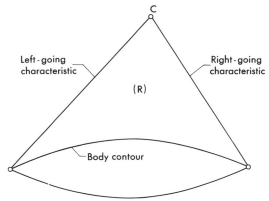

FIGURE 8. Closed body of revolution.

with the flow properties in a region (R) limited by a boundary **B** formed by the body contour, the left-going characteristic through the initial point I, and the right-going characteristic through the final point F. After the drag and the volume are expressed as integrals of quantities evaluated along the body contour IF, the minimal problem can be treated as a Bolza problem, with this understanding: the quantity J is the drag; the constant K is the value prescribed for the volume; and the constraints $\psi_j = 0$ are the irrotationality condition and the continuity equation which hold at every point of the region (R). Of course, the tangency conditions must be satisfied along the body contour IF and the direction and compatibility conditions must be satisfied along the remainder of the contour B, that is, the characteristic lines IC and CF.

6. SOLUTION PROCESS

In the previous sections, a discussion of the principal mathematical models was given. After an optimization problem has been formulated, the classical tools of the calculus of variations must be employed: they involve first-order conditions as well as second and higher order conditions. While a detailed analysis is beyond the scope of this paper, a summary of these conditions is presented in Table 3. We note that the basic equations, the Euler equations, are ordinary differential equations for the problems of Section 4 and partial differential equations for the problems of Section 5. Therefore, the problems of Section 5 are considerably more difficult than those of Section 4.

With the aid of the above variational tools, a wide variety of problems has been solved in recent years. Wings, bodies, and wing-body combinations have been optimized in supersonic, hypersonic, and free-molecular flow. The discussion of all the results obtained goes beyond the scope of this paper. Therefore, the reader is referred to the specialized literature on the subject (see, for example, Refs. 1 and 2).

TABLE 3
OPTIMUM CONDITIONS

First-order conditions	Euler equations, transversality condition, corner conditions
Higher-order conditions	Legendre condition, Weierstrass condition, Jacobi condition

7. ENGINEERING TRENDS AND UNSOLVED PROBLEMS

Despite the variety of the results already obtained, the theory of optimum aerodynamic shapes is only at its beginning. There are interesting and useful variational problems in one independent variable yet to be solved in every flow regime. An analogous remark is even more appropriate for variational problems involving two, three, or four independent variables, since these problems have been treated in the literature only occasionally. Among the engineering problems which deserve to be investigated in the near future, the following deserve to be mentioned:

(a) Supersonic flow: Determination of the axisymmetric closed body, forebody, or ducted forebody which minimizes the total drag, the sum of the pressure drag and the friction drag, for a given volume.

(b) Supersonic flow: Determination of three-dimensional wings, fuselages, and wing-fuselage combinations which minimize the total drag under the condition that the lift is given, the volume is given, and the boom intensity on the ground does not exceed a prescribed limit.

(c) Hypersonic flow: Determination of the axisymmetric body which minimizes the surface-integrated heat transfer rate.

(d) Hypersonic flow: Determination of three-dimensional wings, fuselages, and wing-fuselage combinations which minimize the total drag or maximize the lift-to-drag ratio for given conditions imposed on the lift and the volume.

(e) Free-molecular flow: Determination of three-dimensional shapes having minimum drag for a given volume.

Mathematically speaking, these problems are problems of the Bolza type in one or several independent variables, not generally amenable to analytical solutions. This being the case, numerical techniques must be developed, more specifically, first-variation methods (steepest-descent methods) and second-variation methods (quasi-linearization methods).

While the theory of optimum aerodynamic shapes is only at its beginning, the vista is expanding rapidly on its promising applications. Therefore, it is not difficult to predict that, providing sufficient research effort is expended in this area and providing the present rate of progress is maintained in the design of digital computing machines, the calculus of variations approach will become a fundamental instrument in the design of optimum aerodynamic configurations.

ACKNOWLEDGMENT

The research described in this chapter was supported by the Directorate of Mathematical Sciences, Air Force Office of Scientific Research.

REFERENCES

[1] Miele, A., Editor, *Theory of Optimum Aerodynamic Shapes,* Academic Press, New York, 1965.

[2] Miele, A., *Summary Report on Configurations Having Maximum Lift-to-Drag Ratio for Hypersonic Flight,* Rice University, Aero-Astronautics Report No. 52, 1968.

VII. Arc Jets In Science and Technology

CHARLES SHEER

INTRODUCTION

The generation and management of arc jets is a segment of the broader field of plasma physics which, during recent years, has penetrated deeply into science and industry. Motivated chiefly by the need to solve technical problems involving hyperthermal aerospace environments, the development of the arc jet has, within a suprisingly short space of time, borne fruit in many areas of modern technology.

An arc jet generator is a device for producing a continuous stream of plasma, or "plasmajet," by means of an electric arc. Phenomenologically, the popular notion of the plasma medium is that of an ionized gas in which there exists some mechanism for maintaining a supply of charged particles. Moreover, the concentration of charged particles must be sufficient to impart to the gas the normally absent property of electrical conductivity. This relatively simple idea, however, is transcended by the recently expanded concept of plasma, which includes condensed phases of matter as well as gases. For example, it has been pointed out[1] that the concept of Debye screening, which is a fundamental idea of considerable importance in plasma physics, was first introduced by Debye and Hückel to describe the motion of charged particles in aqueous electrolytic solutions. Similarly, the oscillations of the electron gas within a solid metal were

CHARLES SHEER is Senior Research Associate in the Electronics Research Laboratories, School of Engineering and Applied Science at Columbia University. A scientist whose interests and research experience have ranged from nuclear physics, through electrophysiology and biophysics, electrical and electronic instrument design and development, to his present work in plasma physics, Dr. Sheer is the holder of 18 U.S. and 6 foreign patents. He is the co-inventor, with Dr. Samuel Korman, of the Sheer-Korman process for extractive metallurgy. He has served on a number of advisory bodies to government agencies.

predicted and found by direct analogy with the natural oscillations of a gaseous plasma. The phenomena of charge avalanches and cyclotron resonance, both characteristic of gaseous plasmas, have been observed in semi-conducting solids. In fact, the term "microplasma" has come into common use in solid state physics to describe events featuring the collective motions of charged particles in semi-conductors.

In addition to maintenance of mobile charged particles, there are other requirements[2] which are essential to the generation of plasma, but which are too involved to include here. For our purposes it will

TABLE I

RANGES OF PARTICLE DENSITY AND TEMPERATURE FOR VARIOUS TYPES OF PLASMAS

	Particle Density (No. Per cc)	Temperature (°K)
Natural Plasmas		
Stellar Interiors	10^{22} - 10^{25}	$\sim 10^{8}$
Stellar Atmospheres	10^{10} - 10^{16}	10^{4} - 10^{6}
Nebulae	10^{3}	10^{4}
Interstellar Space	1 - 100	10^{2}
Earth's Ionosphere	10^{10} - 10^{12}	10^{2} - 10^{3}
Man-Made Plasmas		
Thermonuclear Plasma	10^{12} - 10^{14}	10^{8} - 10^{9}
Constricted Arc Plasma Jets	10^{16} - 10^{18}	$1\text{-}5\text{x}10^{4}$
Free Burning Electric Arcs	10^{16} - 10^{17}	$7\text{-}10\text{x}10^{3}$
Combustion Flames	10^{16} - 10^{18}	$3\text{-}5\text{x}10^{3}$
Low Pressure Arcs	10^{14} - 10^{16}	$1\text{-}3\text{x}10^{3}$
Glow Discharges	10^{10} - 10^{12}	300 - 600

be useful to adopt the following qualitative description of the plasma medium:

A macroscopically neutral body of matter containing an appreciable concentration of mobile charge carriers.

Implicit in the rather indefinite term "appreciable" is the notion of an adequate degree of electrical conductivity. In the case of gaseous plasma, the flow of electricity through the medium provides an excellent mechanism (electrical resistance heating) for supplying energy to the medium, a requirement which, as we shall see, is essential to steady-state arc jet generation.

The first appearance of plasma physics as a scientific discipline arose out of the astrophysical inquiries into such topics as solar prominences and the motion of stellar clouds, wherein the ionized nature of the medium and its consequent interaction with magnetic fields led to a new understanding of these phenomena. Thus, widening our scope to a cosmic scale, it might be said that the study of plasma is as old as astronomy.

The various natural and man-made plasmas differ from each other chiefly with respect to particle density (pressure) and average particle kinetic energy (temperature). Table I shows the ranges of density and temperature encountered in the various types of plasma. In particular, for the arc jets to be discussed below, we shall be dealing with free-burning arcs and constricted arc plasma jets. Therefore, for the balance of this chapter we shall restrict our attention to ionized gases having particle densities in the range of 10^{16} to 10^{18} particles per cc, and temperatures in the range 7×10^3 to 5×10^4 °K.

PLASMA GENERATION

All devices or environments in which plasma is generated have in common some mechanism for the continuous ionization of the medium. Since charged particles are continually lost from a given plasma zone, either by direct recombination of oppositely charged species, or by diffusion or convection out of the plasma zone, continual ion production* is mandatory for the continued existence of the plasma state. In the glow discharge, direct ionization by impact of free electrons, which have been accelerated to energies in excess of the ionization energy by the high electric field used in this device, provides for the generation of new ions. In equilibrium, the ion generation rate equals the rate of depletion by volume recombination and diffusion to the walls. In the ionosphere, the mechanism is photoionization by the short wavelength component of solar radiation, which is absorbed

---

* More appropriately, ion-pair production. The most common mechanism is the dislodgement of a free electron from a neutral gas atom, creating a heavy positive ion, which, together with the free electron, forms the ion pair. In any macroscopically small plasma volume there will occur equal numbers of positive gas ions and free electrons. Except in quite rare circumstances, the formation of heavy negative ions, e.g., by the attachment of a free electron to a neutral gas atom, does not occur.

in the upper atmosphere and which makes up for recombination and for the ions lost to outer space.

In the case of the electric arc, the ionization level is maintained by the so-called "thermal" ionization process. As a result of the appreciable electrical conductivity of the arc column, relatively high currents can be made to flow, resulting in the dissipation of Joule (I^2R) heat within the column. This occurs mainly by elastic collisions between the current-carrying free electrons and the neutral gas atoms in the column. Although the energy per collision may be considerably below the energy required for ionization by impact, the gas can be maintained at an elevated temperature. Statistical considerations indicate that a fraction of the gas atoms, namely those comprising the high energy "tail" of the velocity distribution, will receive enough energy to become ionized upon collision.

In a free-burning arc, i.e., one subject only to the influence of natural convection, the depletion rate is relatively small. This is due to the fact that at elevated temperatures and normal pressure (e.g., 1 atm.) volume recombination becomes less likely and ion depletion occurs to a large extent by the slower diffusion process plus gentle convection of the ambient atmosphere. Hence a steady-state situation may be maintained with relative ease. However, this state of affairs is dependent on a rather delicate balance between the generation and depletion of charge carriers. Therefore, when the balance is upset to any significant degree, as for example when the attempt is made to transfer energy from the arc to an external fluid, the arc becomes unstable. Thus a free-burning arc can tolerate the injection of "foreign" material at a rate only slightly in excess of the mild natural convection of the ambient atmosphere. It is therefore inherently ineffective as a heat transfer device.

An arc jet is a device which utilizes the arc to heat a continuous stream of fluid to plasma temperatures. For efficient operation, a major fraction of the energy dissipated within the conduction zone must be transferred to the working fluid. Therefore, the central problem in arc jet generation is the stabilization of the arc against the influence of vigorous forced convection. More specifically, the problem is concerned with the maintenance of the requisite ion concentration in the arc column under conditions of high depletion rate. This is obviously a necessary condition, but it is not in itself sufficient.

It is also necessary to maintain the geometrical integrity of the conduction zone within certain well-defined limits.

In order to appreciate the significance of these requirements, let us consider what happens when a stream of gas is blown against the column of a free-burning arc. The first effect of the convected gas is to cool the column by the admixture of cold gas. This lowers the temperature and hence the ion generation rate. In principle, this effect could be compensated for by increasing the arc voltage while maintaining the current constant. The increased voltage gradient in the column would increase the average kinetic energy of the free electrons and this added energy would be transferred to the gas by elastic collisions, thus restoring the thermal ionization rate to the required level.

A more significant effect arises from the fact that the collision cross-section for momentum transfer between a neutral gas atom and a positive ion is several orders of magnitude greater than that between two neutrals. Interactions between the incoming gas atoms and the ions in the column are therefore highly probable and these interactions displace the ions in the direction of injected gas flow. The free electrons are dragged along with the ions by ambi-polar diffusion with the net result that the column is deformed by an amount depending on the momentum and flux density of the injected atoms. The deformation causes the effective arc gap to increase in length and thus require a high arc voltage to maintain a given voltage gradient in the column. The column of a free-burning arc is very sensitive to this effect and drastic lengthening of the column occurs with only moderate gas flow rates. What usually happens is that the voltage needed to sustain the column in its deformed position becomes greater than the maximum voltage available from the power supply and the arc goes out.

The above description is perhaps somewhat oversimplified since other factors, such as self-magnetic field effects, enter into the phenomena involved in arc instability. However, it serves to delineate the basic requirements for effective arc jet generation. These are:

(1) Availability of a power source which can supply enough additional energy (in the form of increased voltage) to replenish charge carriers at the highest depletion rate to be sustained.

(2) Immobilization of the conduction column, i.e. maintenance of positional integrity, under the influence of the most rapid forced convection to be sustained.

The second of these requirements implies the imposition of some form of physical constraint on the conduction column of the arc. In other words, the discharge in an arc jet generator cannot be allowed to burn freely. A survey of the various forms of arc jet devices developed within the past two decades indicates that these devices may be conveniently classified in terms of the type of physical constraint used to stabilize the arc against convective deformation. Such a classification is shown in Table II. Four basic types of constraint are represented,

TABLE II

CLASSIFICATION OF PLASMA GENERATORS

Type of Constraint	*Physical Form of Constraint*	*Type of Plasma Generator*
(1) Thermal	Water—Cooled Channel	Wall Stabilized Arc; Constricted Arc Torch
(2) Fluid Mechanical	Fluid Vortex	Vortex—Stabilized Arc
(3) Electromagnetic	Lorentz Force Induced by Magnetic Field	Magnetically Stabilized Arc (Stationary or Rotating); RF Induction Torch
(4) Electrostatic	E—Field Due to Electron Space Charge Sheath in Contact with Anode.	High Intensity Arc; Fluid Transpiration Arc.

namely, thermal, fluid mechanical, electromagnetic and electrostatic.

Before the discussion of techniques it will be instructive to dwell briefly on the tributary subject of energy dissipation within the arc column. This will help to focus attention on specific problems and generally illumine the subject of arc jet stabilization.

Figure 1 contains a sketch of a typical free-burning arc. The arc current is carried between the anode and cathode through the discharge zone by means of the charge carriers, i.e., the positive ions and the free electrons. Owing to their small mass and high mobility the electrons are responsible for virtually all of the charge transport. The heavy positive ions are required for charge neutrality, at least in the

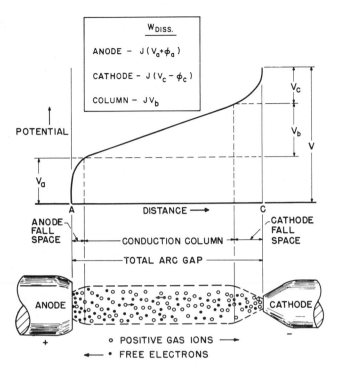

FIGURE 1. Sketch of (a) free-burning arc, and (b) axial voltage distribution of the discharge zone.

column proper, although they carry very little of the arc current. Figure 1 also contains a curve of the axial voltage distribution along the inter-electrode gap. The voltage distribution, a directly measurable quantity, also provides a picture of the primary distribution of energy dissipation within the gap. This follows from the fact that the arc current density does not vary much between the electrodes. The volume rate of Joule heating is given by $\vec{J} \cdot \vec{E}$ where $\vec{J}$ is the current density and $\vec{E}$ is the electric field. For approximately constant $\vec{J}$ this product is determined by the local voltage gradient.

From the voltage curve it is observed that the arc gap may be divided into three regions. The principal region is the column proper, occupying the major portion of the gap and characterized by constant cross-sectional area, relatively low and uniform axial potential gradient, and macroscopic charge neutrality throughout its volume. At the ends of the column are two regions joining the column with the anode and cathode surfaces, known as the "fall space" or "sheath" regions. They are associated with charge transport across the gas-solid boundaries of the discharge, and are characterized by a lack of charge neutrality and consequent high potential gradient. In the cathode fall space a preponderance of positive ions causes a net positive space charge while in the anode sheath a negative space charge is established due to an excess of free electrons. For the present discussion the importance of these regions is that, although they occupy only a very small fraction of the arc gap, they account for a relatively large fraction of the total arc voltage. Since both fall space regions are in intimate contact with the electrode surfaces, we may consider the energy dissipated in the fall spaces to be transferred directly to the electrodes.* Thus if V_a and V_c are the anode and cathode fall space voltages, respectively, and J is the magnitude of the current density, then the energy transferred by the discharge to unit area of electrode surface is JV_a for the anode and JV_c for the cathode. This does not, however, represent the net dissipation on the electrodes, which is influenced also by charge transport considerations. As mentioned earlier the arc current is carried chiefly by electrons. This holds also for the electrode-gas interfaces. At the cathode, electrons are emitted to provide current continuity across the surface. In order to surmount the surface potential barrier the electrons must possess a kinetic energy at least comparable to the height of the barrier; hence, when they leave the cathode they remove a certain quantity of energy, thus effectively cooling the cathode. This may be thought of as removal of heat by electron evaporation, and, per unit surface area, amounts to $J\phi_c$, where ϕ_c is the work function of the cathode material. Similarly, current continuity is maintained by the entry of free electrons into the anode surface. These electrons release energy upon traversing the anode surface potential barrier, which may be considered as heat of electron condensation, and is given by $J\phi_a$ per unit area, where ϕ_a is the work function of the anode

---

* This is consistent with the dissipative mechanism which involves the acceleration of charged particles across the fall voltages. Owing to the short distances involved ($\sim$ one or two mean free path lengths) most of the energy gained in traversing the fall space fields is actually transferred to the surfaces by direct particle bombardment.

material. We have then the following gross division of primary energy dissipation within the arc:

At the cathode: $J(V_c - \phi_c)$
Within the column: JV_b
At the anode: $J(V_a + \phi_a)$

V_b being the total drop across the column.

Whereas V_b is directly proportional to the arc gap distance, V_c, V_a, ϕ_c and ϕ_a are independent of the gap so that the relative amount of energy released in the column, compared with that transferred to the electrodes, depends on this parameter. For a typical laboratory free-burning arc at 1 atm. pressure, the division of dissipated energy will be approximately as follows: 80% to the column, 15% to the anode and 5% to the cathode. This represents the usual compromise between too short an arc, which overloads the electrodes and is inconvenient to handle, and too long an arc which requires an expensive high voltage power supply.

Even for relatively short arcs (1 or 2 cms) most of the energy appears to be dissipated in the column. This is, therefore, the logical zone for transferring the Joule heat to a working fluid.

One additional effect should be mentioned which may significantly alter the distribution of energy dissipation from that depicted above and which may, under some circumstances, influence the performance of a given arc jet generator. This is the cathode jet effect[4] which occurs in all arcs for which there is a significant contraction of the discharge diameter in the transition region of the cathode fall space. The effect may be explained by reference to Figure 2. The arc column near the apex of a conical cathode is shown with a marked contraction of the column cross-section. This configuration is typical of the conical tungsten cathodes used in most plasma jet generators. Since there is a sharp rise in current density in the contraction region, there will also be a similar rise in the flux density of the self-magnetic field generated by the arc current. A magnetic field having a space-variable flux density will exert a body force on a conductor immersed in the field, whose magnitude depends on the space rate of change of flux density and which is oriented in the direction of the maximum decrease in magnetic field.* Since the

---

* This is identical to the so-called "magnetic mirror" geometry used to contain thermonuclear plasmas.

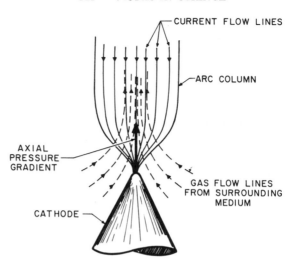

FIGURE 2. Diagram illustrating cathode jet effect.

plasma in the contraction zone is an electrical conductor, it will experience a body force which propels it along the column axis away from the cathode tip. The motion of the plasma away from the cathode decreases the local pressure at the base of the contraction zone, so that the arc in this region aspirates gas from the surrounding atmosphere to form a continuous cathode jet. The strength of this jet depends chiefly on the total arc current and the degree of column contraction near the cathode. In any case, the net effect is to aspirate ambient gas, propel it along the column where it absorbs some of the column energy and, if the arc geometry is collinear, project the heated gas against the face of the anode. Under the right conditions, therefore, a significant fraction of the energy originally dissipated in the column is transferred by convection to the anode due to the cathode jet effect. In extreme cases, as much as 75% of the total energy dissipated in the arc region may be transferred by both direct and convective processes to the anode, resulting in severe thermal loading of the anode structure.

TECHNIQUES OF ARC JET GENERATION[5]

In this section examples of the four classes of arc jet devices listed in

Table II are described. The order of presentation is phenomenological rather than chronological.

A—Thermal

Figure 3 is a diagram of a typical arc jet generator in which the column is stabilized by means of a thermal constraint in the form of a

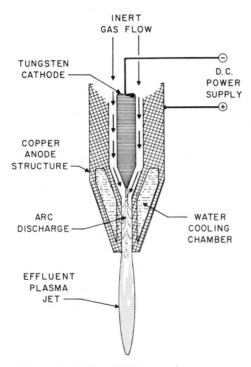

FIGURE 3. Wall-stabilizing arc jet generator.

water-cooled cylindrical channel. The arc is formed between the tip of a tungsten cathode and the inside surface of the channel which serves the anode, as well as the exit orifice for the effluent jet. The nozzle is vigorously water-cooled to prevent thermal damage to the channel surface. The working gas flows axially around the cathode, entering the channel codirectionally with the arc column. In this device the cold wall of the channel immobilizes the column on the axis of the channel, since any lateral deformation of the discharge by the gas flow causes the plasma to contact the cold wall where it is rapidly cooled and deionized. The arc current can, therefore, no longer flow in the layer of gas adjacent to the wall and so must remain centered along the channel. For this reason the arc jet devices employing cold-wall constraints for column immobilization are called "wall-stabilized arcs."

If the channel is sufficiently long, the column will ultimately terminate on the inside surface of the channel* at a point downstream of the entrance, whose location depends on the gas flow rate. If the concentricity of the cathode and anode nozzle is carefully adjusted, the conduction column will flare outward, umbrella-fashion, to contact the nozzle in an annular anode spot. This condition is essential for reasonable nozzle lifetime.

The working gas flows initially in the concentric layer between the hot column and the cool wall. As one proceeds down the channel more and more of the gas stream becomes heated to plasma temperatures and enters the conduction zone. When the column extends across the entire channel (except for a very small film of cool gas at the boundary) the column is said to be "fully developed" and virtually all of the injected gas reaches plasma temperatures. The stream leaves the conduction zone near the nozzle orifice from which it emerges as a high speed plasma jet. The jet, in addition to a considerable quantity of sensible heat, carries away a sizeable number of ion pairs, which must be replenished in the arc zone. For this reason the arc, under these conditions, requires a much larger voltage than a free burning arc of the same length. The power source must be capable of supplying the required voltage for this device to operate stably.

It has been found that the axial temperature of the plasma jet issuing from a wall-stabilized arc operating at a given current can be increased by utilizing a channel orifice smaller than the diameter of the corresponding free-burning arc operating at the same current. In this situation the channel is used to constrict the column, i.e., to squeeze it into a smaller diameter than it would normally occupy,

---

* If the gas flow is too high for the channel length a situation can arise wherein the conduction column extends clear out of the channel and turns backwards to terminate on the outside surface of the nozzle tip. This condition, known as a "blown arc" is generally an unsatisfactory mode of operation.

thus increasing the current density and hence the temperature. For this reason the term "constricted arc" is sometimes applied to this device. Axial jet temperatures for commonly-used wall-stabilized arcs are in the range of 15,000 to 20,000° K, although severe constriction has produced temperatures in excess of 50,000°K.

B—Fluid-Mechanical

In this type of device the column is stabilized by means of a fluid vortex, established by the tangential injection of fluid near the periphery of a cylindrical vessel on whose axis the arc electrodes are posisioned. A schematic diagram of this type of arc jet generator is shown in Figure 4. The arc is ignited between the rod-shaped axial electrode

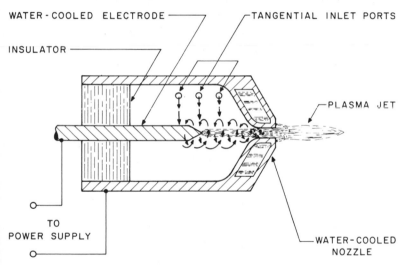

FIGURE 4. Vortex-stabilized arc jet generator.

and the inside surface of the channel comprising the exit port of the nozzle. This configuration is similar to the wall-stabilized arc except that the column is maintained almost entirely in the unconfined region of the chamber instead of almost wholly within the exit channel.

The rapid vortex motion of the injected gas imposes a fluid mechanical constraint on the arc column by virtue of the outwardly directed radial pressure gradient characteristic of a fluid vortex. This means that the gas pressure has its lowest value on the axis of the cylinder. The arc discharge is therefore constrained to remain on the axis in accordance with Steenbeck's minimum energy principle for gas discharges.[6] In effect, this principle states that a gas discharge is most stable in the configuration requiring the least energy for its maintenance. Since the higher the pressure the more the voltage that is needed to sustain unit column length at a given current, it follows that least energy and therefore maximum stability is obtained when the column remains on the vortex axis. This type of device is accordingly known as the "vortex-stabilized" arc jet generator. For sufficiently strong vortex motion the resistance to lateral deformation of the column can be made to approximate that of a water cooled channel. The column can also be constricted by strong vortex motion, thus raising the axial temperature.

Since the vessel is pressurized the swirling gas is gradually forced into the column as it approaches the nozzle and complete mixing occurs in this region. The rotary motion is also largely converted to linear motion* as the gas passes through the nozzle. In addition, the motion has the desired effect of rotating the arc attachment point at the nozzle end of the discharge which mitigates nozzle wear to some extent. Care must be taken to avoid the "blown arc" mode, mentioned earlier, which is caused by too great a gas flow rate and which causes the column to attach on the outside surface of the nozzle (see Figure 4). Electrode polarity in this device is relatively unimportant. However, the rod electrode is usually made of tungsten while the nozzle is copper, both electrodes being vigorously water-cooled.

This represents one of the first types of plasma generator to be developed, having been mentioned as early as 1908.[7]

C—Electromagnetic

There are various ways in which an electromagnetic constraint may be imposed upon an arc in order to stabilize the column against the influence of forced convection. These include both DC and time-

---

* Some remnant of rotary motion usually remains in the effluent jet in this type of device. Proper design can reduce this to a minimum where it might be objectionable, as in wind tunnel applications.

variable discharges and involve both stationary and rotating arcs. The stabilizing force in each case is due ultimately to the fact that the plasma in the column, in addition to being a fluid, is also a good electrical conductor. Hence current flow in a plasma immersed in a magnetic field will induce a Lorentz force on the plasma volume in which the current flows. When properly oriented, this force can be used to resist flow-induced deformation of the conduction column. When applied to an arc jet generator, the device is commonly called a "magnetically stabilized arc."

(1) Stationary Arc

The simplest configuration in which an electromagnetic constraint may be used to stabilize an arc is depicted in Figure 5. Here an arc column is maintained in the vertical (Y) direction, having a current density, $\vec{J}$. The column is immersed in a magnetic field orthogonal to the current flow (i.e., in the horizontal or X-direction) with a magnectic flux density, $\vec{B}$. A Lorentz force $\vec{J} \times \vec{B}$, will therefore be induced in the column, which, in the absence of an external force will deform the column in the Z direction (i.e., orthogonal to both $\vec{J}$ and $\vec{B}$). In fact, for a free-burning arc at 1 atm carrying 100 amps or more, a field of only a few tens of gauss is sufficient to "blow" the arc out, i.e., render its operation in the field unstable. However, if we assume that an external stream of gas is projected against the column so as to produce a net fluid mechanical drag force of magnitude $\vec{F}$ in the $-Z$ direction, then if we adjust either $\vec{B}$ or $\vec{J}$, or both, such that

$$|\vec{F}| = |\vec{J} \times \vec{B}|$$

both forces cancel and the column will remain stationary on the Y axis.

The configuration of Figure 5 is not a very effective type of arc jet generator since much of the gas does not penetrate the column but is deflected around it. The column is "stiffened" by the magnetic field and takes on some of the characteristics of a heated solid cylinder. Also the condition of stability under high flow rates requires critical adjustment of the magnetic field. It does have the virtue of providing a convenient arrangement for studying the basic physics of the interaction of a cross-flow with an arc column.[7]

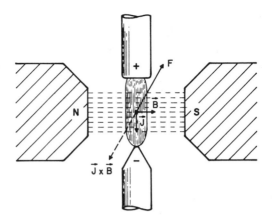

FIGURE 5. Stationary magnetically stabilized DC arc.

(2) Rotating Arc

The first practical use of magnetic stabilization in an arc jet device involves the use of a rotating arc. A typical configuration is sketched in Figure 6. An arc is struck between a central electrode and the inside surface of a cylindrical containing vessel with the the usual water-cooled nozzle orifice at one end. The working gas is introduced at

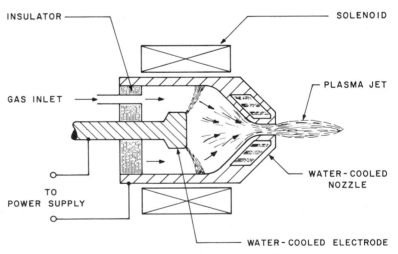

FIGURE 6. Rotating magnetically stabilized arc.

the opposite end and flows axially across the arc zone, emerging in a jet at the nozzle exit. In the absence of a magnetic field the convective force would blow the column toward the nozzle, and, for any reasonable flow rate, would extinguish the arc. A solenoid, concentric to the vessel, establishes a strong axial magnetic field which induces a Lorentz force on the column in the azimuthal direction. The arc therefore rotates about the axis. If the Lorentz force is made much greater than the convective force, the former dominates and the column is displaced only slightly in the direction of flow. In other words, the column is "stiffened" against the effects of cross-flow as a result of the imposition of the electromagnetic constraint.

There are two advantages of the magnetic rotation of the column. As the field strength is increased, the speed of rotation increases, and at sufficiently high rotational speeds the column will merge azimuthally into a pin-wheel shape enclosing the entire cross-sectional aperture of the vessel. This insures that all of the injected gas will be maximally heated by the column. (At lower speeds it is obvious that some of the gas will traverse the device without coming into intimate contact with the column.) The second advantage is the fact that both electrode attachment points move rapidly on the respective electrode surfaces. Thus, the heat dissipated in the fall spaces, which is essentially all transferred to the electrodes, is spread over a much larger surface area than if the arc were stationary. This increases the thermal loading capability of the electrodes and reduces electrode wear, which is of considerable importance at high power levels.

(3) RF Induction Torch

One of the more recently developed arc jet generators is the Radio Frequency induction torch.[8] This device, which has demonstrated interesting properties for many applications, is based on the coupling of high frequency alternating electromagnetic energy into a gas stream. Referring to Figure 7, we observe that the gas is introduced into a confining cylinder, usually of quartz or similar refractory insulating material, which is situated inside a coil designed to carry appreciable RF currents. The coil generally consists of a relatively few turns of heavy copper tubing and is water-cooled during operation. It is energized by a high power RF generator similar to those

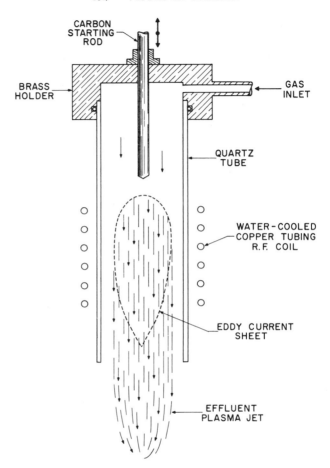

FIGURE 7. RF induction torch.

used in radio transmitters. Frequency of operation is not critical and is chosen in a given apparatus for optimum coupling. It generally lies in the range of 4 to 20 MHz. A movable conductive rod, usually carbon, is used to ignite the RF arc, once the RF power is turned on. The starting rod is lowered into the coil region where it is heated by induction. This heats the gas into the immediate vicinity of the rod. Since the breakdown potential of a gas decreases with increasing temperature, a point will be reached at which the hot gas surrounding the starting rod will become ionized by the RF electric field induced by the coil. An electrical discharge will therefore become established in this region in the form of a local eddy current sheet. This will dissipate more energy in the gas, thus heating neighboring layers to ionizing temperatures and enlarging the conduction zone. This process will continue until the eddy current sheet reaches its maximum size dictated by the size of the coil. The starting rod is then withdrawn from the coil.

Since the induced eddy currents can flow only within the volume enclosed by the coil it follows that the RF arc cannot be displaced by the flowing gas. It is therefore obvious that this device is stabilized by means of an electromagnetic constraint. While it is true that ion pairs are rapidly convected out of the arc zone by the gas stream, the zone of primary dissipation of electrical energy, i.e., the zone of ion generation, is constrained to fixed position within the coil, this being the zone of maximum coupling. The eddy current sheet may be viewed as a one-turn secondary of a transformer of which the coil comprises the primary winding and to which it is constrained to remain in a fixed spatial relationship.

The basic requirement for sustained operation of this device is that the power fed to the coil be sufficient to generate new ions at a rate commensurate with that at which they are lost to the effluent jet. In other words (as in all other arc jets) the power input must be adjusted to the gas flow rate. It is significant that the problem of electrode erosion, which is often a vexing problem in most other arc jet types, does not exist in this device.

D—Electrostatic

(1) The High Intensity Arc

Arc jet generators stabilized by an electrostatic constraint are based on the interaction of the gas stream with the space charge sheath in the anode fall space of the arc (see Figure 1). The prototype of this type of arc jet is the high intensity arc discovered in 1910[9]. This type of discharge is similar in configuration to the ordinary carbon arc (or "low intensity" arc) except that the current density of the anode-column boundary is much higher, and the two electrodes are usually maintained at a mutual angle less than 180°. When an arc is struck between refractory electrodes such as carbon, then at low current densities the heat absorbed by the anode* can be dissipated, by conduction along the anode and radiation from its face, without causing the equilibrium face temperature to reach the melting (or sublimation) point of the anode material. This is the case for the low intensity arc mode of operation. If, however, the current density is increased sufficiently, a point will be reached where the energy absorbed is greater than can be dissipated by conduction and radiation. The anode face temperature will therefore rise. If the net heat absorbed reaches a value great enough to raise the equilibrium anode face temperature to its boiling (sublimation) point and also to supply the requisite latent heat for phase change, the anode will emit a stream of vapor from its face into the arc discharge. This stream of vapor must first traverse the anode fall space region, which is contiguous to the current-receiving surface and normally extends for a few electron mean free path lengths into the column. Although the details of the interaction[10, 11] between the vapor stream and the space charge sheath have not as yet been completely worked out, there is little doubt that this interaction is responsible for the shift to the high intensity arc mode.

The flux of vapor from the anode in the high intensity arc imposes a strong convective force on the column, which would be expected to deplete the column of ion pairs quite rapidly if an equivalent stream were introduced through any other boundary than the anode fall space. In the fall space, the layer of gas adjacent to the electrode is cooled by conduction below the temperature required for thermal ionization. Also the anode vapor, even at the sublimation temperature of carbon (4500°K) is essentially un-ionized. However, because of the excess of free electrons (negative space charge) in this layer a high voltage gradient is established across it in accordance with the well known laws of electrostatics. In a typical arc this may be as high as 5000 volts per cm. Hence, although the high electric field extends for only a fraction of a millimeter, the vapor atoms traversing the layer will have a higher probability of colliding with energetic electrons than in the column. Despite the lower temperature, therefore, a much larger fraction of electron-atom collisions will be characterized by energies exceeding the ionization energy than is the case in the column. The net result is that an appreciable number of the vapor

---

* As discussed earlier, the heat transferred to the anode is at least several times that absorbed by the cathode. Hence the energy balance at the cathode does not enter into the establishment of the high intensity effect.

atoms are ionized by direct electron impact while traversing the sheath, *before* entering the column proper. This mechanism of ionization is known as "field ionization" and, by pre-ionizing the vapor stream, automatically stabilizes the discharge against convective ion loss.

The ionized vapor flux, upon entering the column, becomes superheated within a few millimeters of the surface and exits from the sides of the column as a long plume of hot vapor plasma known as the "anode tail flame." According to one view[11] the superheating of the vapor in the anode end of the column is due to the acceleration of positive ions in the fall space where the high potential gradient imparts to them kinetic energy in excess of the average thermal kinetic energy. This directed kinetic energy becomes randomized by successive collisions and thus establishes a local steep rise in temperature near the origin of the vapor jet.

Since the anode in the high intensity arc is vaporized it is continuously consumed. Steady state operation, therefore, requires that the anode be continuously pushed forward to maintain a constant arc gap. This is accomplished by a suitable feed mechanism which pushes the anode forward at exactly the rate at which it is consumed. Electrical contact to the anode is made by means of sliding brush contacts.

The flow of vapor in significant amounts* through the discharge radically alters the electrical characteristics of the arc. For example, the terminal (volt-ampere) curve, which for the low intensity arc always demonstrates a negative slope, bends upward to assume a positive shape soon after the vapor flow is initiated. This effect is due to the interaction of the vapor stream and the free electrons carrying the arc current, which causes an increase in the potential gradient in and near the anode sheath. This appears to the external circuit as a positive resistance component of the arc which more than compensates for the normal negative resistance characteristic of the arc column. A net positive resistance is therefore established across the arc terminals causing the slope of the volt-ampere curve to bend upwards.

The potential distribution across the arc gap is also considerably altered. A typical distribution for a high intensity arc[12] is shown in

---

* i.e., in amounts such that the vapor particle flux density leaving the anode approximates the electron number density entering the anode.

Figure 8. Comparing this with Figure 1, we note that the anode fall space is enlarged and consumes a major fraction of the total arc voltage. Most of this drop occurs in what may be termed the "transition region" between the space charge sheath and the column proper. This is the region where the vapor from the anode is superheated prior to breaking out of the column to form the plasma tail flame. As much as two thirds or more of the total input energy is therefore transferred to the anode and to the vapor arising therefrom. The high intensity arc is therefore an effective arc jet generator differing from other types mainly in the composition of the plasma jet.

(2) Fluid Transpiration Arc

Although the high intensity arc is finding increasing application, particularly in the field of high temperature chemistry, there are many other uses for which a plasma jet of refractory vapor is objectionable. The question therefore arises whether an arc jet generator might not be constructed based on the same principle, but in which an external gas is substituted for the vapor of the anode, and the

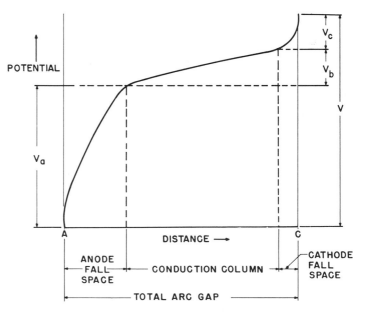

FIGURE 8. Voltage distribution in the high intensity arc.

material of the anode itself is not consumed. This led to the concept of the so-called "fluid transpiration arc,"[13] the most recently developed type of arc jet generator. Like the high intensity arc, it is stabilized by causing the working gas to pass through the space charge sheath at the anode surface where it is preionized sufficiently to compensate for subsequent convective depletion of ion pairs from the conduction column. This is accomplished by using a porous anode through which the gas transpires and emerges into the anode sheath. Since the space charge sheath is constrained by the laws of gas discharge physics to form only at the current-receiving surface, and since the high electric field in this region preionizes the gas before it enters the column, it follows that in this device, as in the high intensity arc, the arc is stabilized against convective force by an electrostatic constraint.

A diagram of a rudimentary form of this device is shown in Figure 9. The anode must be fabricated of a suitably refractory porous elec-

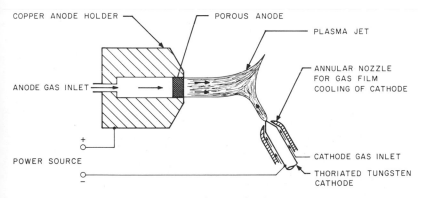

FIGURE 9. Fluid transpiration arc.

trical conductor generally mounted in a copper holder which is water-cooled to retain structural integrity during long term operation. Porous graphite has been used successfully, but a more satisfactory anode consists of sintered tungsten powder, which has been hot-pressed to the right degree of porosity. The tungsten anodes are then conveniently shrunk-fit into a copper anode holder. A conventional cathode is used, but, as noted in Figure 9, the conical cathode tip is provided with a nozzle for introducing some slight additional gas into the column at the cathode end. This is minor compared with the gas introduced through the anode, but has a number of beneficial effects.[14] For example, it provides some gas cooling of the cathode; also, when operating with a particular gas such as argon, in the open air, it inhibits oxidation of the cathode surface and substitutes argon for atmospheric components as the gas aspirated into the column by the cathode jet effect.

A photograph of the fluid transpiration arc operating in the configuration of Figure 9 is shown in Figure 10. This arc was run in the

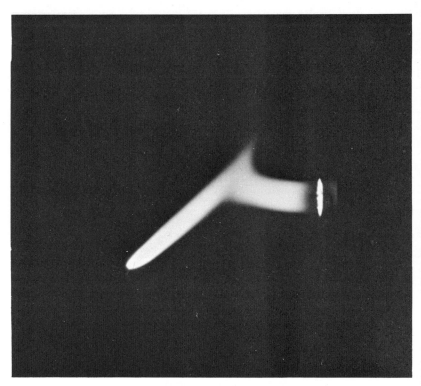

FIGURE 10. Photograph of fluid transpiration arc.

open atmosphere with argon injected at both anode and cathode, in the respective amounts of 50 gm per min through the anode and 6 gm per min around the cathode. The anode face was approximately 1.5 cm² and the arc current and voltage 200 amps and 40 volts, respectively.* In this configuration the cathode is generally inclined at a sufficient angle to the anode to allow the two jets to merge smoothly and minimize turbulence. In Figure 10 the emergent plasma jet is relatively small owing to the large gap (about 12 cms. in the illustration). The merged portion of the jet can be made larger by shortening the gap. However, the jet derived in this way is not so well defined as in the nozzle type of arc jet generators. In the extended position of Figure 10, this device has the same degree of accessibility as a free-burning arc and is therefore quite useful for probe and optical studies of an arc column under the influence of convection.

A well defined jet may, if desired, be generated by an alternative geometrical configuration of the fluid transpiration arc. This is shown in Figure 11. The porous anode in this unit is in the shape of a trun-

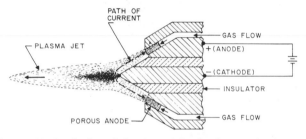

FIGURE 11. Conical modification of the fluid transpiration arc.

cated conical shell providing an annular anode surface as one terminal of the arc. The cathode is positioned axially, with the tip forward of the anode annulus, and separated from the anode holder by a cylindrical insulating insert. The arc column begins at the tip and then reverses, flowing backwards to the anode in the form of a conical lamina (heavy dashed lines in Figure 11). The transpiration gas, after being energized in the annular anode sheath, flows convergently through the conical column and merges with the cathode jet to form

* Reference is made to the relatively non-luminous zone near the anode (or anode "dark space"). Measurements have shown the gas temperature in this region to be in the range of 3000°K which, at atmospheric pressure in argon, is far below that required for electrical conductivity. Yet the measurements of current density and voltage gradient in this region indicated high electrical conductivity. This lends support to the prevalence of the field ionization mechanism described earlier.

a single well-defined plasma jet. It is interesting to note that most of the converging gas flow remains within the column despite the absence of a confining nozzle wall, and emerges in the main jet on the axis. This is evident in the photograph of Figure 12 which depicts

FIGURE 12. Photograph of plasma jet generated by conical fluid transpiration arc.

a conical fluid transpiration arc operating with argon gas at 1 atm and 25 kw power input. This apparent confinement of the gas flow within the column is probably a result of "collision coupling" between the convected nuetral atoms and the ion drift current, which is constrained by the electric field of the arc to remain within a well defined boundary.

ARC JET CHARACTERISTICS

As is usually the case when more than one type of device has been developed to perform a given function, none of the above four classes of arc jet generators can be singled out as being markedly superior to the others in all possible applications. Selection of a particular type is best made after the functional requirements have been specified. Often some advantage is gained by using a hybrid generator employing more than one type of stabilization, particularly at high power levels. Nevertheless, a general comparison of the important features of each type of generator is necessary for an appreciation of the utility of these devices in the manifold applications to which they have been, and will continue to be, used.

No exact comparison among arc plasma generators with respect to a particular feature can be made since the performance of a given generator will vary with design, power level, ambient pressure and other operating conditions. However, a set of performance parameters has been selected with the aid of which generalized comparisons may be made and which indicate performance trends under commonly encountered conditions for the several classes of arc jet devices. These parameters are listed in Table III.

TABLE III

PERFORMANCE PARAMETERS FOR PLASMA GENERATORS

EFFICIENCY — TOTAL JET ENTHALPY/INPUT POWER

MAX. ENTHALPY (h_{max}) — Btu/lb. at EXIT NOZZLE

DIMENSIONLESS MAX. ENTHALPY — (h_{max}/RT_0)

OPERATING LIFETIME — ELECTRODE EROSION RATE

JET CONTAMINATION — PPM OF CONTAMINANT IN JET

The first of these parameters, efficiency, is of obvious importance since the arc jet is a device for converting one form of energy to another and it is of interest to the user to minimize the amount of energy lost in the process. For most applications* the total enthalpy of the effluent jet is the desired form of output energy. Hence the efficiency of an arc jet device may be defined as the ratio of total jet enthalpy to the electrical power input.

The second parameter is the maximum enthalpy (h_{max}) which the device is capable of imparting to the jet and is measured as the Btu content per lb. of gas at the orifice of the exit nozzle (or base of the effluent jet where no nozzle exists). This is not unrelated to efficiency and usually increases when a particular device is operated at reduced efficiency. It does, however, reflect to some degree the quality of the instrument design.

Since h_{max} varies with the molecular weight of the working gas,

---

* Plasma generators are currently under development as high power light sources. For this application effluent jet enthalpy is wasted energy and the efficiency must be redefined as the ratio of total radiated power to electrical power input.

it is also sometimes desirable to make comparisons on the basis of the dimensionless enthalpy, h_{max}/RT_o, where R is the universal gas constant and T_o is a convenient reference temperature (generally taken as $273°$ K.)

The remaining parameters, operating lifetime and jet contamination, are obviously qualitative in nature, although they can be measured in terms of hours and parts per million of contaminant in the jet, respectively. They are both strongly dependent on operating conditions which are often adjusted to meet the requirements of particular applications with respect to each parameter. Obviously, both operating lifetime and contamination have no significance for the consumable anode high intensity arc, and the major limitations on operating lifetime for all other devices, namely, the electrode erosion, is not applicable to the R.F. induction torch.

Table IV lists the efficiency ranges within which the various in-

TABLE IV
COMPARISON OF PLASMA GENERATOR EFFICIENCIES
($\sim$ 1 ATM ARC CHAMBER PRESSURE)

TYPE OF GENERATOR	EFFICIENCY RANGE
WALL - STABILIZED ARC	50 - 75%
VORTEX - STABILIZED ARC	40 - 65%
MAGNETICALLY - STABILIZED ARC (ROTATING)	15 - 45%
RF INDUCTION TORCH	25 - 40%
FLUID TRANSPIRATION ARC	80 - 95%

dicated arc jet generators operate in practice. As a general rule, when long operating lifetimes are required, i.e., hundreds of hours, the best efficiencies obtainable with each device lie near the lower end of the ranges given in Table IV. Conversely, when the use is such that only a few hours of operation (before a maintenance shut-down) is acceptable, the efficiencies can be pushed toward the upper end of the range. In almost every device the major loss in efficiency results from the necessity for water cooling of the nozzle or chamber as the only means of avoiding thermal destruction of the device under operating conditions. In the wall-stabilized arc the confining water-cooled channel is smaller for a given gas flow rate, than, for example, either the vortex or magnetically-stabilized arcs. In both of the latter, and particularly in the magnetically-stabilized device a large arc chamber is essential to provide the required stabilizing force. Therefore, in addition to the heat losses in the water-cooled nozzle, further losses in the arc chamber are suffered due to radiation and conduction to the walls. Hence a higher fraction of the input power is lost with a consequent reduction in efficiency.

In the RF induction torch the efficiency of energy transfer from the high frequency field to the gas is quite high. The relatively low overall efficiency for this device arises from the losses encountered in generating RF power from electrical input at power line frequency. The high efficiency of the fluid transpiration arc arises from the absence of chamber or confining walls and from the fact that energy dissipated at the anode is regeneratively fed back to the plasma via transpiration cooling of the anode by the injected gas on its way through the porous anode.

The influence of the working gas on the maximum enthalpy is illustrated in Table V for the wall-stabilized arc. Although a con-

TABLE V
MAX ENTHALPY OF WALL-STABILIZED ARC IN VARIOUS GASES*
(1-5 ATM ARC CHAMBER PRESSURE)

GAS	MOL. WT.	RT_0 (Btu/lb)	h_{max} (Btu/lb)	h_{max}/RT_0
H_2	2	488	140,000	290
He	4	244	70,000	290
N_2	28	34.8	15,000	430
A	40	24.4	8,000	330

* Taken from reference 5.

siderable variation is observed in h_{max} among the four gases listed, the corresponding values for the dimensionless maximum enthalpy, h_{max}/RT_0, are roughly of the same order. This leads to the approximate generalization that, other things being equal, the amount of energy delivered by an arc jet generator to each particle of the working gas is roughly the same for all gases.

Since the total energy content is different for different gases at the same temperature, it follows that plasma jet temperatures from a particular device operating with a given jet enthalpy will depend on the gas. For example, diatomic gases, such as nitrogen and hydrogen, require more energy to reach a given plasma temperature than monatomic gases like argon and helium, owing to the energy absorbed in molecular dissociation. Also different gases require varying amounts of energy for the ionization process, so that for a particular gas the maximum jet temperature that can be reached is largely dependent on the maximum effluent jet enthalpy.

Both maximum enthalpy and efficiency are strongly influenced by pressure. The curves in Figure 13, illustrating this dependency, were compiled from average operating data for wall, vortex, and rotating magnetically-stabilized arcs. As noted, enthalpy and efficiency decrease

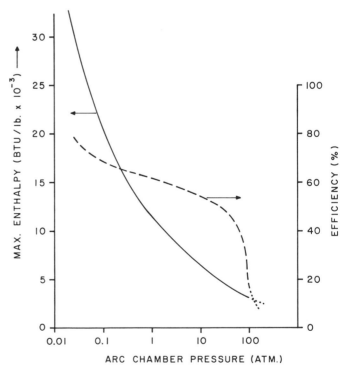

FIGURE 13. Maximum enthalpy and efficiency vs. pressure for typical arc jet generators.

with increasing ambient pressure. The major reason for this effect is the fact that the ratio of the amount of energy radiated from the hot gas in the arc chamber to the amount which leaves the chamber as sensible heat increases with increasing pressure. At high pressures, e.g., near 100 atm, radiation accounts for a major fraction of the electrical energy delivered to the gas. The radiant energy is absorbed by the arc chamber walls and electrodes, and must be removed by water-cooling. Hence less energy leaves the chamber as jet enthalpy and the efficiency is lowered. Thus there exists what might be termed a "radiation barrier" to the efficient operation of arc jet devices at very high pressures.*

APPLICATIONS OF ARC JET DEVICES[15]

The single most valuable feature of arc jet devices for purposes of application is the capability of heating materials in a continuous stream to ultra high temperatures. The historic use of the low intensity electric arc to heat materials was limited by stability considerations to the role of a point source of heat, as in the submerged arc furnace, wherein the maximum temperature achievable in the material itself was necessarily below the temperature of the arc and rarely exceeded 3000° K. With the advent of the arc jet devices described above, the peak temperatures of practically achievable hyperthermal environments were increased by an order of magnitude, and the rates of material through-put in and out of these environments were similarly advanced. It is therefore easy to appreciate that a vast new frontier has been established in both science and technology.

A compilation of the various groups of applications of arc jet technology is shown in Figure 14. The grouping is arbitrary and the examples listed are by no means comprehensive. It does, however, present some of the more important areas in which arc jet devices are already advantageously being used or are under serious development. Lack of space precludes the discussion of all, or even the major part, of the examples shown. In the following a few selected applications are briefly described chiefly to illustrate the breadth of applicability of arc jet devices.

---

* By the same token, the efficiency of plasma light sources increases with increasing pressure.

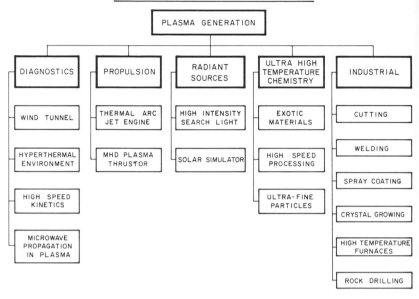

FIGURE 14. Applications of arc jet technology.

A. WIND TUNNELS

The need for upgrading the performance of wind tunnels to provide test facilities for hypersonic and reentry vehicles stimulated the early development of a high power arc jet heater.

There are several parameters which are used to assess tunnel performance, depending on the diagnostic function under consideration.

TABLE VI*

FLIGHT STAGNATION ENTHALPIES FOR VARIOUS REENTRY VEHICLES

VEHICLE CLASS	FLIGHT SPEED	STAGNATION ENTHALPY
ICBM———————	23,000 ft./sec.———————	10,500 Btu/lb.
SATELLITE————	25,000 ft./sec.———————	12,500 Btu/lb.
LUNAR PROBE——	35,000 ft./sec.———————	25,000 Btu/lb.
MARS PROBE————	45,000 ft./sec.———————	40,000 Btu/lb.

* Taken from reference 15.

The most important single parameter for modern aerospace diagnostics is the maximum enthalpy content of the gas leaving the chamber. This must be somewhat greater than the maximum flight stagnation enthalpy developed by the vehicle whose flight is being simulated. Table VI lists the characteristic stagnation enthalpies for four classes of hypersonic vehicles. It is evident that for such vehicles an ultra-high temperature heating device is indicated. In addition to achieving high chamber enthalpy, simulation of the flight Mach number is also desired, as well as low jet contamination (e.g. 1000 PPM) and an operating lifetime of at least several hours.

Until now, no heater has been developed which provides complete simulation for all classes of vehicles under consideration. However, the closest approach to the ideal test conditions is provided by an arc jet heater[16] of the type sketched in Figure 15. This consists of

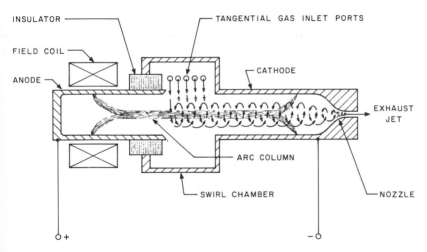

FIGURE 15. Sketch of four megawatt high voltage arc heater developed for wind tunnel use.

two long cylindrical sections comprising the two electrodes, the front (nozzle) section usually serving as the cathode, while the rear section serves as an anode. A larger diameter portion at the base of the front electrode provides a swirl chamber into which the gas is injected tangentially. An early form of this device has been in use for over 20 years in the commercial production of acetylene.[17]

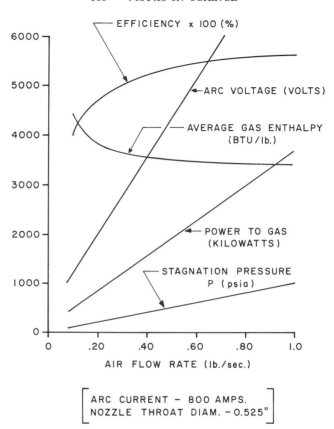

FIGURE 16. Performance curves for four megawatt arc heater. (Courtesy of Linde Division, Union Carbide Company, Indianapolis, Ind.)

B. FABRICATION[18]

Flames have been used to fabricate materials into desired shapes since the dawn of civilization. The basic task in this application is one of heating the material, usually a metal, to its melting point. This is the case whether the objective is cutting, joining (welding), coating (flame spraying or surfacing), or simply massive melting for subsequent casting into molds. Until the introduction of arc jets the flames used in performing such tasks have always been derived from combustion. In modern times the development of oxygen-fuel gas torches has been an important factor in setting the pace of industrial advancement. When practical arc jet devices were developed, almost simultaneously with the need for fabricating refractory metals and alloys, the application of the arc jet to fabrication was a logical consequence.

There are several reasons why an arc jet is superior to combustion torches in flame heating applications.[19] The obvious one is, of course, the high temperature capability of the arc jet. However, because of the greater complexity and cost of arc jet equipment, the relative merits of the two types of flames must be assessed for tasks within the capability of both. A useful comparison for this purpose is provided by Figure 17. The curves in this figure show the percentage of the heat content of the flame which is available for transfer to a material, plotted as a function of the temperature at which the heat transfer takes place. Thus, if it is desired to use a methane-air combustion flame to heat material to 1000° C, only 50% of the heat content of the flame can be transferred, the remainder being carried off as sensible heat of the combustion products. A similar situation would occur at 2500° C for the octane-oxygen flame. At the flame temperature the percentage of heat available for transfer goes to zero, and it is impossible to melt materials such as tungsten, whose melting points are above the flame temperature of oxy-fuel gas combustion flames. No such limitation exists for a plasma flame, which, of course, does not have combustion products. The slight drop of heat content available for transfer in the plasma jet reflects a minor increase in water-cooling requirements for arc jets operated so as to achieve higher temperatures in the work piece. Under practical conditions from 70% to 85% of the effluent jet enthalpy in arc jet torches is available for useful transfer.

In addition to superior heat transfer capability, the use of plasma flames has the important advantage of providing a compatible atmosphere for the heating process. In the case of combustion flames, the combustion products can often contaminate the work piece, particularly in the heat-affected zone, causing scale to form and embrittlement of the material. Metal working plasma jets are characteristically formed in inert gases, such as argon or helium, or mixtures which do not adversely affect the material properties at elevated temperatures. For this reason plasma torches are currently used even in the low temperature region where energy transfer efficiency is no longer a major consideration.

A significant advantage of the arc plasma jet is its high electrical

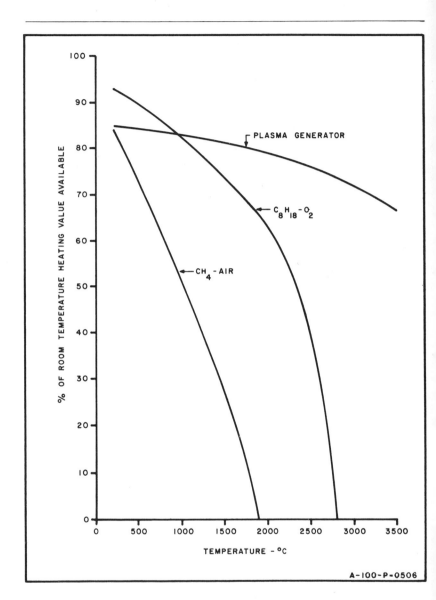

FIGURE 17. Available energy from plasma and combustion flames. (Taken from reference 19).

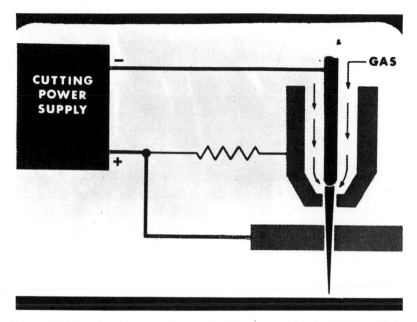

FIGURE 18. Transferred arc cutting torch. (Courtesy of Linde Division, Union Carbide Company, Indianapolis, Ind.)

conductivity which permits operation of the torch in the so-called "transferred arc" mode.[20] This is illustrated in the schematic diagram of Figure 18. Here the (metallic) workpiece is connected directly to the positive terminal of the power supply, while the torch nozzle is connected through a resistor. Initially the torch is ignited only to the torch nozzle; however, as soon as the jet contacts the work piece a major portion of the current flows through the conductive jet and enters the metal at the sides of the cutting kerf. This has the considerable advantage of increasing the enthalpy of the cutting jet by additional Joule dissipation and also largely transferring the anode fall space dissipation from the nozzle, where it is wasted, to the workpiece where it is usefully absorbed. This arrangement increases the rate at which heat may be delivered to a metallic workpiece by a factor of 3 to 5 times. The transferred arc mode is also used in plasma welding and plasma flame spray coating of a metallic substrate. The utilization of arc jets in the fabrication industry, particularly in the areas involving cutting, welding and flame spraying, are now commonplace.

C. Chemical Applications of the High Intensity Arc

Chemical applications of arc jet devices have, with the exception of a few early developments,[17] lagged behind the physical applications listed in Figure 14. A considerable body of research[21, 22] has been accumulating in recent years which delineates the unusual difficulties facing the development of practical techniques employing ultra-high temperature environments for chemical purposes. The media are thermodynamically very complex, even for relatively simple compositions, and are not conducive to theoretical analyses. Residence times at the high temperatures are very short and kinetic behavior in plasma environments are not well understood. Furthermore, the practical matter of handling very hot gases efficiently and of controlling the course of chemical reactions during the rapid quenching phase usually involved in arc jet chemistry pose formidable problems.

Despite these difficulties, the overall technology is fast approaching the point where applications of arc jets to chemical processing are becoming practical. The fixation of nitrogen and the conversion of methane to acetylene have already been cited. In these examples the major problems have been overcome to the extent that, under special circumstances, these processes could be operated competitively with the traditional processing techniques.

Of special interest are several chemical applications of the high intensity arc. These show promise of early incorporation into the industrial processing field. One of the reasons for the advanced status of the high intensity arc in this regard is the fact that no confining walls are involved in this device thus permitting high energy transfer efficiency. Also, the reacting materials for these applications are not gases but refractory solids, which in turn provide a more controllable situation, as will be demonstrated in the following two examples.

(1) Sub-micron Particulates

The use of the high intensity arc to produce an aerosol[23] of silica was one of the first chemical applications of this type of arc jet generator. Since then it has been used[24] to comminute a wide variety of other materials including simple and complex oxides, metals, metallic carbides, etc.

(2) Refractory Metals and Carbides

One of the problems encountered in past attempts to use arc jet techniques for producing refractory metals and carbides from their corresponding oxides has been the difficulty in condensing pure products from the tail flame into which all reactants are initially projected in the vapor state. The high intensity arc (Figure 19)

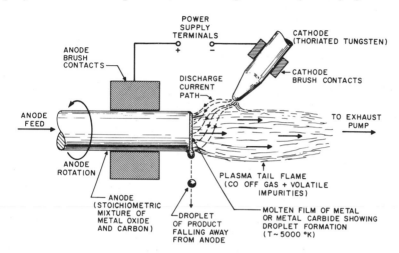

FIGURE 19. Diagram of chemically induced high intensity arc used for production of refractory metals and carbides.

provides unique opportunity for circumventing this difficulty. By controlling the rate of energy transfer to the anode it is possible to establish a high intensity arc discharge without the necessity for all of the electrode constituents to pass into the vapor state.[25] This possibility is based on the nature of the products of a carbothermic reduction of a refractory oxide. The reactions are:

$$MeO + C \rightarrow Me + CO \text{ for a metal;}$$
$$\text{or}$$
$$MeO + 2C \rightarrow MeC + CO \text{ for a metal carbide,}$$

where "Me" stands for a refractory metal.

The high intensity arc process is useful for the production of a variety of high purity metals, such as uranium, thorium, niobium, tantalum, molybdenum, tungsten, etc. It is also applicable to the production of the various carbides of these and similar metals, either as single carbides or as true solid solutions of multiple carbide systems.

CONCLUSION

From the foregoing survey of arc jet technology, it is clear that this field has become a technical discipline in its own right and that it will continue to pervade both research and industry with growing importance within the next few decades. Arc jet technology may properly be regarded as the engineering aspect of the more general fields of plasma physics and chemistry. As such, it is presently involved in the evolution of a number of exciting new developments, including MHD power generation and controlled thermonuclear fusion, whose successful accomplishment can alter the course of civilization.

It is perhaps appropriate to conclude this discussion by quoting an evaluation of the economic impact of arc jet technology on the technical community.[26] Annual expenditures on research, development and testing in the field of plasma technology, approximately 90% of which have been borne by governmental agencies, amount to some $30,000,000. As a direct result of these expenditures, it has been estimated that, in addition to the benefits to defense and space programs, more than $100,000,000 has been added to the gross national product.

ACKNOWLEDGMENT

The author's research reported here has been supported by the Mechanics Division, Directorate of Engineering Sciences, Air Force Office of Scientific Research.

REFERENCES

[1] Tonks, L. *Foundations of Future Electronics,* Chapter 7, Plasma Physics, Ed. by Langmuir and Hershberger, McGraw-Hill Book Co., New York, 1961. (See pp. 155-157).

[2] Boley, F. I., *Plasmas-Laboratory and Cosmic,* Van Nostrand Co., New York, 1966, (See pp. 8-13).

[3] For a review of the charge transport mechanisms in the anode and cathode sheath regions, see Somerville, J. M., *The Electric Arc,* John Wiley & Sons, New York, 1959.

[4] Maecker, H. *Zeit. f. Physik,* 141, 198, (1955).

[5] An excellent review article on this subject is John, R. R., and Bade, W. L. *Amer. Rocket Soc. Journal,* pg. 4 (Jan. 1961).

[6] Steenbeck, M., *Physik. Zeitschr.* 33, 809, (1932).

————————, *Wissenschaftliche, Veröffentlichungenaus den Siemens-Werke,* 19-1 59, 1940.

[7] Myers, T. W., and Roman, W. C., *Survey of Investigations of Electric Arc Interactions with Magnetic and Aerodynamic Fields,* Technical Report No. ARL 66-0184, Wright-Patterson Air Force Base, Ohio, Sept. 1966.

[8] (a) Reed, T. B., *J. Apl. Phys.* **32-5**, 821, (1961).

(b) Thorpe, M. L. *Research & Devel.* p. 28, Jan., 1966.

[9] Beck, H. *Elekt. Tech. Zeit.* **42**, 933 (1921).

[10] Finkelnburg, W., *J. Apl. Phys.,* **20**, 468 (1949).

[11] Mead, L., Marquis, M. A., Sheer, C. and Korman, S. "Qualitative Theory of the Anode Sheath," Part IV. *Arcs in Inert Atmospheres and Vacuum,* John Wiley & Sons, New York, 1956.

[12] Bassett, P. R., *Trans. Amer. Electrochem. Soc.,* **44**, 153 (1923).

[13] Sheer, C., Cooney, J. A., & Rothacker, D. L., *Jour. AIAA,* **2-3**, 483 (1964).

[14] Sheer, C., Stojanoff, C. G. and Tschang, P. S., *Diagnostic Study of the Fluid Transpiration Arc,* Semi-Annual Prog. Report No. P-1/312, Sept. 1964, Contract AF 49(638)-1395, Mechanics Division, AFOSR, Arlington, Va., (See pp. 59-64).

[15] An informative survey of recent applications of plasmajet technology is given in *Plasma Jet Technology,* NASA technology Survey Document No. NASA SP-5033, Oct. 1965 ed by. P. R. Dennis, et al.

[16] Eschenbach, R. C. & Skinner, G. M. *Study of Arc Heaters for a Hypersonic Wind Tunnel,* WADD Technical Report No. WADD-60-354, Wright-Patterson Air Force Base, Ohio, May, 1960.

[17] Gladisch, H. *Hydrocarbon Proc. & Petroleum Refining,* **41-6**, 159 (1962).

[18] Hackman, R. L., *Plasma Arc Techniques in Industry,* ASM Technical Report No. 6-1 presented at the Metals/Materials Congress, Amer. Sci. for Metals, 1963. See also Refs. (6) and (17).

[19] Bryson, D. A. & Eschenbach, R. C., *Arc Plasma Heating, the Key to High Temperature Heating Problems,* Linde research report F-51-408, Union Carbide Corporation, Linde Division, Speedway, Indiana.

[20] Gage, R. M. *High Pressure Arc and Process,* U.S. Patent No. 2,806,124, Sept. 10, 1957.

[21] Reed, T. B. *Plasmas for High Temperature Chemistry,* Vol. I., Advances in High Temperature Chemistry, Academic Press, New York, 1967.

[22] Sheer, C., & Korman, S., *The High Intensity Arc in Process Chemistry,* Arcs in Inert Atmospheres and Vacuum, W. E. Kuhn, Editor, John Wiley & Sons, New York, 1956.

[23] Sheer, C., & Korman, S., *Arc Process for the Production fo Fume,* U.S. Patent No. 2,616,842, Nov. 4, 1952.

[24] Holmgren, J. D., Gibson, J. O., & Sheer, C., *Jour. Electrochem. Soc.,* **111-3**, 362, 1964.

[25] Sheer, C., Korman, S., and Gibson, J. O., *Process for Reduction of Ores to Metals, Alloys, Interstitial and Intermetallic Compounds,* U.S. Patent No. 3,101,308, Aug. 20, 1963.

[26] See reference 15, Page 113-15.

VIII. Biological Sensors

Theodore H. Bullock

Year after year sensory physiologists continue to discover new sensibilities and new forms of transduction. No other system in the body parallels the plethora of distinctively differentiated organs, many of them in lower animals of still unknown function and yielding one by one to combined behavioral and electrophysiological study.

The old five senses, sight, hearing, taste, smell and touch have been replaced in current literature by classes or modalities based on the form of the normally adequate stimulus. These are photoreceptors, phonoreceptors, tactile, vibration, position, acceleration, stretch, pressure and other mechano-receptors, chemoreceptors, thermoreceptors, electroreceptors (a recently discovered whole class, treated below) and nociceptors (stimulated by noxious, often pain-inducing, events). These in turn comprise a larger number of submodalities such as the unit afferent nerve fibers responding to particular assortments of tastes, or smells or colors. A far larger number of lines (we will use as virtually equivalent nerve fibers, axon, unit receptor, channel, and line) are labelled, that is, "known" to the part of the nervous system which receives and analyzes the input. There are labelled lines representing each topographically separate receptive field on the skin, each warm spot and cold spot, each distinguishable unit field of the visual world, the auditory units distinguishable by their frequency response,

THEODORE H. BULLOCK is Professor of Neurosciences in the School of Medicine at the University of California, San Diego, where his present researches are in the fields of comparative neurophysiology. He is a former president of the American Society of Zoologists. He has been a member of many expeditions for experimental physiological investigations on marine, fresh water and terrestrial species in Mexico, Panama, Brazil, Hawaii, Bikini, Eniwetok, Naples and other marine stations. In addition to the University of California, San Diego, he has been a faculty member at Yale, Missouri, UCLA and the Marine Biological Laboratory at Woods Hole.

the muscle, tendon, joint, semicircular canal, blood pressure, and other receptor units geographically defined.

In man there are something more than 10^8 receptor units, most of them rods and cones in the retina.

But to gain some feeling for the process of investigation of biological sensors let us start with an actual experiment.

INFRARED RECEPTORS

If you decide to test the hypothesis inferred from anatomical structure that the curious facial pit of the pit vipers (Fig. 1) is a sense organ, you could perform the following simple maneuver. Exposing the nerve surgically some place between the facial pit, which lies just in front of the eye and its entrance into the skull, one can tie a thread around the nerve and sever it between the knot and the skull pre-

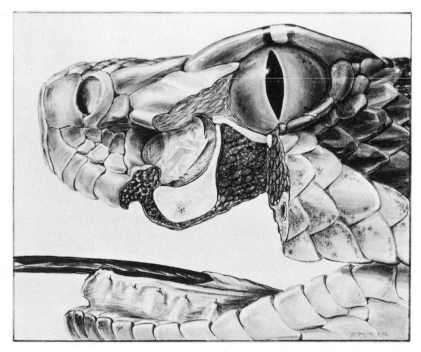

FIGURE 1. Head of a rattlesnake showing the facial pit, dissected to reveal the thin membrane at its bottom, which is the sensory structure.

serving as long as possible a peripheral stump, that is, the length of nerve coming from the facial pit to the point of the cut. One can then lift the whole stump onto an electrode consisting of a platinum wire bent into a convenient hook. Another electrode is placed anywhere else on the snake; we would choose a place close to the nerve in order to avoid picking up the electrical signs of the heart beats or the respiration. Connecting these electrodes to an amplifier, you would find a continual roar or sh-sh-sh sound which is the combined activity of many nerve fibers, each carrying a nerve impulse, which contributes a one millisecond "pop," several times to many times per second.

Now you are ready to test different stimuli and look for effective and ineffective forms of environmental change. You would find that a wide variety of odors had no effect, nor a wide variety of sounds, nor changing the position of the animal, accelerating it this way or that. If you touched the membrane at the bottom of the facial pit with a wisp of cotton or a camel's hair brush you would find a threshold above which the background roar or sh-sh-sh sound would dramatically increase in general level. The same thing happens if you turn on a flash light, directed at the pit from the front and only a few centimeters away or a spot light, like an automobile headlamp, from a few meters away.

Do we then have an ambiguous detector of touch and light? If you filter the light with a thin layer of water and Mohr's salt, the radiation ceases to be effective whereas if you filter with a pitch black infrared-passing glass the lamp is once more effective. Evidently it is the infrared component of the radiant energy that stimulates. Extension of these simple tests shows that the response depends on the contrast between the source of long wave length radiant energy and the prevailing background radiation which is effectively measured by the surface temperature of the objects in the field of view. The temperature of the intervening air is without effect. Even the temperature of the snake and its sense organ is, over a wide range, without effect. We have, then, an infrared change detector which is sensitive over the range of wave lengths, from about 1 to 15 or more microns, responding with a marked acceleration of the spontaneous background activity to a dose of 5×10^{-10} calories delivered in less than 100 milliseconds onto the area of terminal branching of one receptor (Bullock and Diecke, 1956).

This finding has different sorts of significance to different people, depending on their prior interests. For herpetologists the feature that catches attention is the possession of this ability by all species of the family of the pit vipers including the rattlesnakes, copperheads, water moccasins and their allies and by all members of the family of the boas and pythons, which is not a closely related group, and by no other snakes in a considerable series examined in the recent study by Barret and me.

From the point of view of the evolution of the senses in the vertebrates one is struck by the presence of this specialized sensory development in certain branches of the fifth cranial nerve whereas nerves supplying other portions of the skin in the same and other groups of vertebrates either possess no such receptors or they are excessively scarce.

For the general physiologists concerned with mechanisms of transduction the point perhaps most immediately of concern is the evidence that the infrared detector is actually a warm-receptor. That is, its response depends on a rising temperature of the sensory nerve endings (Fig. 2) rather than on the radiation as a wave length-specific or photochemically active stimulus. This means that the organ is in the class of temperature receptors, of which the best studied are cold receptors, that is, those which increase their firing upon cooling. These snake receptors are the best understood warm receptors at present. We believe they are essentially like the warm receptors in our own skin.

However, the differences are what concern the comparative physiologist, who is impressed by the outstanding illustration here of the principle that modest changes in secondary features such as the anatomy can make a profound difference in the use to which an organ is put in the life of an animal. Although the sensitivity seems to be about the same for man and rattlesnake in terms of threshold temperature change, about 1/1000 of a degree centigrade if reasonably abrupt, (Fig. 2), there is a millionfold difference in favor of the rattlesnake when given in terms of calories of flux at threshold. This is mainly due to the sensitive endings being within 2 microns of the surface instead of more than 500 microns as in our own skin. Other anatomical details confer a high resolution of detail and a basis for localization of the radiant source. This, together with integration over time and movement of the snake, can give information on size and distance. The secret here is an extraordinarily fine grain or high

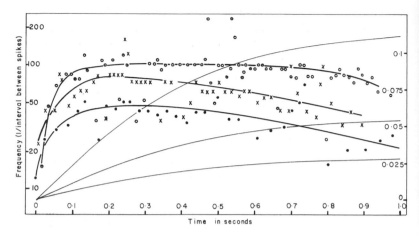

FIGURE 2. Responses of a single sensory fiber in a branch of the Vth cranial nerve supplying the facial pit in a rattlesnake to three different changes in temperature. These were imposed by a tiny stream of flowing water directed onto the membrane and carrying a warm front, due to a loop of resistance wire heated by a sudden current. Note thermocouple records of temperature of water in the pit. Spontaneous firing is reliably increased within less than 50 msec. (From Bullock and Diecke, 1956).

density of sensory nerve fibers per square millimeter of the sensory membrane (Fig. 3), combined with its location at the bottom of a pit with a somewhat restricted mouth that casts shadows on the sensory membrane (Bullock and Fox, 1957).

If you are interested in the ultrastructure of receptor endings, this is one of the most extraordinary. The unmyelinated terminals are free and extremely abundant, ramifying, and packed solidly with mitochondria. The whole layer lies between 2 and 5 microns below the surface.

If you are interested in the mechanisms of transduction at the molecular and chemical level, this should be extraordinarily favorable material but nothing can be said to satisfy your curiosity at present. To pique your interest the equivalent Q_{10} for the increase in firing rate with a threshold stimulus of about $1/1000°$ C is 10^{30}!

Space limitations prevent more than a brief mention of other features of interest. Recent work in Japan has achieved successful microelectrode recording of the subthreshold receptor potentials. The phenomenon of spontaneity referred to at the outset is itself a

FIGURE 3. Nerve endings in the rattlesnake pit membrane as seen in a whole mount, fortunately impregnated with reduced silver. Note capillaries and blood corpuscles for scale. The number of sensory axons per square mm is greater than the number of optic nerve fibers per square mm of retina in man. Each is highly branched; the electron microscope shows even more branching than this silver stain. The scale is 50 micrometers long. (From Bullock and Fox, 1957).

property of major importance in the brain and can be studied here with particular advantages. Certain statistical properties of the spontaneity, both short range irregularity and longer term surging, are of theoretical and mechanistic interest. On and on go the problems of basic principle involved in a given instance of sensory reception.

Let us pass on. We could develop the picture of recent advances in chemoreceptors in the taste buds and in the nose as well as the antennae of insects. A great deal of work has been done on the stretch receptors that measure passive or active pull on a muscle. We could develop the still unknown receptors for many environmental stimuli that animals respond to behaviorally including hydrostatic pressure in the range of a few centimeters of water, x-rays far below lethal dose, gamma rays, magnetic fields and others; in most of these we have no idea whether a nervously innervated sense organ is involved or the detection is a property of generalized cells. Instead of any of these alternatives, I want to tell you about the recent discoveries in electroreception.

ELECTRORECEPTORS IN ELECTRIC FISH

Here is a group of receptors, interesting in their own right as a recently discovered new class of sense organs and also for the insights they provide into questions of general principle.

The encyclopedic ichthyologists of the last century knew about

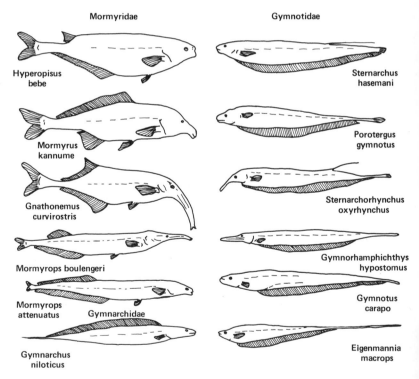

Figure 4. Some of the many genera of electric fish. All of the fresh water families Gymnarchidae and Mormyridae (African) and Gymnotidae (South American) are electric, i.e. possess an electric organ and discharge pulses into the water. (From Lissmann, 1958).

the possession of small electric organs by three families of fresh water fish, the Mormyridae and Gymnarchidae of Africa and the Gymnotidae of South America (Fig. 4). But since the organs were patently too small to generate electricity of offensive or defensive magnitude these fish were referred to as pseudo-electric fish and remained an enigma in evolutionary theory since there was no adequate explanation for the evolution of organs to a stage not yet developed enough to be of value for the only functions that were conceived of.

Only a few years ago Lissman (1958) at Cambridge re-examined these fish and proposed a new theory of the function of these organs, which has opened up a large field of investigation from behavior to cellular mechanism and brain processing. These fish are found to discharge the electric organ in the form of brief pulses from several to many times per second, continuously night and day (Fig. 5). The voltage is low, one or a few volts open circuit, and rapidly attenuated with distance from the fish. Nevertheless, says the hypothesis, this

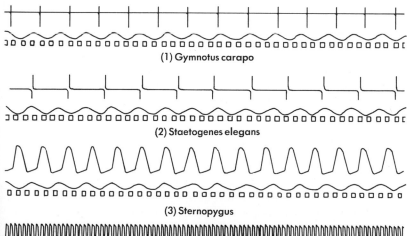

(1) Gymnotus carapo

(2) Staetogenes elegans

(3) Sternopygus

(4) Eiegenmannia virescens

FIGURE 5. Some of the kinds of electric organ discharge pattern. Note lower and higher frequencies, respectively more and less irregular, broader and narrower pulses. (From Lissmann, 1958).

pulsatile field of current is used by the animal to detect inhomo-
geneities in the conductance of the environment such as those caused
by dielectric or conducting objects, therefore virtually anything that
is not identical to the water in its conductance. The distortion of the
field by objects (Fig. 6) is detected, according to this picture, by an
array of special detectors in the animal, each reporting to the brain

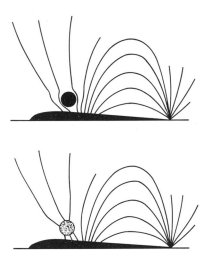

FIGURE 6. Diagram of the field around a (half) fish and its distortions due
to objects in the water, therefore, a diagram of the usual adequate stimulus
according to Lissmann's (1958) hypothesis.

the intensity of the field at its locus, the brain then synthesizing an
analog of the watery world by computation from the many channels
of input.

This proposal has been supported by behavioral, physiological, and
anatomical studies in more than half a dozen laboratories in recent
years. It has led to the discovery of a class of receptors (Bullock et al,
1961; Hagiwara et al, 1962) which cannot be ascribed to any of the
familiar categories such as chemoreceptors, thermoreceptors, photoreceptors, mechanoreceptors and the like. Of course, many kinds of receptors are subject to influence by applied electric current but we
cannot, therefore, call them electroreceptors. The necessary and sufficient evidence in the case of the electric fish receptors was the finding
that they respond systematically to the naturally occurring electric

fields and to its alteration by displacement of objects in the field. Incidental to this was the demonstration of high sensitivity, abundance, wide distribution and antomical specialization from other related sense organs.

Let us examine this sense organ and its properties. The first thing important to realize is that a differentiation into several types has occurred, anatomically and physiologically different, though all answering to the name and criteria of electroreceptors. All these types belong to the system of acousticolateralis sense organs, which are innervated by the lateral line nerves, a common possession of elasmobranchs (sharks and rays), bony fish and aquatic amphibia. This is an extensive series of sense organs in the skin of the tail, trunk and head innervated by branches of the extraordinary nerve that comes directly from the brain though running the length of the body. This system is therefore superimposed upon the regular sensory endings of the segmental nerves from the spinal cord; these latter are generally simple, branched, free nerve endings without structural specialization.

The lateral line receptors are structurally specialized, mainly in two ways. First, there is a nonnervous epithelial cell, usually ciliated, and of special aspect, that appears to be the actual receptor or sense cell. It receives the endings of the afferent nerve fibers of the first order neurons in this sensory pathway. In other words, the excitation of the first order neuron is indirect: the environmental stimulus is detected and transduced by the nonnervous ciliated sense cell, sometimes called a hair cell, and this in turn excites the dendritic terminal of the first order afferent fiber, presumably by chemical transmission. This indirect method involving nonnervous sense cells is nearly unique among all animals and senses; perhaps only in the taste buds of vertebrates is there another comparable situation. The higher vertebrate ear with its cochlea and semicircular canals are special derivatives of the same lateral line system and share this feature.

The second general feature of this system is that instead of diffuse, solitary cells, clusters of hair cells occur in organized relation to each other, permitting the use of the term organ; these may be quite discrete and numerous especially on the head but also scattered over the trunk.

Most receptors of the lateral line system are some variety of mechanoreceptor, from static position (tilt detectors) to movement (acceleration detectors), vibration (transmitted from solid substrate) to near-field water-borne disturbance (displacement detectors) to far-field water-borne sound waves (pressure detectors).

The electroreceptors are the only exceptions since their excitability has not been attributed to mechanical events.

Note the consequence of this arrangement: electroreception is not as simple as one might suppose, electricity directly exciting the nerve fiber, hence by-passing a transduction process; instead electric current presumably excites the sense cell which then, presumably by release of chemical transmitter, excites the sensory nerve endings. One of the fascinating questions of general principle is whether there is a relation between this indirect chain of events and that believed to obtain in the highest and most studied of the acousticolateralis organs, the cochlea or organ of hearing. Here a so-called cochlear microphonic potential faithfully reproduces the sound waves and is thought to mediate the excitation of the cochlear nerve endings; it is not really known whether the hair cells generate the cochlear microphonic and with it excite the nerve endings or rather detect the cochlear microphonic like electroreceptors and thereupon chemically transmit the excitation to the nerve endings.

Within the general scheme of lateral line sense organs the electroreceptors are apparently histologically differentiated though only a few speculative proposals have been made about the relation of structure and function (Szabo, 1965; Waltman, 1966; Wachtel and Szamter 1966; Lissmann and Mullinger, 1968). Little is known at present at the light microscope or electron microscope level which would help to explain the high sensitivity to voltage gradients in the water outside the fish. The structure does offer an explanation of the low sensitivity to mechanical disturbance, since these organs are rather well cut off from direct contact with the external medium or the lateral line canal.

It is quite possible, although the histology alone cannot clarify this, that there is a low resistance electrical path from the surface down to the sense organ and that the surrounding skin is of unusually high resistance, thus providing a funnel for current from the external medium to the inner body tissues which, in turn, offer a low resistance return path to the electric organ.

The sensitivity of the electroreceptors has been measured on the whole animal by behavioral endpoint and on the single sensory fiber of the lateral line nerve by psysiological endpoint on several species of different families with widely divergent results. The most sensitive are behavioral thresholds in the range 0.03 μv/cm (*Gymarchus*, Lissmann) and 0.01 μv/cm (*Raja*, Dijkgraaf and Kalmijn). The basis of estimation, voltage gradient per centimeter in the water, is used in order to compare results. However, an understanding of the receptor will require conversion into current density and resistance of each part of the path, or the voltage drop across the receptor membrane. None of these is known at present.

A principal effort in the physiological analysis of the electroreceptors has been to unravel the types there are and to characterize them. This is done by laboriously and carefully dissecting the lateral line nerve to isolate minute bundles of fibers and eventually a single functional unit and recording its nerve impulses with electrodes and amplifiers while delivering controlled stimuli that reveal its properties.

The unexpected result has been the discovery of several types of nerve impulse code fundamentally distinct from the classical frequency code and this is another main area of interest for general principles of nervous communication.

The classical frequency code has been for many years the answer to the question: How is information represented in streams of nerve impulses in nerve fibers? One of the very first problems we face when we ask how the brain works is this one of the form in which information contained in nervous messages is represented, whether from the sensory receptors to the brain or from the brain to the muscles or from place to place within the brain and spinal cord. As soon as amplifiers and string galvanometers permitted the discovery of nerve impulses in the early decades of this century, it was noticed that nerve fibers from sense organs being stimulated carry more impulses per second the stronger the stimulus. This has been repeatedly confirmed and is so reasonable for a code based on nerve impulses—which are all or none events about a millisecond in duration, that the notion of an average frequency representation is well established. Some of the electroreceptor fibers behave in accordance with this coding scheme (Fig. 7).

In the electric fish we have found several other types of nerve fibers however that do not correspond with this picture. One type has been described from a species of *Sternopygus* that fires its electric organ consistently at 100 per second. This type of nerve fiber follows the electric organ discharge with a single nerve impulse from the electro-

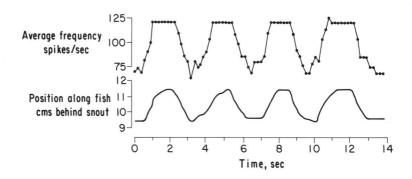

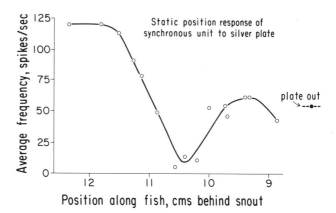

FIGURE 7. Average frequency coding. The response of a unit in the lateral line nerve of a gymnotid, that appears to code by the classical means. Stimulus was an object brought into and out of the receptive field. (From Bullock and Chichibu, 1966).

receptor to the brain and this one-to-one relationship is maintained during stimulation by introducing conducting or dielectric objects into the receptive field of the receptor, for example by moving a metal rod along the side of the fish about a centimeter away. The sensory fiber fires at 100 per second and cannot carry information about the stimulus by its frequency. The parameter which shows the response of the receptor is the time between the electric organ discharge and the sensory nerve impulse. This latent period varies systematically by about 2 milliseconds for a movement of the metal rod of 1 centimeter (Fig. 8). Since there are other sensory fibers which do not change in

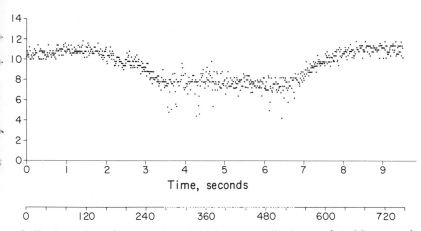

Ordinal number of successive electric organ discharges (at 80 per sec.)

Figure 8. Latency coding. The response of a unit in the lateral line nerve of a gymnotid that cannot be coding by frequency and apparently codes by the magnitude of the delay between its firing and that of another class of units. During the slow vertical sweep of this record an object was moved in and then out of the receptive field. (From Bullock and Chichibu, 1966).

latent period with stimulation the central nervous system has a basis for measurement of latency and hence of the alteration of the electric field by the metal rod. We can call this a latency code (Bullock and Chichibu, 1956).

Another class of fibers is encountered in these fish which does not follow every cycle of the electric organ discharge but misses either occasionally or more frequently according to the presence of a stimulating object in the water. Missing does not occur regularly every second or third or fourth or fifth cycle of the electric organ discharge but is significantly nonrandom and on the average codes a stimulus strength although with a limited dynamic range. This system can, of course, be treated as an average frequency code but is different from the classical form in that the intervals are quantal. Whether the brain reads it in the same way or not is a question for the future. In the meantime we can call this a probability code.

In species of *Hypopomus* the electric organ discharges at from 5 to 30 per second and a class of electroreceptors follows each discharge, not with just one or no impulses, but with zero or one or up to 15 impulses in a short high frequency burst (Fig. 9). These fibers may encode the presence and intensity of a stimulus by the number of impulses in the burst or by its duration; typically there is no systematic change in the intervals between impulses. In any case we cannot treat this as a frequency code because the average frequency will primarily depend upon the number of electric organ discharges per second which varies over a wide range at the will of the fish. It may be called a number code, or what is equivalent, a duration of burst code, since the intervals are not systematically changing.

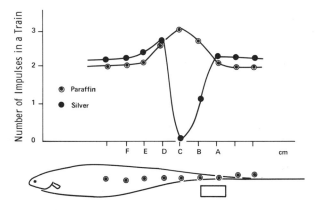

FIGURE 9. Number or duration coding. The response of a unit in the lateral line nerve of a gymnotid that cannot be coding by mean frequency and apparently codes the intensity of the adequate stimulus—presence of an object in its field, by the number of nerve impulses at a nearly fixed frequency. Note the steep function of position and opposite effect of dielectric and conducting objects. (From Hagiwara and Morita, 1963).

The fibers coding by average frequency are as remarkable as any other. For they are smoothly changing frequency with intensity of stimulation in the presence of the pulsatile field of the electric organ discharge, somehow ignoring that frequency. The possibility suggests itself that they are integrating over many electric organ discharge cycles at the expense of promptness of response to a new stimulus. But this can be eliminated because the fibers in question continue to fire and to respond to objects even when the electric organ is silenced by anesthetic or other means. Evidently these receptors have a high cut off filter that prevents the brief event of the electric organ from stimulating and are mainly sensitive to the feeble DC and slowly changing voltages in the water from other sources of current external to the fish. Under any but the most chemically clean conditions there normally exist sources of current in the water and the walls of the container or objects in the water and while the voltages are small the sensitivity of the receptors is quite high enough to respond to such stimuli.

Considerations of electroreceptor sensitivity and function led us to basic principles of neural coding and these in turn have led us back to questions of utility. The discovery of this class of electro-receptors that do not depend upon the electric organ raised the possibility that such organs are widespread among species lacking a specialized electric organ. New evidence, particularly from be-havioral studies on sharks and rays without electric organs, strength-ens the suggestion that such is the case. One of the outstanding puz-zles of sensory physiology since the late '30's has been the function of the characteristic and abundant sense organs in the skin of all sharks, skates and rays called *ampullae of Lorenzini*. Work pub-lished in Holland (Dijkgraef and Kalmijn, 1966) seems to have established the function of these receptors scattered through the skin of elasmobranchs as electroreceptors, responding to the action potentials generated by prey species of fish through their heart beats or respiratory or locomotor movements. I expect still other species of fish to be found which normally make use of electroreception.

The relevance of such studies for basic brain physiology is that ordinary nerve cells in the brain in all probability are normally in-fluenced in the frequency of their firing by standing and slowly changing potentials in the tissue in addition to whatever else con-trols them; common nerve cells are in fact electroreceptors. It is the available stimuli and their meaning that are still in question.

Let us look a little farther into the behavioral function of the electroreception in electric fish. Lissmann and Machin showed (1958) that *Gymnarchus* can learn to distinguish between two ob-jects that differ in electrical conductivity, for example, two porcelain filter candles filled with different mixtures of distilled and tap water. Möhres (1957) indicated a social significance of the discharge in mormyrids, in connection with territorial defense.

I want to tell you of some new evidence that gymnotids use this system in close range navigation, obstacle avoidance and detection of apertures or channels. Preliminary evidence in my laboratory indicated that species of electric fish of the family *Gymnotidae* were much better than a number of species of nonelectric families of fresh water fish from the tropical fish store in a task involving finding the aperture in a baffle between two halves of the aquarium when that aperture was shifted at random between trials. The fish were trained on a so-called shuttle-box operant conditioning paradigm. They learned that when the lights came on, electric shocks would soon follow and shortly thereafter prodding would occur, unless they retreated through a door to the other half of the aquarium, whereupon lights would go off and they would be left in peace. After the fish learned to solve the problem, the clear plastic partition between the two halves of the aquarium was changed to one with eight holes, of which all but one were covered for each trial according to a quasi-random number table. Because of position habits and personality differences a few specimens were refractory to the shuttle box task but fourteen specimens of electric fish *(Eigenmannia, Gymnotus, Hypopomus* and *Sternopygus)* were each trained to rouse, hunt for and pass through the open hole in an average of less than 30 seconds. (The electric fish commonly rested motionless during the 3 to 5 minutes between trials. They did not always rouse and start to hunt with the light-on signal but did so with one or an occasional brief electric shock delivered by hand switch at the judgment of the trainer. Only in the early stages of shaping was prodding necessary. These fish will not work for a food reward.) One or two specimens each of ten species of nonelectric fresh water fish (in the genera *Carassius, Anoptichthys, Barbus, Anostomus, Corydoras, Astronotus, Anguilla, Mastacembelus, Protopterus, Petromyzon)* succeeded in averaging no less than 300 seconds to find the aperture even though continually searching or moving about and intermittently reinforced by shock or prod, having come to plateau performance after a week or two of training at 20 trials a day. Only two species of nonelectric fish tried were able to do as well as 45-60 seconds *(Acanthophthalmus* sp. and *Xenomystus* sp.)

To test the hypothesis that the electroreception was of some aid in finding the apertures (visual, mechanical, and other cues or senses were not eliminated) the following experiment was devised. Clusters of four carbon rod electrodes mounted in the same metal holder above the water were fixed in position near each of the apertures and became part of the normal furniture of the fish's world. External connections permitted shorting together any combination of the eight clusters. A certain fish was then trained with clusters 1, 3, 5 and 7 permanently shorted together and 2, 4, 6 and 8 permanently shorted together. Another fish was trained with 1, 2, 3 and 4 shorted together and 5, 6, 7, and 8 shorted together; another with 1, 2, 5, and 6 shorted together and 3, 4, 7, and 8 shorted together, etc. After reaching plateau performance, measuring the time to find the open aperture, typically about 20 seconds, occasional trials were injected into a session with an unfamiliar pattern of shorting of the electrodes. The results of a preliminary series on fourteen fish was a significant increase in the time required to find the aperture, typically by about 5 to 10 seconds. The same test could not be tried on the nonelectric fish since they were unable to find the aperture in a reasonable or consistent length of time. The conclusion is that in the electric fish a sudden change from the familiar in the shape of the world, conductance-wise—not usually mechanically, or chemically detectable upsets the fish's performance by a significant amount.

To test the reciprocal problem of providing an electrical clue of the position of the correct aperture a new device was constructed. The partition between the two halves of the aquarium was provided with swinging doors of which two were used for a given fish; in any trial one was locked and the other free to swing. A pair of carbon rods in front of each door could be externally shorted or left unconnected; one of these conditions was the indication of the unlocked door. The measurement in this case was not time but departure from chance level in choosing a door to push upon, following the on-signal, to reach the other side of the aquarium. During the many days of testing trials the fish is occasionally given an electric shock if it is not active and near the choice points; this maintains its motivation to get through the partition but does not give any clue as to the unlocked door. The result with our arrangement of clues was a small departure from chance level of choice but at a highly significant level. Each of 14 averages of 100 or more trials in 5 fish, (*Gymnotus carapo* and *Gnathonemus* sp.) were significant at the 0.5% level with the carbon rod clues and an additional 3 averages were slightly less significant at the 1% level. One fish given the same shaping and training failed to choose the correct door significantly above chance level in 100 or more trials with one geometry of the carbon rod clues but achieved 0.5% significance on another geometry.

Since the conditions were uniform with respect to visual, mechanical, and chemical clues the only modality available in these experiments was electrical and in the form of a very minor change in the configuration of the electrical world, avoiding the intentional introduction of voltage gradients (although minute inequalities between the carbon rod electrodes could not be eliminated). The results show that the electric modality is used by these gymnotid electric fishes. However, tasks have not been devised which would bring out the differences we presume must exist in the utilization of electrorecption in object detection between species, for example, the high frequency-fixed frequency species and those discharging the electrical organ at a low and variable frequency.

Some of the difference last referred to may be involved in the social communication function of the electric discharges and electroreception. Experiments (not reported here) in our laboratory and on the Scripps Institution of Oceanography Research Vessel Alpha Helix in the Amazon indicate a wide difference among species in the amount and kind of behavioral response to electric pulse signals of the type of the fish's own species.

Between the properties of the peripheral receptors and the behavioral reactions is another chapter of interest, namely, the study of second order and higher order processing of the sensory input by the analyzers in the brain in order to extract the information of interest to the organism from the large number of parallel channels of unit receptors. Enger and Szabo (1965) have successfully recorded from single neurons in the brain that show responses to objects different from those of the sensory nerve fibers, e.g. phasic change depending on direction of movement regardless of the nature of the object, whether dielectric or conductor.

Instead of expanding on this discussion of electroreception, I want to tell you about some recent work in the same direction in the ultrasonic auditory systems of bats and dolphins, which my colleagues and I (Drs. Nobuo Suga and Alan Grinnell and collaborators in Japan) have worked with in the last few years.

ULTRASONIC AUDITORY ANALYSIS

If an anesthetized bat is mounted in a holder with its head immobilized and the roof of the midbrain is exposed by opening the skull, a microelectrode consisting of a glass capillary drawn to a fraction of a micron diameter at the tip and filled with a conducting salt solution, can be introduced into the portion of the midbrain called the inferior colliculus and advanced in steps of a few microns while the potential difference between this and an indifferent electrode on the skin or muscle is watched on the cathode ray oscilloscope screen. This is, in fact, a widely used technique for hunting for single nerve cells or nerve fibers in the brain in order to study their properties and responses to stimuli of many kinds. It is a technique requiring patience and luck combined with skill since the factors that operate to permit picking up single units that are still functioning are not really understood, while clearly the vast majority of nerve cells the electrode encounters or passes are not heard from or are damaged. We therefore have no way of knowing at present whether the units that we do find and study are a representative sample of the population or selected for some feature that biases the sample.

Let us consider some of the kinds of units that have been encountered in such exploration in bats. The reason for studying bats is that, in association with their elaborate behavioral employment of echolocation, the auditory system in the brain is enormously developed and readily accessible and the range of hearing extending into the ultrasonic above 100 khz gives us more than two extra octaves of room for delivering auditory stimuli.

First, we shall plot the response of each unit by choosing a pure tone that is effective in causing impulses in the unit, when delivered with a gradual rise that prevents the onset click and maintained for a period longer than the latent period of the unit spike. Now, we shall weaken the intensity of the sound until an arbitrary criterion of threshold is reached, for example one spike response in ten repetitions of the tone pip or a spike probability of 0.1. These stimulus conditions establish a point on a graph of frequency against intensity at threshold which we may call the excitatory response area curve. This curve is typically U or V shaped with a best frequency where the threshold is minimal and rising thresholds at higher and lower frequencies. Some of the units encountered have a broad response area. Others have a narrow response area with a much steeper fall in sensitivity on each side of a narrow best frequency. Some units show suppression by high intensities, at an upper threshold, therefore giving a graph which is a closed figure.

Now let us add a further test. Delivering a sound within the response area that is above threshold at some effective frequency, we will now try the effect of superimposing sounds of other frequencies and intensities. In some units, particularly those with the narrow excitatory response area, we find sounds both inside and outside of this area which therefore do not cause any excitation but which are effective in altering the response to the conditioning tone in the direction of suppression. In this way we can plot the threshold intensities at different frequencies for the inhibitory effect and obtain an inhibitory area (Fig. 10). This may overlap the excitatory response area; that is to say tones in the overlap region not only can elicit spikes but at the same time inhibit the responses to other tones simultaneously delivered. Inhibitory areas may occur on either high frequency or low frequency side of the excitatory response area, or on both sides. In the latter case, they may be quite symmetrical or one inhibitory area may have a considerably more sensitive best frequency than the other. On the basis of simple stimuli with pure tones, single or paired, we have found an array of different types of units by the limited criteria of wide versus narrow excitatory response area, high intensity suppression, presence or absence of inhibitory area, one or two inhibitory areas, and symmetry or asymmetry of two inhibitory areas. We would probably find still further differentiation of types of nerve cells if we looked at other criteria such as the time course of response to stimuli at a fixed moderate intensity or at a certain number of decibels above threshold.

Instead, let us introduce another form of stimulation, namely, frequency modulated tones. If during the latent period of response the tone is swept through the frequencies included in the response area we will get a response, providing the intensity is above the best frequency threshold and the sweep rate is suitable—about one octave in 4 msec. If the frequency modulated tone starts in an inhibitory response area there will generally be no response even though the tone sweeps into an excitatory response area. At these sweep rates presumably there is an aftereffect of the inhibition which

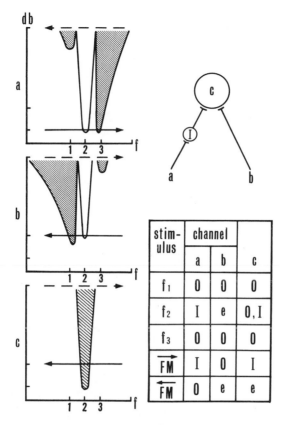

FIGURE 10. Three kinds of auditory nerve cells in the brain of a bat (diagrammatic), and an arrangement of them that would explain the responses specialized so that frequency modulated tones are recognized but fixed frequency tones cause no response. Neurons "a" and "b" do respond to fixed frequency tones (excitatory response area in white); they also have inhibitory areas (hatched) and these are asymmetrical, in the opposite senses for "a" and for "b". The result is that "a" responds to upward sweeping FM tones (solid arrow) at low intensity and not to downward sweeping FM at any intensity (dashed arrow); "b" is the opposite. If "a" is inhibitory to "c" (here shown via an interneuron "i") and "b" is excitatory, the result will be that "c" responds to no pure tone, but has an inhibitory response area and fires only to downward sweeping FM tones in the right range. The table shows the effect of different tones as indicated on the abscissa upon the three neurons. E and e are stronger and weaker excitation, I and i are stronger and weaker inhibition, O represents no effect. (Kindness, N. Suga).

suppresses response during the brief period of the excitatory stimulus. Therefore, in general, there is no response to frequency modulated tones in symmetrical units or units with inhibitory areas well developed on both sides of the excitatory. In asymmetrical units frequency modulated tones can cause a response at low intensity if swept in the right direction, that is, from the excitatory towards the inhibitory frequencies. The variety of types of response to frequency modulated tones is further increased because some units have inhibitory areas to simultaneously delivered tones but not to immediately successive tones so that the frequency modulated stimulus does not show a directional preference.

With this background you may see the great interest in the discovery of some units in the highest level of the auditory system, i.e., in the cerebral cortex, which do not respond to any pure tones whatever but do respond to frequency modulated tones in the correct range and direction (Fig. 10). One of the particularly exciting and pregnant directions in which contemporary neuronal physiology is developing is in the discovery and analysis of what I call recognition units, that is, units which are property detectors responding to moderately complex combinations of features in the stimulus situation, for example, small dark moving objects in the visual field or rectangles in a certain orientation. Here is a particularly good one in the auditory domain, because it is so quantitatively specifiable, of intermediate complexity and readily understood on the basis of a model requiring simply the convergence of two of the simpler kinds of asymmetrical units, one presumed to be excitatory and the other inhibitory to the recognition unit. In no other recognition unit so far is there such a satisfactory model (Suga, 1965) based on known types of simpler units. The model is non-trivial also because it asserts that the crucial interaction is based on inhibitory action and not on augmentation or facilitation.

If we add another complication to the stimulus we quickly find units whose behavior cannot yet be explained fully. In his current work in our laboratory, Dr. Suga is permuting combinations of pure tones, frequency modulated tones and bursts of white noise, bandlimited at chosen upper and lower bounds. These three basic forms of stimulation simulate rather well the major components of human speech, namely, the formants prominent in vowels, the transitions and the wide spectrum bursts dominant in the consonants. Suga

(1968) finds units which respond to each of these three alone, and not to the other two, or to two of the three but not the third form of stimulation or to all three forms given in combinations. There can be inhibitory interaction in many cases but so far no facilitatory interaction. The response to a given vowel or a transition can therefore be very much dependent on the other frequencies present besides the constant frequency or the modulated frequency. Many units are thus sensitive to the sound structure, not only to the frequency, but to the succession of intensities.

Another way of studying the properties of auditory centers is by recording with electrodes that see more than one nerve cell at a time and give us the compound potential resulting from the summed activity of several or many units. We will call these responses evoked potentials and it is evident already that their behavior will not be entirely predictable from what we have learned about units since it is not to be assumed that we have seen all types of units or know their relative contributions or their microdistribution within the tissue.

Grinnell (1963a, b, c, d) has given us a series of thorough studies of the behavior of evoked potentials in bats at different levels of the auditory system and I select here only some features for mention. The evoked potential is chiefly an onset response but is nevertheless quite dependent for its detailed form upon the frequency composition of the tone. It is also very sensitive to slight changes of intensity, down to 0.2 to 0.5 db. A few hundred cycles of difference in frequency around 50 khz produces a distinguishable alteration in the form of the response. The evoked potential is preferable to the unit spike recording for the study of latent period and recovery after a conditioning stimulus since the response is more consistent. The bat is highly specialized for time resolution of auditory signals and shows extremely rapid recovery with nearly complete temporal resolution down to less than 1 msec of interval between two clicks. This recovery is better at low intensity stimulation and, surprisingly, at higher levels of the auditory system. Indeed, at higher levels there is a period following the first tone pip when the response is more excitable than normally, even at periods as short as 1.5 to 2 msec. The case of special interest for the normal behavior of the bat is the case of high intensity sound simulating the bat's own cry and a low intensity second sound like the normal echo. Recovery is still remarkably good when the first sound is 40 to 50 db stronger than the second; the second tone gives 25 to 50 per cent response at 1 to 2 msec interval. Clearly there is central processing between the first and the later auditory centers which enhances the sensitivity to subsequent sounds.

Another evidence of central processing is in the improvement of directional sensitivity from lower to higher centers. Sensitivity to the direction of a source of sound is important for the bat and is highly developed; the maximum difference between the most sensitive direction and the least sensitive direction is from 40 db to 68 db in some experiments. Some single units at higher levels have shown a difference in threshold of as much as 9 db per degree of azimuth.

The central processing involved in directionality is also relevant to the resistance to jamming, which is another evidence of specialization for the echolocation employed by these animals. Sharp tuning of many units is no doubt a major part of jamming resistance; tuning can be as sharp as 35 db per khz. This can be combined with the sensitization brought about by the first tone pip and with the directionality and binaural interaction, especially at higher centers, that will reduce the effect of a noise source coming from a different direction.

A bat and a dolphin are about as dramatic a contrast as the mammals offer—in size, habitat, appendages—and attractiveness to man. Yet it was basically a similarity between them that led a group of Japanese and a group of American scientists, of whom I was one, to collaborate on the first series of electrophysiological recording studies on cetaceans, using the recently developed breakthrough in anesthesia of these difficult animals (Nagel et al, 1964). That similarity is the use of echolocation to detect objects and find and discriminate prey, the use of ultrasonic frequencies, short click-like sounds, rapid and sophisticated analysis of sounds and the possession of large and elaborate brain regions associated with auditory functions. The kind and degree of hypertrophy in different regions, from medulla to colliculus, to geniculate, to cortex is quite different in chironterans and cetaceans, and the overall brain development is mostly greater in dolphins than in bats. Dolphins are highly vocal animals and use a repertoire of sounds, probably largely for social communication, that is one of the widest and most varied in the animal kingdom.

All this makes an examination of the physiological capacities and specializations of the auditory centers of the dolphin brain a most desirable objective. I want to tell you briefly what we learned in two short seasons on the coast of the Izu Peninsula in Japan where numbers of dolphins are caught commercially for food and we were able to do a good series of more than 20 animals. The full report has just appeared and gives details of techniques for solving the formidable problems of anesthesia, surgery, electrode placement, underwater stimulation and so on (Bullock et al, 1968).

We concentrated for this first study on an intermediate level of the auditory pathway, i.e. the inferior colliculus and nucleus of the lateral lemniscus (Fig 11). These are midbrain centers. Higher levels

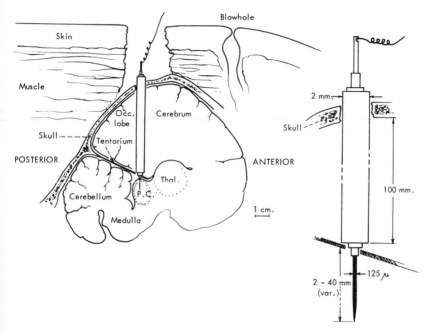

FIGURE 11. Diagram of recording electrode in position in the inferior colliculus (PC) of the dolphin, showing method of approach. The electrode (detail) was inserted through the smallest of three concentric metal tubes designed to hold the whole assembly in place on the membranous tenorium and permit free advancement of the electrode. (From Bullock et al, 1968).

(geniculate or cortex) would mean such a high degree of topographic sorting out that it would be difficult to do two experiments alike before making a complete map. Lower levels are likely to show less of the specialization for processed input that we were interested in

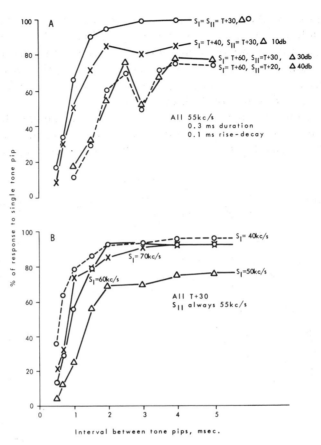

FIGURE 12. A. Recovery of responsiveness to fainter second stimuli: dolphin *(Stenella)* collicular evoked potential. With tone pips of the same frequency (55 khz, 0.3 msec duration, 0.1 msec rise and decay times), recovery of response to the second of two stimuli is plotted as a function of interval, when the stimuli were of equal intensity (30 db above threshold, or T + 30), and when the first was 10, 30, and 40 db louder than the second. Note that although a louder first stimulus does prolong depression of a second response, recovery is still considerable at 2 msec interval when the first is 40 db more intense. Note also the dip in the recovery curve at 3 msec, presumably representing short term inhibition superimposed on refractoriness of receptor elements. B. Comparable measurements showing responsiveness to a 55 kc/s signal following exposure at different intervals to an earlier stimulus of 40, 50, 60 and 70 kc/s. Both stimuli in the pair were chosen to be 30 db above threshold at their respective frequencies. (From Bullock et al, 1968).

studying. The midbrain proved to be an excellent compromise, with a target we could hit and a compound evoked potential in response to suitable sounds, that showed a gratifying degree of repeatability in successive experiments.

An electrode in the inferior colliculus records a fast and complex series of waves, representing activity in a population of well-synchronized neurons. The compound responses of many units making up the evoked potential often shows more subtle responses to stimulus conditions than single units, as well as short latency, earlier recovery and a better sample from which to judge the sound frequency range of the animal's hearing.

The performance of the dolphin midbrain potentials is remarkable compared to ordinary laboratory mammals but much like that of the bat. First, the recovery is so rapid that a substantial to a nearly complete response can be obtained to the second of two clicks only one millisecond or less after the first one (Fig. 12), and it will follow a train of clicks up to 2000 per second. The response is extremely phasic and brief and is just as good to a tone burst 0.4 ms. in duration as to one of 4 or more ms. Though not sensitive to duration, the evoked potential is sensitive to changes in rise time and this in a very fast range, 0.1 to 1.0 ms. It is also sensitive to the frequency within a tone pip even when the duration is only 0.1 ms., therefore containing only 2 to 10 cycles. In certain ranges the amplitude and form of the potential is highly sensitive to changes in sound intensity as small as 1 db. The range of effective frequencies extends at least up to 135 khz and best frequencies are usually around 40 khz. Wave form is markedly altered not only by frequency but by the range, rate and direction of frequency modulation. It is also altered, without necessarily any attenuation, by subtle changes in the quality of sounds, as by a thin paper screen held (Fig. 13) at a critical place near the face. Masking by certain frequencies and especially by white noise, is prominent.

In short, the system is highly developed for rapid, high frequency, brief sound stimuli and for small differences between such stimuli. The dolphin has been shown behaviorally to echolocate. The specializations are in many ways similar to those of bats but we have probably only scratched the surface; in particular we will doubtless find other parts of the system specialized more for the longer, lower frequency sounds of social communication than for the clicks and echos.

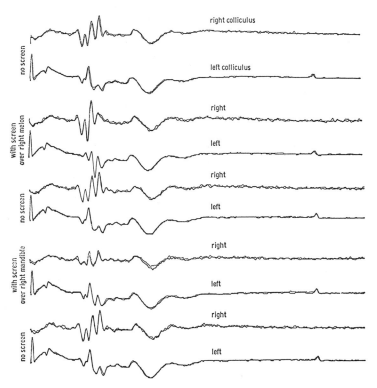

FIGURE 13. Evoked potentials from the midbrain of the dolphin, *Stenella,* showing the sensitivity of waveform to distortion of the sound field. A piece of thin notepaper, 10 x 15 cm. was held 2 cm. from the skin over the portion of the head indicated. Head and loudspeaker were in air. Tone pips of 50 khz, 0.5 ms in duration, abrupt rise and fall (clicks) at 0 db, repeated at 20 per second, delivered by speaker on animal's right. Recording electrodes in both left and right sides of the brain; 64 sweep samples averaged for each line; two successive averages superimposed; time of full sweep equal 32 msec. (From Bullock et al, 1968).

Incidentally, we found the surprising fact that the receptive field does not converge on the external ear. The most sensitive region, mapped with a small roving sound source (animal and source either in air or in water), is the side of the mandible opposite the midbrain whose response is being used as endpoint; the next sensitive is over the ipsilateral melon (forehead) (Fig. 14). The cone of reception is much narrower and steeply falling off than in ordinary mammals.

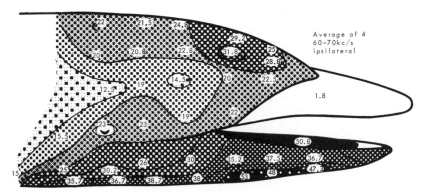

Average of 4
60-70kc/s
ipsilateral

FIGURE 14. Pattern of sensitivity of an individual *Stenella* to sound produced by a hydrophone pressed against the head surface at the points shown. The numerical values represent attenuation at threshold; therefore, the largest numbers represent greatest sensitivity. Contour lines are drawn at intervals of 5 db in sensitivity. Recording was from the inferior colliculus. Note that sensitivity was greatest along the side of the contralateral mandible (except for under the tongue), and on the ipsilateral melon. (From Bullock et al, 1968).

These examples have been chosen to indicate about where we are today in understanding biological sensors. They illustrate a heterogeneous and irregular, shifting frontier. We can be confident not only that many of our ideas and interpretations today will prove to be wrong but that new types of questions and mysteries will continue to emerge faster than old ones are cleared up.

ACKNOWLEDGMENTS

Experimental work reported here was supported by the Air Force Office of Scientific Research, Office of Naval Research, National Science Foundation, and National Institutes of Health.

REFERENCES

Bullock, T. H. and Chichibu, S. 1965. Further analysis of sensory coding in electroreceptors of electric fish. *Science,* **148**:664-665 (abs.), *Proc. Nat. Acad. Sci., Wash.,* **54**:422-429.

Bullock, T. H. and Diecke, F. P. J. 1956. Properties of an infrared receptor. *J. Physiol.,* **134**:47-87.

Bullock, T. H. and Fox, S. W. 1957. The anatomy of the infrared sense organ in the facial pit of pit vipers. *Quart. Jour. Micr. Sci.,* **98**:219-234.

Bullock, T. H., Grinnell, A. D., Ikezono, E., Kameda, K., Katsuki, Y., Nomoto, M., Sato, O., Suga, N., Yanagisawa, K. 1968. Electrophysiological studies of central auditory mechanisms in cetaceans. *Zeit. für vergl. Physiol.* (in press)

Bullock, T. H., Hagiwara, S., Kusano, K., and Negishi, K. 1961. Evidence for a category of electroreceptors in the lateral line of gymnotid fishes. *Science,* 134:1426-1427.

Dijkgraaf, S. and Kalmijn, A. J. 1966. Versuche zur Biologischen Bedeutung der Lorenzinischen Ampullen bei den Elasmobranchiern. *Zeit. für vergl. Physiol.,* 53:187-194.

Enger, P. S. and Szabo, T. 1965. Activity of central neurons involved in electroreception in some weakly electric fish (*Gymnotidae*). *J. Neurophysiol.,* 28:800-818.

Grinnell, A. D. 1963a. The neurophysiology of audition in bats: intensity and frequency parameters. *J. Physiol.,* 167:38-66.

Grinnell, A. D. 1963b. The neurophysiology of audition in bats: temporal parameters. *J. Physiol.,* 167:67-96.

Grinnell, A. D. 1963c. The neurophysiology of audition in bats: directionality and binaural interaction. *J. Physiol.,* 167:97-113.

Grinnell, A. D. 1963d. The neurophysiology of audition in bats: resistance to interference. *J. Physiol.,* 167:114-127.

Hagiwara, S., Kusano, K. and Negishi, K. 1962. Physiological properties of electroreceptors of some gymnotids. *J. Neurophysiol.,* 25:430-499.

Kalmijn, A. J. 1966. Electro-perception in sharks and rays. *Nature,* 212:1232-1233.

Lissman, H. W. 1958. On the function and evolution of electric organs in fish. *J. exp. Biol.,* 35:156-191.

Lissmann, H. W. and Machin, K. E. 1958. The mechanism of object location in *Gymnarchus niloticus* and similar fish. *J. exp. Biol.,* 35:451-486.

Lissmann, H. W. and Mullinger, A. M. 1968. Organization of ampullary electric receptors in *Gymnotidae (Pisces). Proc. Roy. Soc.,* 169:345-378.

Möhres, F. P. 1957. Elektrische Entladungen in Dienste der Revierabgrenzung bei Fischen. *Naturwissenschaften.* 15:431-432.

Nagel, E. L., Morgane, P. J. and McFarland, W. L. 1964. Anesthesia for the bottle nose dolphin, *Tursiops truncatus. Science,* 146:1591-1593.

Suga, N. 1965. Functional properties of auditory neurones in the cortex of echo-locating bats. *J. Physiol.,* 181:671-700.

Suga, N. 1968a. Analysis of frequency-modulated and complex sounds by single auditory neurones of bats. *J. Physiol.,* (in press).

Suga, N. 1968b. Classification of inferior collicular neurones of bats in terms of responses to pure tones, FM sounds and noise bursts. (mansucript)

Szabo, T. 1965. Sense organs of the lateral line system in some electric fish of the Gymnotidae, Mormyridae and Gymnarchidae. *J. Morph.,* 117:229-250.

Wachtel, A. W. and Szamier, R. B. 1966. Special cutaneous receptor organs of fish: the tuberous organs of *Eigenmannia. J. Morph.,* 119:51-80.

Waltman, B. 1966. Electrical properties and fine structure of the ampullary canals of Lorenzini. *Acta Physiol. Scand.,* Suppl 264.

IX. Recent Advances In Organic Fluorine Chemistry

Joseph D. Park

THE FIELD OF ORGANIC FLUORINE chemistry was given a great impetus in the United States by the pioneering work of the late Drs. Thomas Midgley and Albert H. Henne who were instrumental in starting the fluorocarbon refrigerant and propellant industry.

Serendipity has always played an important part in chemistry. Let us take the above case leading up to the development of the Freons— the non-toxic, nonflammable refrigerant now universally used in electrical refrigeration and air conditioning. In 1929, Midgley, the inventor of Ethyl gas, and Henne, his assistant, were called upon by Charles F. Kettering of the General Motors Research Corporation to find a substitute for sulfur dioxide, a toxic and corrosive chemical then in use as a refrigerant. An error in the literature led these men to the use of CCl_2F_2, now known as Refrigerant-12, as the desirable substitute. From this first pound of Freon made in 1929, United States production reached over 600 million pounds for the year 1967. More than two-thirds of this tonnage is presently utilized as aerosol propellants for products necessary for milady's vanity and convenience.

Again, the long arm of coincidence and serendipity played a repeat performance, as if on demand, in the case of Teflon. True, Teflon was an accidental discovery, but it was Dr. Roy J. Plunkett's curiosity and persistence which eventually paid off.

He and I were assigned to the same project—the syntheses of new fluorine refrigerants at du Pont. As an intermediate, he had to synthe-

JOSEPH D. PARK is Professor of Chemistry at the University of Colorado. His interests have been in calorimetry involving heats of reaction of fluorinated organic compounds and in the syntheses of various organofluorine compounds of possible interest as intermediates for the preparation of thermally stable fluids, fluorinated elastomers, plastics, anesthetics, etc. At present, he is Chairman of the Fluorine Division of the American Chemical Society. He was named University Lecturer on Research and Creative Work for 1967-1968 at the University of Colorado.

size and store tetrafluoroethylene in a pressure cylinder. This compound, which boils at —80° C., was previously reported to be incapable of undergoing polymerization. After about six months' storage, Dr. Plunkett had occasion to use the gas again. When he opened the valve on the cylinder, no gas evolved. Many of us would have discarded the cylinder as being empty. However, Dr. Plunkett had a good record of the net, tare and gross of the cylinder, which told him that the cylinder was not empty. Suspecting a clog in the valve, we cooled the cylinder in liquid nitrogen and unscrewed the valve, which was found to be unclogged. Looking down into the cylinder with the aid of a flashlight, we found a dense white deposit in the bottom. In order to secure the material, the cylinder had to be cut open with a hacksaw. Thus, out of a research for new refrigerants came the unsought-for miracle polymer, Teflon, which survived many abortive attempts to bring about its demise.

Lest one gets the impression that all important advances and developments in chemistry are the result of serendipity, we must not forget that the key is that the researcher must retain at all times a sensitive curiosity which is stimulated to examine these unexpected results.

Wonderful serendipity had previously reared its beautiful head in the synthesis of tetrafluoroethylene—the monomer so necessary for the production of Teflon. Starting out on a program based on a hypothesis which later proved to be incorrect, I first began to study the pyrolysis of various fluorinated compounds. Availability of the starting materials determined the order in which the various compounds were to be subjected to this study. Only the first four compounds studied yielded economically desirable products, among them being tetrafluoroethylene, a product which we were *not* looking for. This method, first carried out in 1939, is still in use as the major process for the synthesis of tetrafluoroethylene—another windfall and unlooked for "spin-off." This one product gave organic fluorine chemistry the biggest boost, not only in economics, but also by giving greater impetus to fundamental research in fluorine chemistry.

This material has been the basis for the production of not only Teflon but also for Viton-A, Poly HFP, Fluorel, Krytox, E-Fluid, material of great economic importance, as well as of scientific interest.

Another accidental discovery was that of "squaric acid" in our laboratories at the University of Colorado. I first passed up this most interesting material, chemically known as 1, 2-dihydroxy-3, 4-cyclobu-tenedione, which one of my students, Dr. Cohen, had accidentally prepared. Preliminary examination showed this compound to be devoid of any fluorine atom. I told him to let it lie since we just couldn't be caught synthesizing, even accidentally, a non-fluorine-containing organic molecule. Eventually, however, we allowed this material to see the light of chemical day in order to justify Dr. Cohen's doctoral dissertation. It may be ironical that if posterity is to remember both Dr. Cohen and me for our chemical contributions, it may well be for our discovery of "squaric acid"—a non-fluorinated product emanating from a laboratory devoted to fluorine chemistry. Such is serendipity.

At this point, it may also be quite apropos to introduce the steps leading to the filament formation of Nylon-4. Study of this new polymer was being carried out by one of my students, Dr. Pavlow. All attempts to draw filaments were unsuccessful. One day, a stirring rod was accidentally left in the polymer dissolved in formic acid. Several days later, in pulling out the stirring rod from the sticky mess, we obtained filaments which could be oriented and therefore economically useful. This, we later found out, was how Dr. Julian Hill of the du Pont Company first obtained a filament from Nylon-6 polymer which made economically feasible the great new synthetic textile field.

We first embarked on the syntheses of reactive monomers for polymerization studies on the basis of a seminal suggestion by Professor Paul Flory, than an advisor for AFOSR. He suggested that a heteroatom in the fluorocarbon backbone should be of some help in preparing elastomers with desirable low and high temperature properties. Studies on this basis led researchers to the development of fluorinated nitroso rubbers. My group at the University of Colorado contributed quite significantly to the synthesis of $CF_3—N{=}O$ which copolymerized with $CF_2{=}CF_2$ to lead to the elastomeric nitroso product.

It is our belief that it is in this pregnant field of fluorine endeavor that eventual solution of the sealant program for the supersonic transport (SST) will be made.

With this historical treatment as the prologue, we will now consider the various chemical facets relating to some recent advances in organic fluorine chemistry under the following headings:

I.) The utilization of photochemical and thermal reactions leading to new synthetic routes to unsaturated polycyclic compounds containing polyfunctional groupings in highly fluorinated compounds.

II.) Recent advances and progress in the reaction of polyfluorocycloalkenes with various nucleophiles and the probable pathways of the reactions.

The above methods lead to the syntheses of new compounds useful as intermediates capable of undergoing further reaction, i.e., polymerization, telomerization, etc.

A. Synthesis and Chemistry of Unsaturated Polycyclic Fluorocarbons

The early work in this field is that of Park and Frank[1a,b,c,d] covering the chemistry of the bicyclobutyl derivatives of the following type:

where X=H or F. In this series of studies we

showed how the various compounds were synthesized by a process involving co-dimerization under thermal conditions.

1-Chloro-1,2,2-trifluorethylene (F1113) adds to 1,1,4,4-tetrafluorobutadiene (I) in good yield to form 1-(β,β-difluoro)-vinyl-2,3,3,4,4-pentafluoro-2-chlorocyclobutane (II). No diadduct was obtained in this reaction at 160° or 220° C.

Similarly, 1,1-dichloro-2,2-difluoroethylene (F112A) codimerizes with I to afford 1-(β,β-difluoro)vinyl-2,2-dichloro-3,3,4,4-tetrafluorocyclobutane (III) in varying yields. The yield of III was 39% when the reaction was conducted at 205° but rose to 93% at 220°. In addition to III and 1112A dimer a substantial high boiling fraction (137-160°) is obtained in this experiment. Three components were isolated from this fraction whose structure cannot be determined. The hoped for diadduct of 1112A and I was not present in the mixture.

Dehydrohalogenation of the vinyl cyclobutanes, II and III, has been the subject of extensive investigation. As reported previously,

both compounds react with KOH in mineral oil but yields are uncertain with considerable polymerization or decomposition and loss of both HF and HCl occurs to give a mixture of products (IV, V, VI).

The reaction of II with KOH in ethanol gives a very complex mixture of the three possible dienes (IV, V, VI) (HF and HCl elimination) (~35%) and at least ten ethers (~65%). Although a complete analysis of this complex mixture was impossible, some components were identified. An interesting major product (~11%) was assigned the structure VII on the basis of its IR and mass spectra. It might arise from F⁻ attack on II or addition of HF to IV. The major ether

product (~17%) has tentatively been assigned structure VIII. This is based largely on the IR spectrum as a molecular ion is absent in the mass spectrum. Most of the products are highly reactive diene ethers and are unsuitable for analysis.

Reaction of III with KOH and ethanol similarly gives a mixture of products. Two unsaturated ethers and one saturated ether were isolated in addition to the diene, V. Data collected on these ethers has not yet allowed structure assignments.

Several other dehydrohalogenation mediums were investigated in

hopes of obtaining exclusive dehydrochlorination in good yield. Tri-
ethylamine reacts violently with III even if highly diluted and at
−76°C. Pyridine and aniline react less violently but with appreciable
discoloration or polymerization. Aniline might react suitably in cold
dilute solutions. Dilute aqueous KOH again gave HF and HCl elimination in a slow reaction. Hydrolysis for degradation caused rapid
base depletion and a poor recovery of fluorocarbons. Silver oxide in
DMF and diglyme gave mixtures of products in low conversion.

Silver oxide in ethanol is the best solvent yet discovered for the dehydrohalogenation of III. The reaction is complete under mild conditions and affords the diene, V, in 55% yield and 1-(β,β-difluro-β-
ethoxy)-ethaneyl-2-chlorotetrafluorocyclobutene (IX) and 1-(β-fluoro-

β-ethoxy)-vinyl-2-chlorotetrafluorocyclobutene (X) in 25 and 20%
yields respectively. X has been shown to be the trans (H-F) isomer by
proton NMR. No cis isomer is produced. Since IX is not stable with
respect to X under the reaction conditions it must be concluded that
X results from nucleophilic attack on the diene, V. This is confirmed
quantitatively by monitoring the ratio of the two products as the
reaction progresses. The reason for such an attack giving rise to trans
X exclusively is unclear.

Investigations on the hydrolysis of the ethers IX and X were conducted. Treatment of either compound with concentrated sulfuric
acid results in a rapid and quantitative conversion to 1-carboxy-
methyl-2-chloro-3, 3, 4, 4-tetrafluorocyclobutene (XI).

A codimerization of the mixed dienes obtained from dehydrohalogenation of II with Genetron 1113 led to a complex mixture as anticipated. A substantial portion of the dienes was recovered unreacted
and no cyclobuteneylcyclobutanes were observed. Two bicyclobu-

tenes were in the product mixture resulting from thermal dehydro-fluorination of the missing adducts. Other products may be present and further investigations are in progress. The lowest boiling adduct has been assigned structure VII.

This is supported by the mass spectrum ($m/e = 302$ with one Cl), partial analysis and an IR spectrum showing a strongly conjugated unsymmetrical diene system. The second adduct collected has been assigned a structure. It is 2,2′-dichlorooctafluorobicyclobutene. A third isomeric component has been isolated. Its IR spectrum and melting point distinguish it from the preceding compound. Consideration of possible products leads to the conclusion that the compound has structure XIII or XIV. Fluorine NMR will serve to distinguish between these possibilities.

A codimerization between Genetron 1112A and the diene, III, was also carried out but has not yet been worked up. Considerable unreacted diene was recovered.

A significant advance in the synthesis of the title compounds has been accomplished by S. K. Choi of this Laboratory in a reaction in which 1-iodo-2-chlorotetrafluorocyclobutene has been coupled on passing over hot copper. Studies have indicated the need for a long contact time and a trace of DMF— as a catalyst. Yields are nearly

quantitative with complete conversion with sufficient contact time over copper powder. The 2,2′-dichlorooctafluorobicyclobutene (XV) obtained has been the subject of numerous additional studies.

This was made possible by our discovery of a new method of preparing vinylic iodo compounds prepared by the following sequence of

$$(CF_2)_n \overset{C-Cl}{\underset{C-Cl}{\Big\|}} \xrightarrow{\text{HBr}} (CF_2)_n \overset{C-Br}{\underset{C-Cl}{\Big\|}} \quad + \quad (CF_2)_n \overset{C-Br}{\underset{C-Br}{\Big\|}}$$
$$\text{(A)} \qquad\qquad \text{(B)}$$

$$[A] + [B] \xrightarrow[\text{KI}]{\text{DMF}} [CF_2]_n \overset{C-X}{\underset{C-I}{\Big\|}} \qquad n=2,3,4- \quad X = I,Br,Cl.$$

reactions. In addition to the thermal reaction of $\boxed{F}^{\,I}_{\,Cl}$, the ultra-

violet irradiation of $\boxed{F}^{\,I}_{\,I}$ over mercury yielded $\langle\!\!\langle{}_{I}^{F}\rangle\!\!\rangle\!\!-\!\!\langle\!\!\langle{}_{I}^{F}\rangle\!\!\rangle$. Sim-

ilar coupling results were obtained from the corresponding diiodo
perfluorocyclohexene.

These vinylic monoiodo and diiodo compounds gave us an entry
to compounds, heretofore unknown and inaccessible, through the
isolation of the corresponding vinylic mono-lithio and dilithio organic derivatives.

The preparation of the cyclic vinyllithium reagents was accomplished by treating either 1-iodo-2-haloperfluorocycloalkenes with
methyl lithium in ether at −78°. Subsequent treatment with either
dry ice or, more preferably, with gaseous carbon dioxide yielded, after
hydrolysis, the corresponding carboxy derivatives.

Not surprisingly, lithium halogen exchanges were confined exclusively to the vinylic iodo and bromo substituents. Indeed, the chemical
literature is bereft of any references to fluoro or chloro substituents
entering into halogen metal interchanges except in highly specialized
instances. Treatment of the 1,2-diiodocycloolefins with two equiv-
alents of methyllithium in ether at −78° afforded, interestingly, the
dilithio specie—characterized by their conversion to the corresponding diacide derivatives. In contrast, treatment of 1,2-dibromotetra-

$$(CF_2)_n \overset{C-I}{\underset{C-I}{\Big\|}} + 2\ CH_3Li \longrightarrow (CF_2)_n \overset{C-Li}{\underset{C-Li}{\Big\|}} + 2\ CH_3I$$

fluorocyclobutene-1 with excess ethylmagnesium bromide in ether
reportedly yields none of the analogous di-Grignard reagent. In the
following chart is given a schematic flow diagram of some of the
reactions.

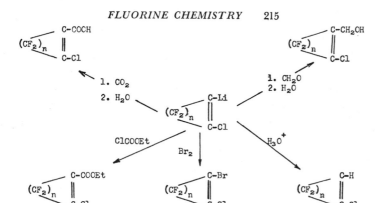

The lithio derivatives have also been utilized to prepare other organometallic compounds. The following method of preparation for

$$\boxed{F \; \substack{Hg \\ Cl}} \; \boxed{\substack{\\ Cl} \; F} \text{ is typical. } \boxed{F \; \substack{Li \\ \\ Cl}} + HgCl_2 \longrightarrow \boxed{F \; \substack{Hg \\ \\ Cl}} \; \boxed{\substack{\\ \\ Cl} \; F}$$

In like manner, $\boxed{F \; \substack{Sn\phi_3 \\ Cl}}$, $\boxed{F \; \substack{Si(CH_3)_3 \\ Cl}}$, etc. have been prepared.

The reactions of $(CF_2)_n \substack{C-Cl \\ \parallel \\ C-Cl}$ with other nucleophiles have also

been investigated and the results found interesting and worthy of further studies. Other nucleophiles are being studied.

$$\boxed{F \; \substack{Cl \\ \\ Cl}} \xrightarrow{S^=} \boxed{F \; \substack{S \\ \\ S} \; F}$$

$$\substack{F \\ \diagup} \substack{Cl \\ \diagdown \\ Cl} \xrightarrow{Se^=} \substack{F \diagup \substack{Se \\ \diagdown} F}$$

These cycloalkene diiodides also undergo thermal reactions in the presence of copper to yield heretofore unavailable fused aromatic derivatives containing fluorine.

$$3 \; \boxed{F \; \substack{I \\ \\ I}} \xrightarrow[heat]{Cu} \substack{\text{(aromatic structure)}}$$

$$\substack{F \\ \diagup} \substack{I \\ \diagdown \\ I} \xrightarrow[heat]{Cu} \substack{\text{(aromatic structure)}}$$

The chemistry of these compounds is now under study. Due to the large cluster of fluorine atoms in the fused ring system, the aromaticity of the benzene nucleus should be lessened and also it should be possible to prepare the radicalanion of compounds of this type.

Utilization of similar cycloalkenes with pendant functional groups should lead to the synthesis of compounds of the following type:

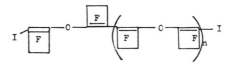

This or similar compounds should have interesting polymeric properties.

REFERENCES A

[1] J. D. Park and W. C. Frank, (a) J. Org. Chem. **29**, 1445 (1964).

(b)	ibid	**32**, 1333 (1967).
(c)	ibid	**32**, 1336 (1967).
(d)	ibid	**32**, 1340 (1967).

A major portion of the work described above was carried out by Messrs. Bruce Nakata, H. E. Romine, S. K. Choi and Clarence Bertino. To them and to my other students should go most of the credit.

B. The Reaction Of Halogenated Cycloalkenes with Nucleophiles

Although the reaction of alicyclic polyhalogenated olefins with nucleophiles has been studied since the late nineteen-forties, a cohesive explanation of the experimental data was not available until recently. E. W. Cook[1a] and J. R. Dick[1b] rationalized the products of alkoxide displacement on polyhalogenated cyclobutenes in terms of the stabilization of a discrete carbanion intermediate. The intermediacy of carbanions in these and similar reactions has been assumed by all subsequent workers in this laboratory, even though attempts to trap these carbanions have failed thus far.

INTRODUCTION

The reactions of halogenated alicyclic olefins with nucleophiles have received considerable attention in the last decade.[2] Enough work has now been carried out to warrant a review and to attempt to encompass the available data within a general mechanistic interpretation. This review is concerned chiefly with the most extensively studied class of nucleophiles, the alkoxide ion, although several other nucleophilic species will be examined briefly in the concluding section.

GENERAL MECHANISTIC CONSIDERATIONS

The generally accepted mechanistic interpretation of nucleophilic substitution reactions of fluoroolefins involves a bimolecular, rate-determining carbanion formation, a concept first advanced by Miller[3] in rationalizing the base-catalyzed addition of alcohols to chlorotrifluoroethylene. The following mechanism has been proposed as a compromise between a concerted displacement of vinylic halide and an addition-elimination of hydrogen halide, the differentiation between which cannot be made on the basis of available data.

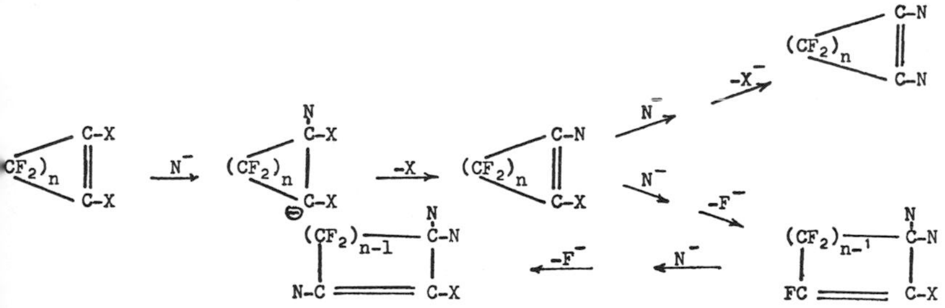

ELECTRONIC DIRECTIVE EFFECTS

Although the consequences of electronic control of nucleophilic attack on halogenated cycloalkenes are well documented, the mechanism of this electronic control is somewhat more subtle. A useful criterion for predicting the course of alkoxide attack on halocycloalkenes has evolved from the reaction scheme illustrated above. Comparison of the relative stability of carbanions arising from nucleophilic attack on an asymmetrically substituted olefin indicates that products are generally derived from the more stable intermediate, e.g., formation of the more stable carbanionic intermediate determines the direction of attack. Implicit to this conclusion is the assumption that the transition state leading to the carbanionic intermediate closely resembles the charged species in question.*

There is, however, an increasing bulk of evidence which has accumulated indicating that this premise must be modified to rationalize the behavior of vinyclic fluorine. The susceptibility of a fluorine-carrying carbon toward attack by nucleophiles has been attributed to a mesomeric drift of electron density to the pi-system; the inability of an α-fluorine to stabilize the negative charge of a carbanionic intermediate; and attack at the more electropositive (fluorine-carrying) carbon. Although the intramolecular competitions discussed in this review cannot distinguish between these possibilities, there is strong evidence that the reactivity of fluorine reflects a special activation of vinyclic F and not a deactivation of the alternate site of attack.

When a mixture of chloroheptafluorocyclopentene and 1,2-dichlorohexafluorocyclopentene were allowed to compete for an insufficient amount of alkoxide ion, 1-chloroheptafluorocyclpentene was found to react to the near exclusion of the latter.[5a] Since the relative stabilization by substituents β to the negative charge ("β-effects") actually favor the carbanion not involved** and the α-stabilization ("α-effects") are identical, the results support the concept or ground state activation. The speed and exothermic nature of these reactions

fit the Hammond conditions for a transition state[6] more closely re

---

* Although a discrete carbanion may not actually be involved in these reactions, the transition state leading to a concerted displacement of halide would presumably possess considerable bond formation between the attacking alkoxide and relatively slight bond cleavage between the carbon and the leaving halogen, a conclusion in agreement with the generally accepted concept of transition states for other reactions at unsaturated centers of low electron density such as carbonyl[4a] and phosphoryl.[4b]

** It has been demonstrated that a β-chlorine is superior to a β-fluorine in stabilization of a carbanionic intermediate. For a more detailed examination of β-substituent effects on product distribution, see page 226.

sembling the cycloalkene than the products or intermediates. The first step is, thus, rapid and independent of the relative stability of the carbanion being formed. The reversibility of this first step; e.g., the possibility of the anion proceeding to product through the slow step, cannot be excluded at present.

It should also be noted that in many of the examples cited in this review, attack at the more electron deficient carbon, presumably the carbon bearing the more electronegative halogen, would lead to an order of reactivity similar to that predicted by relative carbanion stability.

A spectra of examples falling between the two extremes may well exist where both factors contribute to the observed result and where relatively minor changes in structure of the reactants may have a marked effect on the course of the reaction.

STERIC DIRECTIVE EFFECTS

In contrast to the wealth of data proving electronic differences between halogen substituents vital in halide displacements, only limited evidence is available concerning the possible role of steric factors.

Park and Coates[5b] have investigated the reaction of various alkoxides with 1-bromo-2-chlorotetrafluorocyclobutene and found no significant differences in ether-product distribution. These results sug-

$$OR = OMe, OEt, n\text{-}PrO, n\text{-}BuO, I\text{-}PrO, \text{piperidine, phenoxy, t-BuO.}$$

gest steric differences of the halides to be of minimal importance in halocyclobutene-alkoxide reactions but do not necessarily exclude steric interactions at the α-carbon if the assumption is made that the effective bulk of the two halogens is similar; e.g., unequal solvation of the two halogens and/or the interatom C-X distance increases at a rate equal to, or faster than, the increase in Van der Waals radius of X.*

In a similar fluorocarbon system, Mill[7a] and co-workers observed

---

* A similar argument has been advanced by Brown and Klimisch[7] in the rationale of E-2 elimination reactions.

the reactivity of 1-alkoxy-2-chlorohexafluorocyclopentene toward attack by a 2° amine to be in the order $MeO^{-} > EtO^{-} >> iPrO^{-}$, and

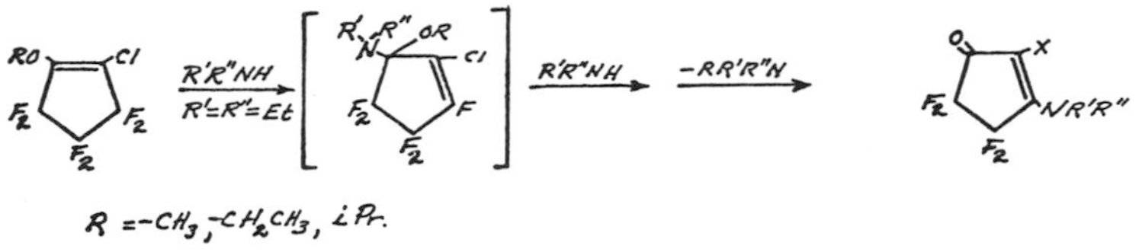
RO
Cl
R'R"NH
R'=R"=Et
R'R"NH
-RR'R"N
NR'R"
R = -CH3, -CH2CH3, iPr.

concluded that this order must be associated with steric hindrance at the double bond. Caution must be exercised in equating these results with those of Coates as this displacment of halide with rearrangement could conceivably arise from a concerted pathway differing from that of vinylic displacement of halogen.

Coates and Park[5b] also investigated the reaction of 1,2-dichloro-3, 3-dialkoxydifluorocyclobutene with alkoxide and found that the ratio of 2,3,3-triether relative to 1,3,3-triether increased from 0.89 to 3.5 when methoxide was employed in place of ethoxide,[8] a result

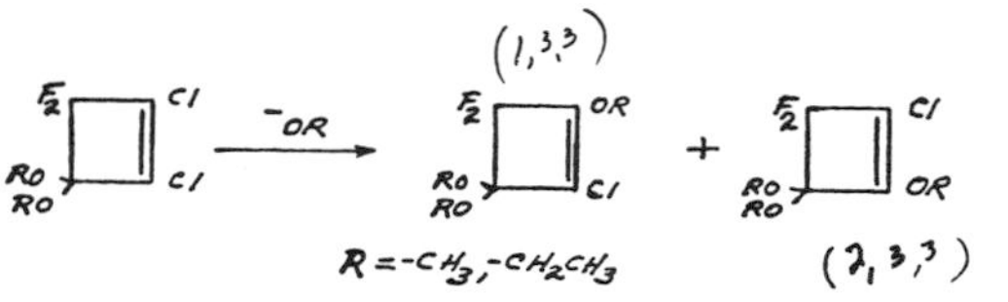
(1,3,3)
⁻OR
R = -CH3, -CH2CH3
(2,3,3)

consistent with a steric effect.

Unfortunately, similar data are not available concerning attack on compounds possessing dissimilar β-halogens.

Conclusions based on this evidence are tenuous but do suggest that stereochemical factors may influence the reaction, particularly when electronic effects are of the same magnitude.

Subsequent Course of the Reaction

If a discrete intermediate is involved in these reactions, the subsequent course of the reaction should be dependent only on the nature of the substituents in the β-positions. Results obtained with cyclobutenes and cyclopentenes substantiate this view that the more electronically favorable loss of halide occurs; the order of leaving group ability being: I > Br > Cl > F.[8]

In cases where the halide is the same at both β-positions relative to the carbanion, there is often a close competition depending on the other substituent.[8]

Tatlow and co-workers[9] have found, however, that additional factors must be considered with the cyclohexenes where both "inward" (vinylic displacement) and "outward" (displacement with rearrangement) loss of fluoride occurs from methoxide ion attack on nonafluorocyclohexenes. They concluded that the data could best be explained on the basis of a trans addition of nucleophile with retention of configuration of the carbanion formed during the short lifetime. Product distribution results from the competition between electronically favored "inwards" elimination of F from $>C(F)OR$ and stereochemically favored trans–"outward" elimination of F from $>C(F)F$.

R	%	%
$-H$	48.5	51.5
$-CH_3$	54.	46.
$-OCH_3$	38.	62.

Since stereochemical opposition to cis-coplanar eliminations ("inward" eliminations in these examples) has been shown to be much less in fluorocyclopentenes and butenes than in cyclohexenes, one would expect this criterion to become important only with cyclohexenes.

Alternatively, vinylic displacement and displacement with rearrangement may not proceed through a common intermediate, the conformational requirements for a S_N2' being improved in the more flexible ring system.

SYNTHESIS OF MONOETHERS
X = F

Park, Sharrah and Lacher[10] were the first to react a cyclobutene

with alkoxide ion as they found that methoxide, ethoxide, n-propox-
ide and n-butoxide ion displaced (stepwise) both vinylic fluorines in

I.

perfluorocyclobutene.

Stockel, Beachem and Megson[11] reported similar results with the
perfluorocyclopentene system. However, a recent reinvestigation of

I.

this work by Tatlow indicates that 4% of 3-methoxyheptafluorocyclo-
pentene is formed in addition to the previously reported[11] 1-methoxy
isomer. Similarly, a trace of a compound believed to be 3-methoxy-
pentafluorocyclobutene was detected in the analogous cyclobutene
reaction. In the cyclohexenyl system, formation of the 3-methoxy
ether appears to compete favorably with that of the 1-methoxy ether.

X = Cl

The first chloroether was synthesized by Park, Snow and Lacher[12]
from 1,2-dichlorotetrafluorocyclobutene. A similar result in the cyclo-

II.

n	ref.
2	12
3	13

pentyl system was reported by Latif[13a] and Shepard.[13b]

DISSIMILAR VINYLIC HALOGEN

The reactions of chloropentafluorocyclobutene and 1-chloroheptafluorocyclopentene have been studied by Lorenzi[14] and Edelson,[15] respectively, with exclusive displacement of fluoride ion observed in both cases. Bromononafluorocyclohexene yields a mixture of mono-

	n	ref.
	2	(14)
	3	(15)

ethers resulting from "inward" and "outward" F elimination following attack at the fluorine bearing trigonal carbon.[16]

The reaction of perhalocycloalkenes with vinylic halogens other than fluorine present one of the strongest arguments for a common mechanistic interpretation of these reactions.[17] The relative amounts of monoethers isolated is in agreement with α-substituent effects on carbanion formation observed in other studies.

n	X_1	X_2	%II	%I	II/I
2	Cl	Br	75	25	3
2	Br	I	90	10	9
2	Cl	I	97.5	2.5	39
3	Cl	Br	77	23	3.3
3	Br	I	89	11	8.1
3	Cl	I	97	3	32

A similar ratio of mono vinylic ethers was observed with 1-bromo-2-chlorooctafluorocyclohexene although this reaction is complicated by the formation of several fractions of longer g.l.c. retention time, presumably arising from initial "outward" expulsion of fluoride followed by rapid subsequent displacement of fluoride to yield the 1, 3-diethoxy ethers.[18]

VINYLIC SUBSTITUENTS OTHER THAN HALOGEN. FORMATION OF MONO-, DI-, AND TRIETHERS.

The reactions of 1-alkoxy perfluorocycloalkenes are noteworthy in that of the over forty cycloalkenes studied, they are the only ones to yield 1,2-dialkoxyethers with excess alkoxide ion.[9, 10, 11]

No Vinylic Fluorines Present

The reaction of 1-chloro-2-alkoxyperfluorocycloalkenes with additional alkoxide leads to the formation of 1,3,3-triethers, the first

reported example being synthesized by Park, Snow and Lacher from 1-ethoxy-2-chlorotetrafluorocyclobutene.[12]

The analogous reaction with 1,2-dichlorohexafluorocyclopentene was investigated by Shepard and co-workers[13b] who proposed the 1,3,3-triether structure in preference to the previously reported 1-chloro-2,3,3-trialkoxy ether.[13]

The reaction mechanism was believed to have proceeded via an S_N2' displacement rather than a S_N2 displacement of allylic fluorines because of the isolation of the extremely reactive diether by McBee and co-workers.[19] A vinylic fluorine is highly reactive to alkoxide ion and is seldom isolated under basic conditions.

Park, Dick and Lacher[20, 21] positively eliminated the allylic displacement mechanism by reacting 1-ethoxy-2-chlorotetrafluorocyclobutene with methoxide ion.

Drier, Duncan and Mill[7a] repeated the experiment in the five membered ring series and obtained the same result. They pointed out that the data did not distinguish between an S_N2' or a stepwise formation via a carbanion intermediate mechanism but professed their belief in the latter.

Other 2-halo-1,3,3-triethers that have been synthesized are the following.[17]

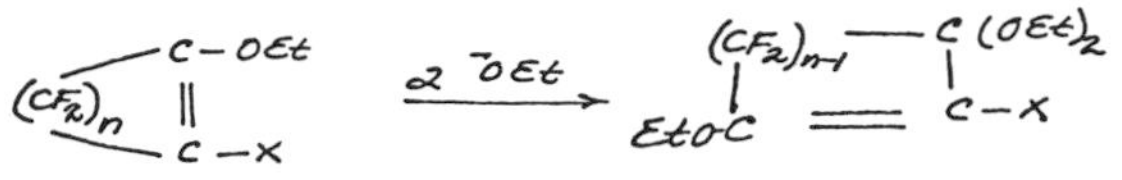

n	X
2	—Br
2	—I
3	—Br
3	—I

Vinylic Hydrogen, Alkyl, and Aryl Substituents

Ethoxide attack on 1-hydropentafluorocyclobutene results in displacement of vinylic fluoride.[22] When the vinylic halide is chlorine,

VII

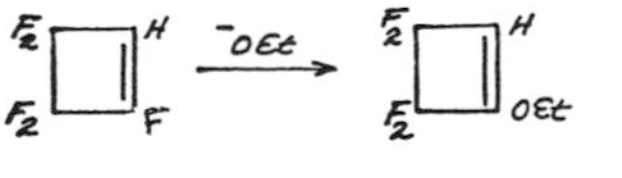

however, attack occurs at the hydrogen bearing trigonal carbon.[23]

VIII

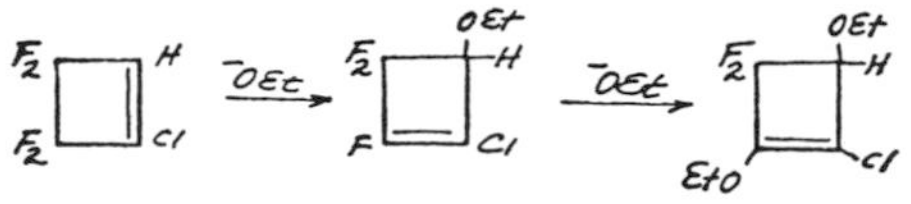

Treatment of 1-chloro-2-phenyltetrafluorocyclobutene with methoxide leads to displacement of vinylic chloride, a result consistent with the stability of α-phenyl stabilized carbanion.[5]

IX

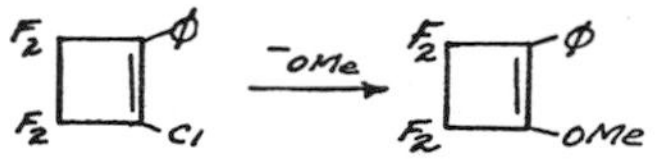

Although alkylhalofluoroolefins give rise to competing 1,4-elimination of HF with vinylic halogen other than fluorine,[5, 29] displacement of vinylic fluoride does proceed smoothly with 1-ethylheptafluorocyclopentene[5] suggesting that the energy requirements for attack at the chlorine bearing carbon in 1-chloro-2-ethylhexafluorocyclopentene are so markedly higher that 1,4-elimination can compete successfully with halide displacement. Conversely, one may

argue that the α-chlorine has lowered the energy of the transition state for the 1,4-elimination. Both explanations may well be related to the observed results.

Analogous displacement of vinylic fluorine from 1-hydro- and 1-methylnonafluorocyclohexene were reported by Tatlow and co-work-

ers[9] although, as with other displacements in cyclohexenes, considerable amounts of products resulting from "outward" elimination of fluoride ion were isolated along with the 1-hydro-2-methoxy- and 1-methyl-2-methoxyoctafluorocyclohexenes, respectively.

SIMILAR VINYLIC HALOGENS AND DISSIMILAR ALLYLIC SUBSTITUENTS

The direction of alkoxide attack on cyclobutenes with chlorines in both vinylic positions has been shown to be influenced by the substituents in the allylic or β-position.[8]

R	R₁	R₂	products % I	products % II
Et	Cl	Cl	89	11
Et	EtO	Cl	71	29
Et	F	Cl	61	39
Et	EtO	EtO	53	47
Me	MeO	MeO	22	78
Et	H	H	0	100

The above results were interpreted as showing that β-substituents stabilize the intermediate carbanion in the order $CL > F > OCH_3 > H$. A previously mentioned β-diethoxy group is large enough to cause a steric hindrance and thus appears more effective than the difluoro group at controlling the ethoxide ion attack. Whether the directive influence is electronic or steric is not yet clear as pointed out in the case of the different α-halogens on pages 219 and 223.

Ethoxide attack on 1,2,3,3-tetrafluorocyclobutene apparently yields a single monoether, 1-ethoxy,2,3,3-trifluorocyclobutenes.[22] A similar selectivity is exhibited in ethoxide attack on 1,2,3,3,4-tetrafluorocyclo-

butene.[22] These results have considerable significance since they imply a profound effect by β-substituents on the course of reaction even in the case of vinylic fluorine.

DISSIMILAR VINYLIC AND ALLYLIC SUBSTITUENTS

Whenever fluorine has been at one of the vinylic positions, alkoxide attack has occurred at that position regardless of the nature of the β-substituents.

R	R₁	R₂	X
Et	H	H	Cl
Et	H	OEt	Cl
Et	H	H	H
Me	H	H	$-CH = CH_2$[5]

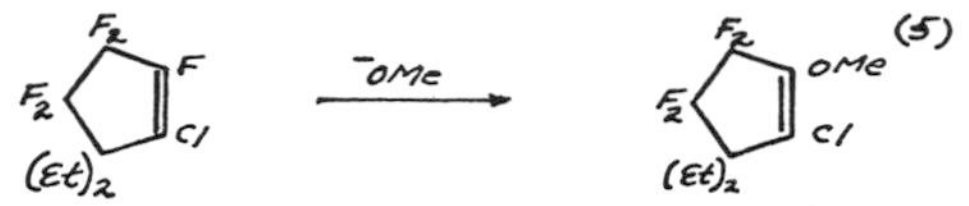

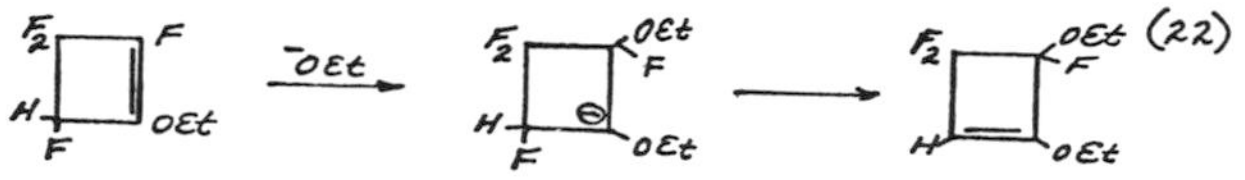

(5)

(22)

The latter example is of interest as it shows the fluoride ion leaving from only the β-CHF group and leaving the β-CF(OEt) group intact.

In other cases with no vinylic fluorine, alkoxide attack is directed by the α-substituents.

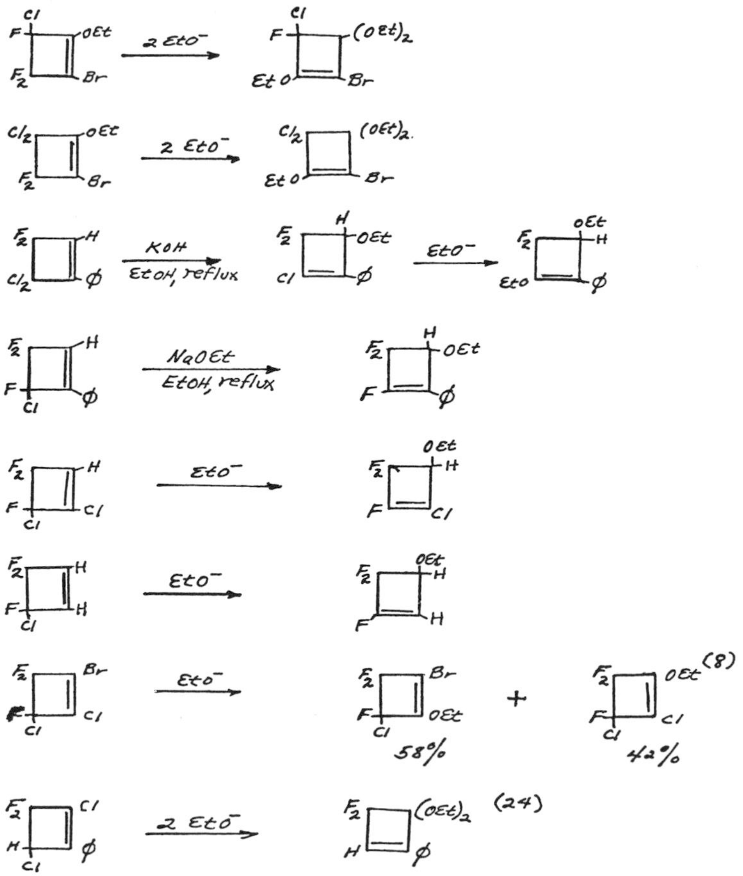

(8)

58%   42%

(24)

$$(8)$$

The last two reactions are particularly noteworthy as they are the only examples to date of the limiting case where both α and β-substituents contribute their influence on product distribution.

Of interest is the similar magnitude of the two effects.

NUCLEOPHILES OTHER THAN ALKOXIDE

The available experimental data are far more limited in these cases but the results obtained have generally paralleled those obtained with alkoxide. The most interesting deviations occur when complex metal hydrides and organometallic reagents are employed although these may be a reflection on the metal ion present rather than the nucleophilic species.

The following examples are not intended to constitute an exhaustive review of the subject but do demonstrate the generality and limitations of the alkoxide data when applied to other nucleophilic species.

SULFUR CONTAINING NUCLEOPHILES

Addition of n-butylmercaptan to perfluorocyclobutene yields sat-

urated products in addition to products resulting from displacement of vinylic halogen, products which can best be accounted for on the basis of successive addition-elimination sequences.[25]

Sulfur attack occurs exclusively in the base-catalyzed reaction of 2-mercaptoethanol with hexafluorocyclobutene.[25]

$$2 \ HO\text{-}CH_2CH_2SH + \begin{array}{c} \overset{F}{\underset{F_2}{\square}} F \\ \end{array} \longrightarrow \begin{array}{c} \overset{F_2}{\underset{F_2}{\square}} S\text{-}CH_2CH_2OH \\ S\text{-}CH_2CH_2OH \end{array}$$

NITROGEN CONTAINING NUCLEOPHILES

The reaction of hexafluorocyclobutene with dialkylamines yields stable tertiary perfluorocyclobutenylamines.[26a] Arylamines failed to add under similar, uncatalyzed conditions.

The reactions of perhalocycloalkenes with ammonia and primary cumines, however, yield derivatives of 1-amino-2-halo-3-iminoperfluorocycloalkenes.

$$(CF_2)_n \begin{array}{c} C\text{-}X \\ \| \\ C\text{-}X^- \end{array} \xrightarrow{RNH_2} (CF_2)_{n-1} \begin{array}{c} C = NR \\ | \\ C \\ \underset{NHR}{\|} \ C\text{-}X \end{array}$$

n	X	$ref.$
2	F	26*
3	Cl	27
4	F	28

* Although a rigorous structure proof was not undertaken, the 1,2-iminoamine,
$\begin{array}{c} RHN \\ F \end{array}\square\begin{array}{c} NHR \\ F_2 \end{array}$, was suggested in reference 26.

Two competitive reaction paths are available in this reaction: 1,4-elimination of HF or additional attack by amine. The isolation of the 1,3-iminoamine from the reaction of perfluorocycloalkenes supports the latter conclusion since all previous work in these systems indicates that the remaining vinylic fluorine would be displaced preferentially.

$$(CF_2)_n \begin{array}{c} C\text{-}NHR \\ \| \\ C\text{-}X \end{array} \quad \nearrow \quad (CF_2)_{n-1} \begin{array}{c} C = NR \\ | \\ F\text{-}C = C\text{-}X \end{array} \quad \searrow \quad (CF_2)_{n-1}\begin{array}{c} C = NR \\ | \\ C = C\text{-}X \\ \underset{NHR}{} \end{array}$$

$$\searrow \quad (CF_2)_{n-1} \begin{array}{c} C\text{-}NHR \\ | \ NHR \\ F\text{-}C = C\text{-}X \end{array} \quad \nearrow$$

Analogous results have been reported by McBee[30] concerning the reaction of both 1,2-dichlorohexafluorocyclopentene and octafluorocyclohexene with hydroxylamine. The isolation of the 1,3-iminohydroxyamine from octafluorocyclohexene was cited as supporting the 1,4-elimination pathway.

The similarity of these reactions to the hydrolysis of perhaloolefins with potassium hydroxide in polar aprotic solvents[31] and the 1,4-elimination of hydrogen fluoride from 1-chloro-2-alkylperfluorocycloalkenes by alkoxide ion[32] is apparent since a 1,4-elimination is apparently the prepared pathway in each case.

Only in the reaction of 1-chloro-2-chloroformylhexafluorocyclopentene with ammonia has the initial substitution product been isolated with a primary amine or ammonia as the nucleophile.[29] Hydrogen bonding with the carboamide group may serve to retard sub-

sequent dehydrofluorination in this example.[29]

McBee's report[30] that the reaction of 1,2,3,3-tetrachloroterafluorocyclopentene with hydroxylamine gave only 2,3-dichlorotetrafluoroclopent-2-eneone oxime is contrasted to Adams'[33] findings concerning alkoxide attack on 1,2,3,3-tetrachlorodifluorocyclobutene.

CARBON AS THE NUCLEOPHILE

The reactions of haloalicyclic olefins with organolithium and Grignard reagents are characterized by competing halogen-metal interchange reactions when vinylic bromine or iodine are present in the molecule.

Treatment of 1-bromo-2-chlorotetrafluorocyclobutene with ethylmagnesium bromide, for example, yields the cyclobutenyl Grignard reagent.[34] A similar exchange followed by loss of magnesium halide may be involved in the rapid decomposition of 1-bromoperhalocyclo-pentenes with ethylmagnesium bromide or magnesium turnings.[5]

Metallation may also occur in preference to nucleophilic displacement of halide ion as in the reaction of nonafluorocyclohexene with methyl lithium.[35]

Only with chlorofluoro- and perfluoroalyicyclic olefins do the results obtained with organometallic reagents parallel those with alkoxide. Park and Fontanelli[36] found that generally high yields of mono-alkylated olefins were obtained with Grignard reagents and the per-

$$X = F, Cl$$
$$n = 2, 3$$
$$R = primary\ alkyl,\ phenyl.$$

haloolefin and similar results have recently been demonstrated with the analogous cyclopentenes.[5] Substantially lower yields of mono- and di-substitution products had previously been obtained with organolithium reagents.[37]

Preferential displacement of vinylic fluorine in 1-chlorohepta-fluorocyclopentene was obtained in the reaction with ethylmagnesium bromide,[38] a result in agreement with preferential displacement of fluoride by alkoxide in this compound.

When 1-alkyl-2-chloroperfluorocycloalkenes are treated with additional Grignard reagent, displacement of vinylic chlorine occurs along with the "expected" displacement with rearrangement. Both cyclobutenes and cyclopentenes yield mixtures of products although

n	%	%
2	82	18
3	60	40

the amount of rearranged alkene is greater with the cyclopentenes.[38]

The extent to which solvent effects, steric bulk and metal ion participation affect these reactions is uncertain at present. These reactions, along with similar ones encountered with metal hydrides, may well constitute examples where both ground state and intermediate stabilities play an important role in directing the course of reaction.

METAL HYDRIDES AS NUCLEOPHILES

Facile displacement of halogen by metal hydrides occurs in a manner generally consistent with alkoxide attack on similar compounds although several striking anomalies have recently been reported.

Lithium aluminum hydride and sodium borohydride displace vinylic fluorine from perfluorocycloalkenes in the manner predicted from alkoxide studies but there is substantially less product result-

n	N	%	%	ref.
2	NaBH$_4$	100	—	41
2	LiAlH$_4$	mixtures		40,41
3	NaBH$_4$	100	—	40
3	LiAlH$_4$	mixtures		40,41
4	LiAlH$_4$	mixtures		40

ing from "outward" elimination of fluoride ion.

Subsequent attack on the 1-H compounds takes place almost exclusively at the 2-carbon to give chiefly the 1,2-dihydroperfluorocyclo-alkene.[40]

Initial substitution on 1,2-dichloroperfluorocycloalkenes results in displacement of vinylic chlorine but subsequent reaction of the chloroalkene with additional hydride leads to a mixture of products arising from attack at both the hydrogen and chlorine bearing carbons in a manner similar to that of Grignard reagents. Burton[41] has suggested several factors which may contribute to this behaviour: a

$$(CF_2)_n \overset{C-H}{\underset{C-Cl}{\|}} \xrightarrow{MX_4^-} (CF_2)_n \overset{C-H}{\underset{C-H}{\|}} + (CF_2)_{n-1} \overset{H}{\underset{F-C}{\overset{|}{\underset{}{\longrightarrow}}}} \overset{C H}{\underset{C-Cl}{|}}$$

simple steric effect with the larger nucleophile, a solvent effect, or an active participation of the metal atom (B, Al) in the displacement reaction.

Perhaps even more striking is the preferential displacement of chlorine from both 1-chloro-5,5-dihydropentafluorocyclopentene and 1-chloro-6,6-dihydroheptafluorocyclohexene by lithium aluminum hydride.[40] Exclusive displacement of fluorine occurs in the reaction 1-chloro-2,3,3-trifluorocyclobutene and ethoxide ion.

The reaction of 1-chloroheptafluorocyclopentene with lithium

$$(CF_2)_n \overset{CH_2}{\underset{}{\underset{C-F}{\overset{C-Cl}{\|}}}} \xrightarrow[Et_2O]{LAH} (CF_2)_n \overset{CH_2}{\underset{}{\underset{CF}{\overset{CH}{\|}}}}$$

$$n = 2, 3$$

aluminum hydride, however, does lead to the same result as alkoxide attack: displacement of vinylic fluorine.[41]

$$\underset{F}{\overset{Cl}{\langle\!\rangle}} \xrightarrow[Et_2O]{LAH} \underset{H}{\overset{Cl}{\langle\!\rangle}}$$

ACKNOWLEDGMENT

This research was supported by the Air Force Office of Scientific Research, the Army Natick Laboratories and the Minnesota Mining & Manufacturing Company.

REFERENCES

[1a] E. W. Cook, Organic Seminar, University of Colorado (1963).

[1b] J. R. Dick, Ph.D. Thesis, University of Colorado (1963).

[2] For a comprehensive of ionic reactions of fluoroolefins, see R. D. Chambers and R. H. Mobbs in *Advances in Fluorine Chemistry*, IV, Bitterworth, 1965, p. 50.

[3] W. T. Miller, E. W. Fager and P. H. Griswold, *J. Am. Chem. Soc.*, **70**, 431 (1948).

[4a] M. L. Bender, *Chem. Rev.* **60**, 53 (1960).

[4b] R. F. Hudson, *Advances in Inorganic Radiochemistry*, **5**, 362 (1963).

[5a] R. J. McMurtry, Ph.D. Thesis, University of Colorado, 1967.

[5b] J. S. Coates, Ph.D. Thesis, University of Colorado, 1966.

[6] G. S. Hammond, *J. Am. Chem. Soc.*, **77**, 334 (1955).

[7] H. C. Brown and R. L. Klimisch, *J. Am. Chem. Soc.*, **88**, 1425 (1966).

[7a] F. Drier, W. Duncan and T. Mill, *Tetrahedron Letters*, **29**, 1951 (1964).

[8] J. D. Park, J. R. Dick and J. H. Adams, *J. Org. Chem.*, **30**, 400 (1965).

[9] A. B. Clayton, J. Roylance, D. R. Sayers, R. Stephens and J. C. Tatlow, *J. Chem. Soc.* 7358 (1965).

[10] J. D. Park, M. L. Sharrah and J. R. Lacher, *J. Am. Chem. Soc.*, **71**, 2337 (1949).

[11] R. F. Stockel, M. T. Beachem and F. H. Megson, *Can. J. of Chem.*, **42**, 2880 (1964).

[12] J. D. Park, C. M. Snow and J. R. Lacher, *J. Am. Chem. Soc.*, **73**, 2342 (1951).

[13a] K. A. Latif, Ph.D. Thesis, Ohio State University (1952).

[13b] R. S. Shepard, H. Lessoff, J. D. Domijan, D. B. Hilton and T. F. Finnegab, *J. Org. Chem*, **23**, 2011 (1958).

[14] F. J. Lorenzi and J. D. Park, unpublished work, this laboratory (1954).

[15] N. A. Edelson, Ph.D. Thesis, Cornell University, 1962.

[16] S. F. Campbell and R. Stephens, *J. Chem. Soc.*, 7367 (1965).

[17] J. D. Park, R. J. McMurtry and R. Sullivan, *J. Org. Chem.*, **33**, 33 (1968).

[18] Unpublished results, this laboratory, 1965.

[19] E. T. McBee, D. L. Crain, L. R. Belohlov, and H. P. Braendlin, *J. Am. Chem. Soc.*, **84**, 3557 (1962).

[20] J. D. Park, J. R. Dick and J. R. Lacher, *J. Org. Chem.*, **30**, 400 (1965).

[21] Unpublished results, this laboratory.

[22] E. A. Kjehlgaard, Ph.D. Thesis, University of Colorado, 1966.

[23] J. D. Park, L. H. Wilson and J. R. Lacher, *J. Org. Chem.*, **28**, 1008 (1963).

[24] Y. Kitahara, M. C. Caserio, F. Scardiglia and J. D. Roberts, *J. Am. Chem. Soc.*, **82**, 3106 (1960).

[25] K. E. Rapp, R. L. Pruett, J. T. Barr, C. T. Bahner, J. D. Gibson and R. H. Lafferty, *J. Am. Chem. Soc.*, **72**, 3642 (1950).

[26] R. L. Pruett, J. T. Barr, K. E. Rapp, C. T. Bahner, J. D. Gibson and R. H. Lafferty, *J. Am. Chem. Soc.*, **72**, 3642 (1950).

[27] C. O. Parker, *J. Am. Chem. Soc.*, **81**, 2183 (1959).

[28] P. Robson, J. Roylance, R. Stephens, J. C. Tatlow, and R. E. Worthington, *J. Chem Soc.*, 5748 (1964).

[29] T. Mill, J. O. Rodin, R. M. Silverstein and C. Woolf, *J. Org. Chem*, **30**, 3698 (1965).

[30] E. T. McBee, J. J. Turner, C. J. Morton, and A. P. Stefani, *J. Org. Chem.*, **30**, 3698 (1965).

[31] R. F. Stockel, M. T. Beachem and F. H. Megson, *J. Org. Chem.*, **30**, 1629 (1965).

[32] J. D. Park and R. J. McMurtry, *J. Org. Chem.*, **32**, 2397, (1967).

[33] J. D. Park, C. Groppelli and J. H. Adams, *Tetrahedron Letters,* 103, (1967).

[34] R. Sullivan, J. R. Lacher and J. D. Park, *J. Org. Chem.,* 29, 3664 (1964).

[35] S. F. Campbell, R. Stephens and J. C. Tatlow, *Chem. Comm.,* 151, (1967).

[36] J. D. Park and R. Fontanelli, *J. Org. Chem.,* 28, 258 (1963).

[37] S. Dixon, *J. Org. Chem.,* 21, 400 (1956).

[38] J. D. Park, R. Sullivan and R. J. McMurtry, *Tetrahedron Letters,* 173, (1967).

[39] C. Fuller and J. C. Tatlow, *J. Chem. Soc.,* 3198 (1961).

[40] W. J. Feast, D. R. A. Perry and R. Stephens, *Tetrahedron Letters* 433 (1966).

[41] D. J. Burton and R. L. Johnson, *Tetrahedron Letters,* 2681, (1966).

X. Muonium

VERNON W. HUGHES

I UNDERSTAND THAT THE central theme of The Thirteenth AFOSR Science Seminar is the interdisciplinary nature of much of modern science. Muonium is an excellent example of a topic with interdisciplinary aspects. Research on muonium started about eleven years ago when parity nonconservation was discovered and it is still active.

Muonium is the atom consisting of a positive muon and an electron and hence can be considered as an isotope of hydrogen. Muonium is of great interest in several subfields of physics and chemistry, including elementary particle physics, atomic physics, and chemical physics. First, it is the simplest system involving the muon and the electron and hence is the best one for studying with precision the interaction of these two elementary particles. The muon is a particularly mysterious particle because it appears to behave in all respects like a heavy electron and hence there appears to be no interaction which could account for the large value of the muon mass relative to the electron mass. It thus occupies an anomalous role in the spectrum of the elementary particles. We have been able to study the electromagnetic interaction of the electron and the muon through a precise measurement of the hyperfine structure interval in the ground state of muonium. Second, since muonium is a light isotope of hydrogen in which the positive muon replaces the proton, muonium has a rich chemistry and its interactions with other atoms and mole-

VERNON W. HUGHES is Professor of Physics at Yale University and from 1961 to 1967 was Chairman of the Physics Department. His present researches are in elementary particle physics and in atomic physics. Eight years ago, he and three associates discovered the muonium atom—an extraordinary new atom—in an experiment performed at the Nevis Laboratories of Columbia University. He has been a consultant to the Los Alamos Scientific Laboratory, the Oak Ridge National Laboratory, the NASA Institute for Space Studies and for industry. In addition to Yale, he has served on the faculties of Columbia University and the University of Pennsylvania.

cules have been studied. Third, muonium provides a useful system for studying certain aspects of the weak interaction of the muon and the electron, in particular a possible weak interaction coupling muonium to antimuonium, which is the atom consisting of a negative muon and a positron.

Mass: $m_\mu = (206.767 \pm 0.003)\ m_e$

Charge: $+\ e$

Spin: $I = 1/2$

Magnetic Moment: $\dfrac{\mu_\mu}{\mu_p}\ =\ 3.18338 \pm 0.0004$

Gyromagnetic Ratio: $g_\mu\ =\ 2(1.001162 \pm 0.000005)$

Lifetime (mean): $\tau_\mu\ =\ (2.2000 \pm 0.0015)\ \mu sec$

FIGURE 1. Properties of Positive Muon.

Figure 1 lists the properties of the positive muon. Its mass is well known and is about 207 times the electron mass. The charge of the positive muon is the same as the positron charge. The spin is ½ and the magnetic moment is somewhat more than 3 times the proton magnetic moment. The g-value is greater than 2 by the anomalous magnetic moment factor, and the excellent agreement between the experimental and theoretical values of the anomalous magnetic moment factor provides the most critical proof that the muon is a heavy Dirac particle with the usual coupling to the electromagnetic field. The mean lifetime of the muon is 2.2 μsec.

The tool for studying muonium is provided by parity nonconservation in the weak interactions involved in the production and decay of the muon. (See Fig. 2) The positive pi meson decays into a positive muon and a muon-type neutrino. In the rest frame of the pion the muon spin angular momentum, indicated by the double line arrow, is in the direction opposite to its linear momentum, indicated by the single line arrow. This correlation of spin direction and velocity direction is a consequence of parity nonconservation and provides us with polarized muons. The positive muon decays into a positron and two neutrinos with a continuous positron energy spectrum extending up to 52 MeV. The angular distribution of the positrons with respect to the muon spin direction, $I_{e^+}(\theta)$, is asymmetric due to parity nonconservation. The quantity θ is the angle between the

$$\pi^+ \longrightarrow \mu^+ + \nu_\mu$$

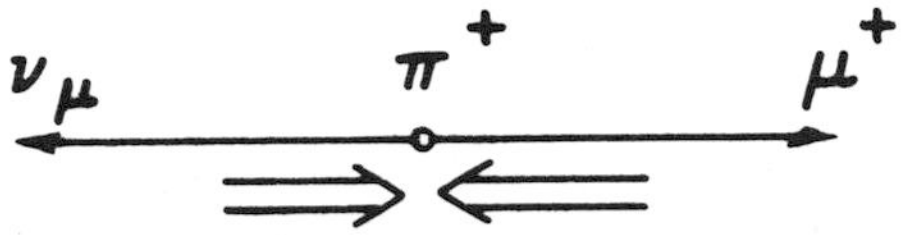

$$\nu_\mu \qquad \pi^+ \qquad \mu^+$$

$$\mu^+ \longrightarrow e^+ + \nu_e + \bar{\nu}_\mu$$

$$I_{e^+}(\theta) \propto 1 + A \cos \theta$$

FIGURE 2. Decays of pion and of muon.

muon spin direction and the direction of emission of the positron and A is approximately $+\frac{1}{3}$, so positrons are emitted preferentially along the muon spin direction. This characteristic of the muon decay provides the means for detecting the muon spin direction.

FORMATION

The gross energy levels of muonium as given by the Schroedinger equation are the same as those of hydrogen except for a slightly different reduced mass factor in the Rydberg constant. Figure 3 shows the energy level diagram for the hyperfine structure levels in the ground 1 $^2S_{1/2}$ state of muonium. Energy in units of the hyperfine structure (hfs) interval is plotted as a function of a dimensionless parameter x, which is proportional to magnetic field. At zero magnetic field there are two levels—the upper triplet state with total angular momentum quantum number $F = 1$ and the lower singlet state with $F = 0$. The energy separation is the hfs interval which is due to the magnetic interaction between the spin magnetic moments of the electron and the muon. In the presence of an external magnetic field H the triplet state splits into its three magnetic substates designated by the magnetic quantum number M_F with the values $+1, 0$ and -1. At strong magnetic fields, where the magnetic interaction of the electron and muon magnetic moments with the external field is large compared to the hfs interval ($x \gg 1$), the energy levels are as shown and the good quantum numbers are M_J, the magnetic quantum number for the electron spin, and M_μ, the magnetic quantum number for muon spin. The states are numbered from 1 through 4 for convenience.

Muonium is formed when positive muons are stopped in a gas. It is formed directly in its ground state by the capture of an electron from an atom by a positive muon. Argon has been used in most of our experiments:

$$\mu^+ + Ar \rightarrow \mu^+ e^- + Ar^+$$

This capture reaction has a maximum cross-section for a muon kinetic energy of about 200 eV. Because the muons are polarized and the charge capture reaction is primarily due to the Coulomb interaction, which does not alter the muon spin direction, polarized muonium is formed. Thus, if we have a strong magnetic field opposite to the direction of the muon beam and hence in the direction of the muon spins so that $M_\mu = +\frac{1}{2}$, then only the two states $(M_J, M_\mu) = (+\frac{1}{2}, +\frac{1}{2})$ and $(-\frac{1}{2}, +\frac{1}{2})$ are formed. One-half of the muonium atoms formed will be in each of these states. In a weak magnetic field polarized muonium is also formed. However, in weak magnetic fields M_μ is not a good quantum number and the hfs interaction will par-

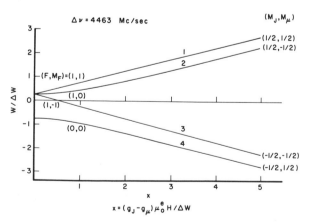

FIGURE 3. Energy level diagram of the muonium ground $1\,^2S_{1\,2}$ state in a magnetic field.

tially depolarize the muons, so the distribution in the low field (F,M_F) states will be $(1,1) = \frac{1}{2}$, $(1,0) = \frac{1}{4}$, $(1,-1) = 0$, and $(0,0) = \frac{1}{4}$.

The original search for muonium involved the attempt to observe its characteristic Larmor precession frequency in a weak external magnetic field. The Larmor precession frequency f_L of a magnetic moment μ associated with an angular momentum $F\hbar$ in an external magnetic field **H** perpendicular to μ is given by:

$$f_L = \frac{\mu H}{F\hbar}$$

In weak field the only muonium state formed that has a magnetic moment is the triplet state $(F,M_F) = (1,+1)$. Since the magnetic moment is approximately the electron spin magnetic moment and $F = 1$,

$$f_L \simeq \frac{\mu_0^e H}{h} = 1.40H \text{ Mc/sec}$$

Figure 4 shows the schematic diagram of the experiment. All our

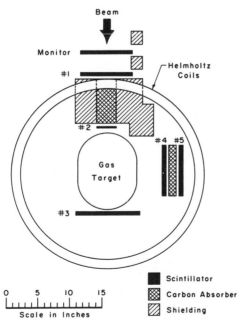

FIGURE 4. Experimental arrangement for muonium formation experiments.

experiments have been done at the Columbia University Nevis synchrocyclotron. The 380 MeV proton beam strikes an internal target forming π^+ mesons which decay to positive muons, and an external meson beam is formed with a momentum of about 140 MeV/c. The meson beam has π^+ and μ^+ mesons. The pions are stopped in an absorber and muons with energies up to several MeV enter an argon gas target with a pressure of some 50 atm. The muon loses energy by ionization and excitation of Ar atoms and forms muonium stably with kinetic energies in the keV range. The muonium is then rapidly thermalized. The slowing down process occurs in less than 10^{-9} sec. It was necessary to purify the argon by recirculating it over titanium heated to about 700° C. The numbered black lines indicate scintillation counters, and the stopping of a muon in the gas target is indicated by a coincident 12 but anticoincident $\overline{3}$ count. Helmholtz coils are indicated which provide a magnetic field of about 4G perpendic-

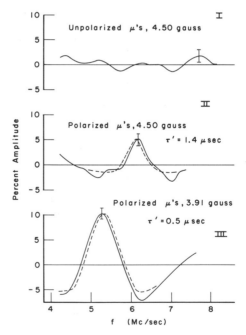

FIGURE 5. Frequency analysis for muonium precession experiment. The quantity τ' is a parameter used to account for various experimental sources of line breadth.

ular to the plane of the diagram. The decay positrons are observed by the 45 counter telescope as coincident 45 counts and the time delay of the positron count with respect to the time of the arrival of the muon is measured. If polarized muonium is formed, the triplet $M_F = +1$ state should process in the external magnetic field. Since the decay positron is emitted preferentially in the direction of the muon spin, this precession should be observed from the measurement of the time distribution of the decay positrons as a modulation of the muon lifetime decay curve with the characteristic Larmor precession frequency.

Figure 5 shows the analysis of the data in which the amplitude of the frequency component is plotted versus the frequency. For case II the solid curve is the result of a least squares Fourier-type analysis of the experimental data and the typical error bar corresponds to one standard deviation. The dashed curve is a theoretical line shape centered at the muonium precession frequency corresponding to the measured value of the magnetic field. With a field of 4.5 G a resonance is clearly seen at the predicted frequency. Similarly for case III for a different field of 3.9 G the resonance is seen. As expected, no resonance is seen in case I when pions are stopped in the target and hence unpolarized muons are obtained. These results prove that polarized muonium is formed in argon. The data indicate that the fraction of muons which form muonium is between $\frac{1}{2}$ and 1.

The existence of muonium with its characteristic Larmor precession frequency serves as a proof that the spin of the muon is $\hbar/2$, since the approximate expression for the Larmor precession frequency depends on the muon only through its spin value.

HYPERFINE STRUCTURE INTERVAL

In view of the results on muonium formation we were encouraged to plan a precision magnetic resonance experiment to measure the hfs interval $\Delta\nu$. As was mentioned, the interval $\Delta\nu$ arises from the magnetic interaction between the spin magnetic moments of the electron and the muon, which is different for the triplet state in which the two spins are parallel than for the singlet state in which the two spins are antiparallel. The interval $\Delta\nu$ in muonium is analogous to the well known hfs interval of 1420 Mc/sec in hydrogen, and would be expected to be about 4460 Mc/sec since the muon magnetic moment is 3.18 times larger than the proton magnetic moment.

The detailed theoretical formula for $\Delta\nu$ of muonium is indicated in Figure 12 and is based on the assumption that the muon is a heavy electron. The leading bracketed term is the Fermi formula in which α is the fine structure constant, c = velocity of light, R_∞ = Rydberg constant, and $\mu_\mu/\mu_0{}^e$ = ratio of muon magnetic moment to the electron Bohr magneton. The remaining terms include reduced mass, relativistic and virtual radiative corrections. Use of known values of the fundamental constants gives the value:

$$\Delta\nu = 4463.16 \pm 0.10 \text{ Mc/sec}(\pm 22 \text{ ppm})$$

in which the error arises primarily from uncertainty in α. The value of α used is that given from the deuterium fine structure measurement of Lamb et al.

The principle of the experiment is simple. Suppose we have a strong external static magnetic field **H**, along the direction of the spins of the incident muons; muonium will be formed only in states 1 and 4 that have $M_\mu = +\frac{1}{2}$. If nothing is done to perturb this distribution of muonium states, the decay positrons will be emitted preferentially in the direction of **H**. However, suppose a microwave magnetic field is introduced with the proper Bohr frequency so it can induce a resonance transition of muonium from one hfs state to another—e.g., from state 1 to state 2. In state 2 the muon spin points in the opposite direction, having $M_\mu = -\frac{1}{2}$, and the decay positrons from the state are emitted preferentially in the direction opposite to the direction of the static field **H**. Hence an induced transition can be detected through the change in angular distribution of the decay positrons.

Transitions have been studied both at strong magnetic field and at weak magnetic field. Figure 6 gives the energy levels and transition frequencies. The Hamiltonian includes the hfs interaction, the interaction of the electron spin magnetic moment with the external magnetic field **H**, and the interaction of the muon spin magnetic moment with **H**. The energy levels are given by the Breit-Rabi formula whose solution was shown in Fig. 3 of the hfs energy levels. We take the viewpoint that the electron magnetic moment (or g_J-value) and the muon magnetic moment (or g_μ) are determined in other experiments,

$$\mathcal{H} = a \vec{I}_\mu \cdot \vec{J} + \mu_0^e \, g_J \, \vec{J} \cdot \vec{H} + \mu_0^e \, g_\mu \, \vec{I}_\mu \cdot \vec{H}$$

$$W_{F = \frac{1}{2} \pm \frac{1}{2}, \, M_F} = - \frac{\Delta W}{4} + \mu_0^e \, g_\mu \, H \, M_F \pm \frac{\Delta W}{2} \, (1 + 2 M_F x + x^2)^{\frac{1}{2}}$$

Where

$$x = \frac{(g_J - g_\mu) \, \mu_0 \, H}{\Delta W}$$

$$\nu \left[(M_J, M_\mu) = \left(\tfrac{1}{2}, \tfrac{1}{2} \right) \rightarrow \left(\tfrac{1}{2}, -\tfrac{1}{2} \right) \right]_{\text{Strong Field}} \simeq \frac{a}{2} + \frac{\mu_0 \, g_\mu \, H}{h}$$

$$\nu \left[(F, M_F) = (1, 1) \rightarrow (0, 0) \right]_{\text{Weak Field}} \simeq a + \frac{\mu_0 \, g_J \, H}{h}$$

FIGURE 6. Energy Levels and Transition Frequencies.

so that the measurement of a single resonance transition determines the hfs interaction constant a, which is the only unknown. The transition observed at strong field is between states 1 and 2 with $(M_J, M_\mu) = (\tfrac{1}{2}, \tfrac{1}{2})$ and $(\tfrac{1}{2}, -\tfrac{1}{2})$. The approximate frequency for this transition is the hfs interval divided by 2 plus the frequency associated with muon spin flip. At weak field the transitions $(F, M_F) = (1, \pm 1) \longleftrightarrow (0, 0)$ have been observed. The resonance frequency is ap-

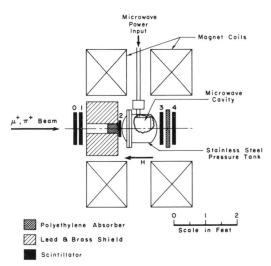

FIGURE 7. Experimental arrangement for measurement of $\Delta \nu$ in an experiment which employs a strong static magnetic field and involves an induced microwave transition. The scintillation counters are numbered.

proximately the constant a, plus a term associated with the electron spin flip.

Figure 7 shows the experimental setup. The muons are stopped in the high pressure argon gas target and indicated by coincident 12 but anticoincident $\bar{3}$ counts. A split solenoid provides a strong magnetic field along the direction of the spins of the incident muons. Microwave power can be fed into a high Q microwave cavity contained within the pressure vessel. Decay positrons are observed in the counter telescope 34 during a time interval following the arrival of the muon. Observations are made as the field H is varied with the microwave frequency fixed. The signal will be the ratio

$$S = \frac{\left.\dfrac{\overline{34}}{12\bar{3}}\right|\ \text{ON}}{\left.\dfrac{\overline{34}}{12\bar{3}}\right|\ \text{OFF}} - 1, \text{ which is positive on resonance.}$$

Figure 8 shows a typical resonance curve for signal versus static magnetic field. Bars indicating one standard deviation error are

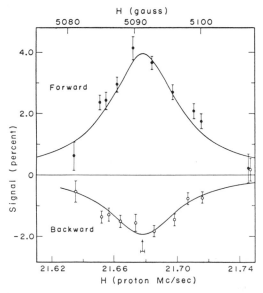

FIGURE 8. Typical resonance curves for the transition $(M_J, M\mu) = (\frac{1}{2}, \frac{1}{2}) \leftrightarrow (\frac{1}{2}, -\frac{1}{2})$. The backward signal is obtained by the observation of positrons emitted toward counter 2.

shown at the experimental points. The solid curve is a least squares fit of the theoretical Lorentzian line shape to the experimental points. The amplitude of the signal is about 4% and agrees with the expected amplitude under the assumption that all muons form muonium. The width of the curve is about 15 G which is due to the muon decay rate and to microwave power broadening. From such a curve we obtain corresponding resonance values of microwave frequency and magnetic field. From these resonance values we can compute $\Delta\nu$ by use of the Breit-Rabi formula.

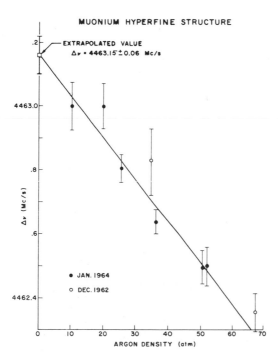

MUONIUM HYPERFINE STRUCTURE

EXTRAPOLATED VALUE
$\Delta\nu = 4463.15 \pm 0.06$ Mc/s

JAN. 1964
DEC. 1962

ARGON DENSITY (atm)

FIGURE 9. Experimental values of $\Delta\nu$ versus the argon gas density. The solid line is the least squares linear fit which was used for extrapolation to zero pressure.

Figure 9 shows the results of such $\Delta\nu$ measurements as a function of argon pressure. There is clearly a substantial dependence of $\Delta\nu$ on pressure. This dependence is the so-called hfs pressure shift and is due to distortion of the muonium wave function in the many collisions muonium makes with argon atoms during its lifetime. The solid curve is a straight line fit to the experimental data. The linear fit assumes that only two-body collisions and not collisions involving two argon atoms are important. Theoretical estimates of three-body collisions as well as a quadratic fit to the data support this view. The procedure of fitting the data with a straight line is also justified by the agreement within experimental error of the hfs pressure shifts for muonium and hydrogen in argon. The value of $\Delta\nu$ extrapolated to zero pressure is taken as $\Delta\nu$ for free muonium:

$$\Delta\nu_M = 4463.15 \pm 0.06 \, \text{Mc/sec},$$

in which the error of one standard deviation is due to counting statistics and to magnetic field errors.

Within the past two years extensive measurements have been completed of transitions at weak magnetic field with $\Delta F = \pm 1$. This measurement provides the most direct determination of $\Delta\nu$. The principal technical problems with this experiment were, first, the requirement of a homogeneous, stable low static magnetic field near the large synchrocyclotron magnet. Second, the signal intensity is

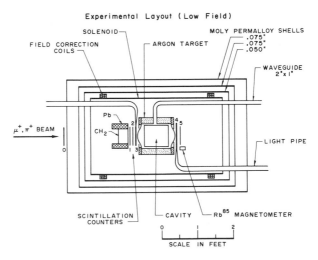

FIGURE 10: Experimental arrangement for measurement of $\Delta\nu$ in an experiment which employs a weak magnetic field and involves an induced microwave transition.

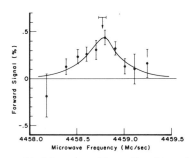

$(F,M_F)=(1,-1)\leftarrow(0,0)$
Magnetic Field = 2.8 gauss

FIGURE 11. Muonium Hyperfine Transition.

smaller than that for the strong field transition due to the relative populations of muonium hfs states and the small change in muon polarization accompanying the transition. Figure 10 shows the magnet arrangement. There are three moly permalloy shields. Inside these there is a solenoid and correction coils. This system provides an axial magnetic field of about 3 G with homogeneity and stability to better than 10 mG. Figure 11 shows an observed resonance curve for the transition $(F,M_F) = (1, -1) \leftrightarrow (0,0)$ observed at a field of 2.8 G fitted with the theoretical line shape. Low field data were taken also for unresolved $\Delta F = \pm 1$ transitions with both argon and krypton as the stopping gases.

Figure 12 summarizes the results of the muonium hfs measure-

	High Field Measurement	Low Field Measurement	Average
$\Delta \nu_{expt.}$ (Mc/sec)	4463.15 ± 0.06	4463.31 ± 0.04	4463.26 ± 0.04 (1std. dev.)

$$\Delta \nu_{theor.} = \frac{16}{3}\alpha^2 c R_\infty \frac{\mu_\mu}{\mu_0^e} \left(1 + \frac{m_e}{m_\mu}\right)^{-3} \left[1 + \epsilon\left(\alpha, \frac{m_e}{m_\mu}\right)\right]$$

In Which

$$\frac{\mu_\mu}{\mu_0^e} = \frac{\mu_\mu}{\mu_p}\frac{\mu_p}{\mu_e}\left(1 + \frac{\alpha}{2\pi} - 0.328 \frac{\alpha^2}{\pi^2}\right)$$

Where

$$\frac{\mu_\mu}{\mu_p} = 3.183355 \pm 0.000095 \quad (\pm 30\,\text{ppm}, 95\% \text{ confidence limit})$$

Fine Structure Constant, α^{-1} = 137.0368 ± 0.0025 (± 18 ppm, 95% confidence limit)

FIGURE 12. Muonium Hyperfine Structure.

ments. The values obtained from the high field and low field measurements are in satisfactory agreement and give a combined result of

$$\Delta \nu = 4463.26 \pm 0.04 \text{ Mc/sec}$$

in which a one standard deviation error is given. This value agrees with the theoretical value given earlier.

This agreement confirms the basis of the theory which was that the muon is a heavy Dirac particle or heavy electron. Since $\Delta \nu_M$(expt) is known with about the same accuracy as $\Delta \nu_M$(theor), which is limited principally by our knowledge of α, we can use $\Delta \nu_M$(expt) to determine an alternative value of the fine structure constant. The theoretical formula for $\Delta \nu$ is given in Figure 12. After α, the least well-known constant appearing is the muon magnetic moment or actually the ratio of the muon to proton magnetic moments. This ratio is obtained from the measured ratio of the precession frequency of muons stopped in water to the proton resonance frequency in water. Since the chemistry of muons in water may be different from the chemistry of protons in water due principally to the different vibrational energies, the magnetic shielding of the proton and the muon may be different. The value shown is meant to be a limit of error to take account of this ambiguity as well as two standard deviations in the experimental errors. Hence we obtain the value of α shown with a limit of error of 18 ppm. Other determinations of α are given in Figure 13.

Source	Value of α^{-1} (Limit of Error; 95% Confidence Limit)
Deuterium Fine Structure $2\,^2P_{3/2} \rightarrow 2\,^2P_{1/2}$	$137.0388 \pm 0.0012 \ (\pm 9 \text{ ppm})$
Hydrogen Fine Structure $2\,^2P_{3/2} \rightarrow 2\,^2P_{1/2}$	$137.0353 \pm 0.0016 \ (\pm 12 \text{ ppm})$
Muonium Hyperfine Structure $1\,^2S_{1/2},\ F=1 \rightarrow F=0$	$137.0368 \pm 0.0025 \ (\pm 18 \text{ ppm})$
Hydrogen Hyperfine Structure $1\,^2S_{1/2},\ F=1 \rightarrow F=0$	$137.0357 \pm 0.0008 \ (\pm 6 \text{ ppm})$
Josephson Effect	$137.0359 \pm 0.0008 \ (\pm 6 \text{ ppm})$

Average: $\alpha^{-1} = 137.0363 \pm 0.0011$ (8 ppm; 1 std. dev.)

FIGURE 13. Values of the fine structure constant α.

Except for the early experiment on deuterium fine structure all the values of α are in good agreement.

MUONIUM CHEMISTRY

Muonium will behave as a light isotope of hydrogen with regard to its atomic interactions and chemical reactions since the muon mass is 207 times the electron mass and since the muon mean life-time of 2.2 μsec is long compared to the electron atomic orbital times. In the history of the discovery of muonium, chemistry played an important negative role and many post-parity experiments which searched for the characteristic muonium precession frequency failed, due to the subsequent chemical reactions of muonium with molecules. As I mentioned, it was necessary to purify the argon gas in order to observe the muonium precession and the hfs transitions.

Figure 14 shows data on explicit studies of the interactions of muonium. The amplitude of the resonance signal for a strong field transition is shown as a function of the concentration of various molecules introduced in small fractional amounts as impurities in the argon. Note that the resonance signal is decreased by the addition of O_2 and NO, and with less effectiveness by C_2H_4 (ethylene); H_2

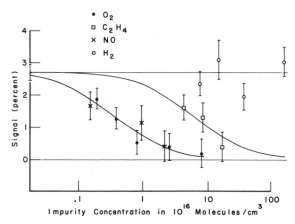

FIGURE 14. Resonance signal for the transition $(M_J, M_\mu) = (\frac{1}{2}, \frac{1}{2}) \leftrightarrow (\frac{1}{2}, -\frac{1}{2})$ at 5200 G versus impurity concentration. The solid curves are fitted theoretical curves which involve the signal quenching cross section as a parameter.

does not affect the signal. Decrease of the resonance signal implies collisions which remove muonium from the resonant states. In the theory of the line shape the collision rate can be added to the muon decay rate and the data can be analyzed to yield a cross-section for signal quenching.

For thermal muonium the Born-Oppenheimer approximation is valid as it is for hydrogen. As to the nature of the reactions, NO and O_2 are paramagnetic with free electron spins and we expect that electron spin exchange will dominate. This reaction is determined by the Coulomb interaction and the Pauli exclusion principle. The exchange of the muonium electron with an argon electron can result in the transference of muonium from one hfs state to another. C_2H_4 is an unsaturated hydrocarbon and in a collision with muonium we believe that a muonium-containing molecule is formed. For H_2 there is no reaction. H_2 is not paramagnetic so electron spin exchange reactions are not possible. Furthermore, a reaction such as $M + H_2 \rightarrow MH + H$ is energetically forbidden for thermal muonium because of the high zero point vibrational energy of MH.

A simpler method of studying the molecular interactions of muonium involves the measurement of the polarization of the muons as a

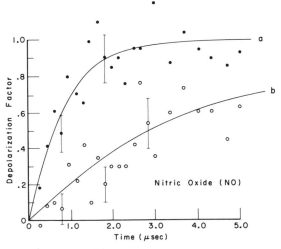

FIGURE 15. Depolarization factor, $1 - e^{\lambda_2 t}$, versus time for NO where λ_2 is the fitted depolarization rate, under the assumption that the muon depolarization varies as $P = P_0 e^{\lambda_2 t}$.

function of time and of impurity concentration by use of a precision digital time analyzer following the scintillation counters. The method is, of course, based on the fact that a change in muon polarization implies a change in positron angular distribution. Figure 15 shows such data for NO. Depolarization is plotted as a function of time during a period of several muon mean lives for two different NO concentrations; for the lower curve the pressure of NO was 0.13 mmHg and for the upper curve, 0.37 mmHg. Typical statistical errors are shown. The solid curves are simple exponential functions. If the reaction mechanism is electron spin exchange, the theoretical curve is an exponential and the coefficient in the exponent is proportional to the electron spin exchange cross-section.

A more detailed study of the nature of the depolarizing collisions can be made by observation of the depolarization rate as a function of the static magnetic field. At strong field an electron spin exchange collision will leave the muon spin direction unchanged and hence the effective depolarizing cross-section will be zero. At weak field, on the other hand, the coupling of the electron and muon spins by the hfs interaction results in a change of muon spin direction when an electron spin exchange occurs. The variation of depolarizing cross-section as a function of magnetic field depends only on the spin eigenfunctions and is simply predicted. Figure 16 shows data for NO, which has a single free electron spin—$^2\pi$ state—as a function of H. The experimental points are in good agreement with the theoretical

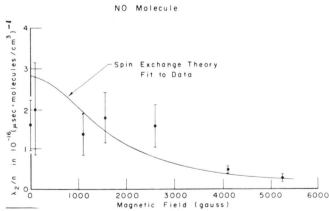

FIGURE 16. Depolarization rate per impurity molecule versus magnetic field. The solid curve is a fitted theoretical curve.

solid curve and hence the spin exchange nature of the collision is confirmed. Similar confirmation has been established for O_2.

Figure 17 summarizes the data on muonium-molecule cross-sections obtained thus far. For NO_2 we have a lower limit of 23 x 10^{-16} cm²

Muonium – Molecule Cross Sections in $10^{-16} cm^2$

Added Gas	Postulated Interaction	σ_R from Signal Quenching Data at 5250 G.	$\sigma_{S.E.}$ from Depol. Rates at Several Fields
NO_2	$+M \rightarrow NO+OM$	23 ($^{lower}_{limit}$)	—
O_2	Spin Exchange	5.4 ± 2.5	5.9 ± .6
NO	Spin Exchange	3.2 ± 1.5	7.1 ± 1.0
C_2H_4	$+M \rightarrow C_2H_4M$	.29 ± .16	—
H_2, N_2, SF_6	—	.01 ($^{upper}_{limit}$)	—

FIGURE 17.

from the resonance signal quenching data and we believe the reaction is $NO_2 + M \rightarrow NO + OM$. For O_2 and NO the reaction mechanism is an electron spin exchange reaction and the cross-sections are 5.9 and 7.1 x 10^{-16} cm² for NO and O_2. Corresponding spin exchange cross-sections for H with NO and O_2, measured with the use of the hydrogen maser, are about 3 or 4 times larger than for muonium. We believe this difference is due to the fact that for a given kinetic energy M and H have different momenta and hence different numbers of partial waves contribute to the reaction. For C_2H_4 the cross-section is 0.29 x 10^{-16} cm² and we believe that a muonium-containing molecule is formed. No reaction was observed for H_2, N_2, and SF_6. The absence of a reaction for H_2 was discussed and similar remarks apply to N_2.

Our work on muonium chemistry is in an early stage and a rich variety of reactions could be studied and compared with those of hydrogen. Indeed, in some ways, muonium chemistry is easier to study than H atom chemistry because the behavior of a single muonium atom can be detected through its energetic positron decay by the methods of particle physics.

MUONIUM-ANTIMUONIUM CONVERSION

Muonium provides an interesting system for study of the weak interactions, or of the nature, of the muon quantum number (Figure

18). The conversion of muonium to antimuonium (μ^-e^+) would violate the usual additive law of muon number conservation but would be allowed by a multiplicative law of muon number conservation,

Muonium – Antimuonium Conversion

$$\mu^+e^- \longrightarrow \mu^-e^+$$

Violates Additive Law of Muon Conservation.

Allowed by Multiplicative Law of Muon Conservation.

$$\mathcal{H} = G_{M\overline{M}} \, \overline{\psi}_\mu \, \gamma_\lambda \, (1+\gamma_5) \, \psi_e \, \overline{\psi}_\mu \, \gamma^\lambda \, (1+\gamma_5) \, \psi_e$$

$$(\overline{M}|\mathcal{H}|M) = \frac{\delta}{2} = \frac{8 G_{M\overline{M}}}{\pi a_0^3} \qquad (\text{for } G_{M\overline{M}} = G_V \;,\; \delta = 2.1 \times 10^{-12} \text{ eV})$$

$$\psi(t) = a\phi_M + b\phi_{\overline{M}} \qquad (\text{at } t = 0 \,,\, a = 1 \,,\, b = 0)$$

$$P(\overline{M}) = \frac{\delta}{2\Lambda^2} \left(\frac{G_{M\overline{M}}}{G_V} \right)^2 = 2.6 \times 10^{-5} \left(\frac{G_{M\overline{M}}}{G_V} \right)^2 \qquad (\text{in Vacuum}), \text{ where } \Lambda = \hbar\gamma$$

$$P_{gas}(\overline{M}) \simeq \frac{1}{N} P_{vac}(\overline{M})$$

$$\overline{M} + A \longrightarrow \mu^- A$$

$$G_{M\overline{M}} \lesssim 2 \times 10^5 \; G_V$$

FIGURE 18.

which would be consistent with present knowledge about the weak interactions. A Hamiltonian term which couples M and $\overline{M}$ is shown, and the value of the matrix element is shown for the case in which the coupling constant is taken as the universal Fermi constant G_V.

Muonium and antimuonium are degenerate as regards their electromagnetic interaction. If initially M is formed, then due to the coupling, a component of $\overline{M}$ is formed in the wave-function. Hence there is a probability that muon decay will occur in the $\overline{M}$ mode with the emission of an energetic electron. This probability $P(\overline{M})$ is 2.6 x 10^{-5} for muonium in vacuum. In the presence of a gas the degeneracy of M and $\overline{M}$ is removed due to the different electromagnetic interactions of M and $\overline{M}$ with atoms—e.g., argon. Hence the development of the $\overline{M}$ component is inhibited, and $P(\overline{M})$ is reduced by the factor 1/N, the number of collisions of the M-M system with Ar atoms during its lifetime. The collisions of the antiatom $\overline{M}$ with Ar are dominated by an inelastic rearrangement collision in which the muonic argon atom is formed. Hence the argon gas will change the mode of $\overline{M}$

decay, since μ^- nucleus capture will predominate over μ^- decay. We have done an experiment to search for the characteristic muonic Ar X-rays as a sensitive test for the $M \to \overline{M}$ conversion, and have established that $G_{M\overline{M}}$ is less than several thousand times the universal Fermi coupling constant G_V.

FUTURE

As to future work on muonium let me just remark that all our work has been done with only about 10^{10} muonium atoms; work on the hydrogen atom, on the other hand, has available hydrogen atom beam intensities of 10^{14} atoms/sec. Research on muonium is now severely limited by the number of muonium atoms available or by muon beam intensities. When higher intensity accelerators—so-called meson factories—get built, great improvements and extensions of studies of muonium will be possible.

ACKNOWLEDGMENT

This research has been supported by the Air Force Office of Scientific Research, the Office of Naval Research and the National Science Foundation.

REFERENCES

[1] Hughes, V. W., *Bull. Am. Phys. Soc.* **2**, 205 (1957).

[2] Hughes, V. W., McColm, D. W., Ziock, K., and Prepost, R., *Phys. Rev. Letters* **5**, 63 (1960).

[3] Prepost, R., Hughes, V. W., and Ziock, K., *Phys. Rev. Letters* **6**, 19 (1961).

[4] Ziock, K., Hughes, V. W., Prepost, R., Bailey, J. M., and Cleland, W. E., *Phys. Rev. Letters* **8**, 103 (1962).

[5] Cleland, W. E., Bailey, J. M., Eckhause, M., Hughes, V. W., Mobley, R. M., Prepost, R., and Rothberg, J. E., *Phys. Rev. Letters* **13**, 202 (1964).

[6] Thompson, P., Amato, J. Hughes, V. W., Mobley, R., and Rothberg, J., *Bull. Am. Psys. Soc.*, **11**, 343 (1966).

[7] Mobley, R. M., Bailey, J. M., Cleland, W. E., Hughes, V. W., and Rothberg, J. E., *J. Chem. Phys.* **44**, 4354 (1966).

[8] Morgan, D., *Bull. Am. Phys. Soc.* **9**, 393 (1964).

[9] Hughes, V. W., *Ann. Rev. Nucl. Sci.* **16**, 445 (1966).

[10] Thompson, P., Amato, J. J., Hughes, V. W., Mobley, R. M., and Rothberg, J. E., *Bull. Am. Phys. Soc.* **12**, 75 (1967).

[11] Mobley, R. M., Amato, J. J., Hughes, V. W., Rothberg, J. E., and Thompson, P. A., *J. Chem. Phys.* **47**, 3074 (1967).

[12] Amato, J. J., Crane, P., Hughes, V. W., Rothberg, J. E., and Thompson, P. A., *Bull. Am. Phys. Soc.* **13**, 635 (1968).